The Works
of
Bret Harte

BLACK'S READERS SERVICE COMPANY

ROSLYN, NEW YORK

CONTENTS

v

POEMS

AUTHOR'S PREFACE

A series of designs—suggested, I think, by Hogarth's familiar cartoons of the Industrious and Idle Apprentices—I remember as among the earliest efforts at moral teaching in California. They represented the respective careers of the Honest and Dissolute Miners: the one, as I recall him, retrograding through successive planes of dirt, drunkenness, disease, and death; the other advancing by corresponding stages to affluence and a white shirt. Whatever may have been the artistic defects of these drawings, the moral at least was obvious and distinct. That it failed, however,—as it did,—to produce the desired reform in mining morality may have been owing to the fact that the average miner refused to recognize himself in either of these positive characters; and that even he who might have sat for the model of the Dissolute Miner was perhaps dimly conscious of some limitations and circumstances which partly relieved him from responsibility. "Yer see," remarked such a critic to the writer, in the untranslatable poetry of his class, "it ain't no square game. They've just put up the keerds on that chap from the start."

With this lamentable example before me, I trust that in the following sketches I have abstained from any positive moral. I might have painted my villains of the blackest dye,—so black, indeed, that the originals thereof would have contemplated them with the glow of comparative virtue. I might have made it impossible for them to have performed a virtuous or generous action, and have thus avoided that moral confusion which is apt to arise in the contemplation of mixed motives and qualities. But I should have burdened myself with the responsibility of their creation, which, as a humble writer of romance and entitled to no particular reverence, I did not care to do.

I fear I cannot claim, therefore, any higher motive than to illustrate an era of which Californian history has preserved the incidents more often than the character of the actors,—an era which the panegyrist was too often content to bridge over with a general compliment to its survivors,—an era still so recent that in attempting to revive its poetry, I am conscious also of awakening the more prosaic recollections of these same survivors,—and yet an era replete with a certain heroic Greek poetry, of which perhaps none were more unconscious than the heroes themselves. And I shall be quite content to have collected here merely the materials for the Iliad that is yet to be sung.

SAN FRANCISCO, *December* 24, 1869.

INTRODUCTION

What would have happened if . . .? The game is as fascinating as it is futile. What would have happened, shall we say, if Alexander had fallen at the battle of Granicus; if Caesar had survived the Ides of March; if Napoleon had won instead of lost at Waterloo; if a Bosnian student had not fired two lethal shots in the city of Sarajevo, on June 28th, 1914? Or, descending from questions of prime historical importance to one less momentous, but pertinent to our present subject, what would have happened to Bret Harte as an author if he had not, at the impressionable age of fifteen, in the year 1854, made the long journey westward from Albany on the Hudson to the city of the Golden Gate? Kipling, we may be sure, could have done without India and its local color; and been much without it. But what would Bret Harte have been without the California of the fifties and the sixties, and *that* local color? It is all guesswork, of course, but it is hard to believe that he would have been more than a writer of small fame and consequence; an imitator of others, following Irving and Dickens at a distance, rather than an influence on others, and a factor of undeniable importance in the development of his native literature.

Whatever our guess, we do know certain facts:—that Bret Harte's best stories were all inspired by a brief youthful experience, the experience chiefly of a spectator rather than a participant, for it was as a school-teacher that he lived for a time among the rough miners of Sonora; that these tales were mainly written within the two-year period, from 1868 to 1870, when he was editor of the *Overland Monthly* in San Francisco; that during his thirty years of life thereafter he never wrote anything to equal them, never found scenes or incidents or characters that fired his imagination as California had fired it; and that it was to California, to the very last, that he always looked backward when his literary energy and invention flagged,—looked backward in the hope that by imitating himself he could duplicate his earliest successes. But that he never did. Between 1867 and 1898 he published forty-four volumes of prose and verse, but his place in literature would be the same to-day if he had written only one book; the one that contains "The Luck of Roaring Camp," "Tennessee's Partner," and "The Outcasts of Poker Flat." It is a strange story, Bret Harte's life, and rather a pathetic one; the story of a man who outlived his best work by thirty years, but who managed somehow to cling to the benefits of the position that work had won him, to repeat himself, and feed upon his past, and go on selling what he wrote for a good price, even though the eminence to which he had suddenly been lifted had cruelly exposed the limits of his power and the paucity of his talents.

When the pupils of the Albany Female College lost their professor of Greek, Francis Bret Harte was left fatherless. He was a frail youth, whose education was limited to four or five years at school and the reading that he had done for himself at home; reading that gave him an early and intimate acquaintance with the best of the English novelists, and that moved him to the composition of very juvenile verse. He was a dreaming, mooning lad, not of the stuff that makes young prospectors; and we are not quite sure what prompted him and his mother to undertake the arduous migration to California, by way of Panama, five years after the first gold seekers had shown the way. Perhaps an elder son and brother had preceded them. However, westward they went, and arrived in San Francisco when that city was entering its most picturesque era; when, behind a mask of self-conscious civic virtue, humanity was very crude and colorful and various indeed. Soon afterwards young Harte had his brief contact with mining life in

Calaveras County, and the depth of the impression it made upon him was undoubtedly in proportion to the extreme sensitivity of the Eastern youth, uprooted from a gentle domestic environment, and set down at a rough outpost of civilization. When he returned to San Francisco, in 1858, he had collected the small fund of material upon which he was to subsist through his literary lifetime: he had taught school in a primitive community, done a very little placer mining, been express messenger and tax collector and druggist's clerk, and learned the useful trade of type-setting. He was ready for a sedentary career. But he was not quite ready to write, for, as he tells us himself, several years were required for "the great mass of primary impressions" to become "sufficiently clarified for literary use."

It was as a compositor on *The Golden Era*, and later as one of its editorial staff, that he wrote his first sketches in imitative vein. Then came the "Condensed Novels," parodies of famous fiction, contributed to weekly numbers of *The Californian*, and collected between covers in 1867; and then the editorship of *The Overland Monthly*, and the publication of "The Luck of Roaring Camp" in the second number of that magazine. Triumph followed. No sooner had this story appeared, says Fred Lewis Pattee, "than the foremost publishing house of Boston hailed it as a new classic. Its author immediately was offered ten thousand dollars a year to write for *The Atlantic Monthly*, and the progress of his train east as he came to accept his unprecedented commission was indicated by daily bulletins in the newspapers as if he were a royal personage on a tour of the land. When was short story ever so advertised before?" When indeed? But the royal progress eastward did not follow so soon after the appearance of "The Luck" as this would imply; it was "The Heathen Chinee" that, in H. W. Boynton's words, "served to clinch the general conviction that Bret Harte was too important a person to live in California," and it was in the spring of 1870 that he left San Francisco.

Years of life were before him; he would manufacture

Stories

THE LUCK OF ROARING CAMP

THERE was commotion in Roaring Camp. It could not have been a fight, for in 1850 that was not novel enough to have called together the entire settlement. The ditches and claims were not only deserted, but "Tuttle's grocery" had contributed its gamblers, who, it will be remembered, calmly continued their game the day that French Pete and Kanaka Joe shot each other to death over the bar in the front room. The whole camp was collected before a rude cabin on the outer edge of the clearing. Conversation was carried on in a low tone, but the name of a woman was frequently repeated. It was a name familiar enough in the camp,—"Cherokee Sal."

Perhaps the less said of her the better. She was a coarse, and, it is to be feared, a very sinful woman. But at that time she was the only woman in Roaring Camp, and was just then lying in sore extremity, when she most needed the ministration of her own sex. Dissolute, abandoned, and irreclaimable, she was yet suffering a martyrdom hard enough to bear even when veiled by sympathizing womanhood, but now terrible in her loneliness. The primal curse had come to her in that original isolation which must have made the punishment of the first transgression so dreadful. It was, perhaps, part of the expiation of her sin, that, at a moment when she most lacked her sex's intuitive tenderness and care, she met only the half-contemptuous faces of her masculine associates. Yet a few of the spectators were, I think, touched by her sufferings. Sandy Tipton thought it was "rough on Sal," and, in the contemplation of her condition, for a moment rose superior to the fact that he had an ace and two bowers in his sleeve.

It will be seen, also, that the situation was novel. Deaths

1

were by no means uncommon in Roaring Camp, but a birth was a new thing. People had been dismissed from the camp effectively, finally, and with no possibility of return; but this was the first time that anybody had been introduced *ab initio*. Hence the excitement.

"You go in there, Stumpy," said a prominent citizen known as "Kentuck," addressing one of the loungers. "Go in there, and see what you kin do. You've had experience in them things."

Perhaps there was a fitness in the selection. Stumpy, in other climes, had been the putative head of two families; in fact, it was owing to some legal informality in these proceedings that Roaring Camp—a city of refuge—was indebted to his company. The crowd approved the choice, and Stumpy was wise enough to bow to the majority. The door closed on the extempore surgeon and midwife, and Roaring Camp sat down outside, smoked its pipe, and awaited the issue.

The assemblage numbered about a hundred men. One or two of these were actual fugitives from justice, some were criminal, and all were reckless. Physically, they exhibited no indication of their past lives and character. The greatest scamp had a Raphael face, with a profusion of blond hair; Oakhurst, a gambler, had the melancholy air and intellectual abstraction of a Hamlet; the coolest and most courageous man was scarcely over five feet in height, with a soft voice and an embarrassed, timid manner. The term "roughs" applied to them was a distinction rather than a definition. Perhaps in the minor details of fingers, toes, ears, &c., the camp may have been deficient; but these slight omissions did not detract from their aggregate force. The strongest man had but three fingers on his right hand; the best shot had but one eye.

Such was the physical aspect of the men that were dispersed around the cabin. The camp lay in a triangular valley, between two hills and a river. The only outlet was a steep trail over the summit of a hill that faced the cabin, now illuminated by the rising moon. The suffering woman

might have seen it from the rude bunk whereon she lay,—
seen it winding like a silver thread until it was lost in the
stars above.

A fire of withered pine-boughs added sociability to the
gathering. By degrees the natural levity of Roaring Camp
returned. Bets were freely offered and taken regarding the
result. Three to five that "Sal would get through with
it;" even that the child would survive; side bets as to the
sex and complexion of the coming stranger. In the midst
of an excited discussion an exclamation came from those
nearest the door, and the camp stopped to listen. Above
the swaying and moaning of the pines, the swift rush of the
river, and the crackling of the fire, rose a sharp, querulous
cry—a cry unlike anything heard before in the camp. The
pines stopped moaning, the river ceased to rush, and the
fire to crackle. It seemed as if Nature had stopped to
listen too.

The camp rose to its feet as one man! It was proposed
to explode a barrel of gunpowder, but, in consideration of
the situation of the mother, better counsels prevailed, and
only a few revolvers were discharged; for, whether owing
to the rude surgery of the camp, or some other reason,
Cherokee Sal was sinking fast. Within an hour she had
climbed, as it were, that rugged road that led to the stars,
and so passed out of Roaring Camp, its sin and shame,
for ever. I do not think that the announcement disturbed
them much, except in speculation as to the fate of the child.
"Can he live now?" was asked of Stumpy. The answer
was doubtful. The only other being of Cherokee Sal's sex
and maternal condition in the settlement was an ass. There
was some conjecture as to fitness, but the experiment was
tried. It was less problematical than the ancient treatment
of Romulus and Remus, and apparently as successful.

When these details were completed, which exhausted
another hour, the door was opened, and the anxious crowd
of men who had already formed themselves into a queue,
entered in single file. Beside the low bunk or shelf, on
which the figure of the mother was starkly outlined below

the blankets, stood a pine table. On this a candle-box was placed, and within it, swathed in staring red flannel, lay the last arrival at Roaring Camp. Beside the candle-box was placed a hat. Its use was soon indicated. "Gentlemen," said Stumpy, with a singular mixture of authority and *ex officio* complacency,—"Gentlemen will please pass in at the front door, round the table, and out at the back door. Them as wishes to contribute anything toward the orphan will find a hat handy." The first man entered with his hat on; he uncovered, however, as he looked about him, and so, unconsciously, set an example to the next. In such communities good and bad actions are catching. As the procession filed in, comments were audible,—criticisms addressed, perhaps, rather to Stumpy, in the character of showman,—"Is that him?" "mighty small specimen;" "hasn't mor'n got the colour;" "ain't bigger nor a derringer." The contributions were as characteristic: A silver tobacco-box; a doubloon; a navy revolver, silver mounted; a gold specimen; a very beautifully embroidered lady's handkerchief from Oakhurst (the gambler); a diamond breastpin; a diamond ring (suggested by the pin, with the remark from the giver that he "saw that pin and went two diamonds better"); a slung shot; a Bible (contributor not detected); a golden spur; a silver teaspoon (the initials, I regret to say, were not the giver's); a pair of surgeon's shears; a lancet; a Bank of England note for £5; and about $200 in loose gold and silver coin. During these proceedings Stumpy maintained a silence as impassive as the dead on his left, a gravity as inscrutable as that of the newly born on his right. Only one incident occurred to break the monotony of the curious procession. As Kentuck bent over the candle-box half curiously, the child turned, and, in a spasm of pain, caught at his groping finger, and held it fast for a moment. Kentuck looked foolish and embarrassed. Something like a blush tried to assert itself in his weather-beaten cheek. "The d—d little cuss!" he said, as he extricated his finger, with, perhaps, more tenderness and care than he might have been deemed

capable of showing. He held that finger a little apart from
its fellows as he went out, and examined it curiously.
The examination provoked the same original remark in regard to the child. In fact, he seemed to enjoy repeating
it. "He rastled with my finger," he remarked to Tipton,
holding up the member, "the d—d little cuss!"

It was four o'clock before the camp sought repose. A
light burnt in the cabin where the watchers sat, for Stumpy
did not go to bed that night. Nor did Kentuck. He drank
quite freely, and related with great gusto his experience,
invariably ending with his characteristic condemnation of
the new-comer. It seemed to relieve him of any unjust
implication of sentiment, and Kentuck had the weaknesses
of the nobler sex. When everybody else had gone to bed,
he walked down to the river, and whistled reflectingly.
Then he walked up the gulch, past the cabin, still whistling
with demonstrative unconcern. At a large red-wood tree
he paused and retraced his steps, and again passed the
cabin. Half-way down to the river's bank he again paused,
and then returned and knocked at the door. It was opened
by Stumpy. "How goes it?" said Kentuck, looking past
Stumpy toward the candle-box. "All serene," replied
Stumpy. "Anything up?" "Nothing." There was a
pause—an embarrassing one—Stumpy still holding the
door. Then Kentuck had recourse to his finger, which he
held up to Stumpy. "Rastled with it,—the d—d little
cuss," he said, and retired.

The next day Cherokee Sal had such rude sepulture as
Roaring Camp afforded. After her body had been committed to the hill-side, there was a formal meeting of the
camp to discuss what should be done with her infant. A
resolution to adopt it was unanimous and enthusiastic. But
an animated discussion in regard to the manner and feasi-
bility of providing for its wants at once sprung up. It
was remarkable that the argument partook of none of those
fierce personalities with which discussions were usually
conducted at Roaring Camp. Tipton proposed that they
should send the child to Red Dog,—a distance of forty

miles,—where female attention could be procured. But the
unlucky suggestion met with fierce and unanimous opposition. It was evident that no plan which entailed parting
from their new acquisition would for a moment be entertained. "Besides," said Tom Ryder, "them fellows at Red
Dog would swap it, and ring in somebody else on us." A
disbelief in the honesty of other camps prevailed at Roaring Camp as in other places.

The introduction of a female nurse in the camp also met
with objection. It was argued that no decent woman could
be prevailed to accept Roaring Camp as her home, and the
speaker urged that "they didn't want any more of the other
kind." This unkind allusion to the defunct mother, harsh
as it may seem, was the first spasm of propriety,—the first
symptom of the camp's regeneration. Stumpy advanced
nothing. Perhaps he felt a certain delicacy in interfering
with the selection of a possible successor in office. But
when questioned, he averred stoutly that he and "Jinny"—
the mammal before alluded to—could manage to rear the
child. There was something original, independent, and
heroic about the plan that pleased the camp. Stumpy was
retained. Certain articles were sent for to Sacramento.
"Mind," said the treasurer, as he pressed a bag of gold-
dust into the expressman's hand, "the best that can be
got,—lace, you know, and filigree-work and frills—d—n the
cost!"

Strange to say, the child thrived. Perhaps the invigorat-
ing climate of the mountain camp was compensation for
material deficiencies. Nature took the foundling to her
broader breast. In that rare atmosphere of the Sierra
foothills,—that air pungent with balsamic odour, that
ethereal cordial at once bracing and exhilarating,—he may
have found food and nourishment, or a subtle chemistry
that transmuted asses' milk to lime and phosphorous.
Stumpy inclined to the belief that it was the latter, and
good nursing. "Me and that ass," he would say, "has been
father and mother to him! Don't you," he would add,

apostrophizing the helpless bundle before him "never go back on us."

By the time he was a month old, the necessity of giving him a name became apparent. He had generally been known as "the Kid," "Stumpy's boy," "the Cayote" (an allusion to his vocal powers), and even by Kentuck's endearing diminutive of "the d—d little cuss." But these were felt to be vague and unsatisfactory, and were at last dismissed under another influence. Gamblers and adventurers are generally superstitious, and Oakhurst one day declared that the baby had brought "the luck" to Roaring Camp. It was certain that of late they had been successful. "Luck" was the name agreed upon, with the prefix of Tommy for greater convenience. No allusion was made to the mother, and the father was unknown. "It's better," said the philosophical Oakhurst, "to take a fresh deal all round. Call him Luck, and start him fair." A day was accordingly set apart for the christening. What was meant by this ceremony the reader may imagine, who has already gathered some idea of the reckless irreverence of Roaring Camp. The master of ceremonies was one "Boston," a noted wag, and the occasion seemed to promise the greatest facetiousness. This ingenious satirist had spent two days in preparing a burlesque of the church service, with pointed local allusions. The choir was properly trained, and Sandy Tipton was to stand godfather. But after the procession had marched to the grove with music and banners, and the child had been deposited before a mock altar, Stumpy stepped before the expectant crowd. "It ain't my style to spoil fun, boys," said the little man, stoutly, eyeing the faces around him, "but it strikes me that this thing ain't exactly on the squar. It's playing it pretty low down on this yer baby to ring in fun on him that he ain't going to understand. And ef there's going to be any godfathers round, I'd like to see who's got any better rights than me." A silence followed Stumpy's speech. To the credit of all humorists be it said, that the first man to acknowledge its justice was the satirist, thus stopped of his fun. "But," said Stumpy, quickly, following up his advantage, "we're here for a christening, and we'll have it. I proclaim you Thomas Luck, according to the laws of the United States and the State of California, so help me God." It was the first time that the name of the Deity had been uttered otherwise than profanely in the camp. The form of christening was perhaps even more ludicrous than the satirist had conceived; but, strangely enough, nobody saw it, and nobody laughed. "Tommy" was christened as seriously as he would have been under a Christian roof, and cried and was comforted in as orthodox fashion.

And so the work of regeneration began in Roaring Camp. Almost imperceptibly a change came over the settlement. The cabin assigned to "Tommy Luck"—or "The Luck," as he was more frequently called—first showed signs of improvement. It was kept scrupulously clean and whitewashed. Then it was boarded, clothed, and papered. The rosewood cradle—packed eighty miles by mule—had, in Stumpy's way of putting it, "sorter killed the rest of the furniture." So the rehabilitation of the cabin became a necessity. The men who were in the habit of lounging in at Stumpy's to see "how the Luck got on" seemed to appreciate the change, and, in self-defence, the rival establishment of "Tuttle's grocery" bestirred itself, and imported a carpet and mirrors. The reflections of the latter on the appearance of Roaring Camp tended to produce stricter habits of personal cleanliness. Again, Stumpy imposed a kind of quarantine upon those who aspired to the honour and privilege of holding "The Luck." It was a cruel mortification to Kentuck—who, in the carelessness of a large nature and the habits of frontier life, had begun to regard all garments as a second cuticle, which, like a snake's, only sloughed off through decay—to be debarred this privilege from certain prudential reasons. Yet such was the subtle influence of innovation that he thereafter appeared regularly every afternoon in a clean shirt, and face still shining from his ablutions. Nor were moral and social sanitary laws neglected. "Tommy," who was sup-

posed to spend his whole existence in a persistent attempt
to repose, must not be disturbed by noise. The shouting
and yelling which had gained the camp its infelicitous title
were not permitted within hearing distance of Stumpy's.
The men conversed in whispers, or smoked with Indian
gravity. Profanity was tacitly given up in these sacred
precincts, and throughout the camp a popular form of
expletive, known as "D—n the luck!" and "Curse the
luck!" was abandoned, as having a new personal bearing.
Vocal music was not interdicted, being supposed to have
a soothing, tranquillizing quality, and one song, sung by
"Man-o'-war Jack," an English sailor, from her Majesty's
Australian colonies, was quite popular as a lullaby. It
was a lugubrious recital of the exploits of "the Arethusa,
Seventy-four," in a muffled minor, ending with a prolonged
dying fall at the burden of each verse, "On b-o-o-o-ard of
the Arethusa." It was a fine sight to see Jack holding
The Luck, rocking from side to side as if with the motion
of a ship, and crooning forth this naval ditty. Either
through the peculiar rocking of Jack or the length of his
song—it contained ninety stanzas, and was continued with
conscientious deliberation to the bitter end—the lullaby
generally had the desired effect. At such times the men
would lie at full length under the trees, in the soft summer
twilight, smoking their pipes and drinking in the melodious
utterances. An indistinct idea that this was pastoral happiness pervaded the camp. "This 'ere kind o' think," said
the Cockney Simmons, meditatively reclining on his elbow,
"is 'evingly." It reminded him of Greenwich.

On the long summer days The Luck was usually carried
to the gulch, from whence the golden store of Roaring
Camp was taken. There, on a blanket spread over pine-
boughs, he would lie while the men were working in the
ditches below. Latterly there was a rude attempt to deco-
rate this bower with flowers and sweet-smelling shrubs, and
generally someone would bring him a cluster of wild honey-
suckles, azaleas, or the painted blossoms of Las Mariposas.
The men had suddenly awakened to the fact that there

were beauty and significance in these trifles, which they had so long trodden carelessly beneath their feet. A flake of glittering mica, a fragment of variegated quartz, a bright pebble from the bed of the creek, became beautiful to eyes thus cleared and strengthened, and were invariably put aside for "The Luck." It was wonderful how many treasures the woods and hillsides yielded that "would do for Tommy." Surrounded by playthings such as never child out of fairy-land had before, it is to be hoped that Tommy was content. He appeared to be securely happy, albeit there was an infantine gravity about him, a contemplative light in his round gray eyes, that sometimes worried Stumpy. He was always tractable and quiet, and it is recorded that once, having crept beyond his "corral,"— a hedge of tessellated pine-boughs, which surrounded his bed,—he dropped over the bank on his head in the soft earth, and remained with his mottled legs in the air in that position for at least five minutes with unflinching gravity. He was extricated without a murmur. I hesitate to record the many other instances of his sagacity, which rest, unfortunately, upon the statements of prejudiced friends. Some of them were not without a tinge of superstition. "I crep' up the bank just now," said Kentuck, one day, in a breathless state of excitement, "and dern my skin if he wasn't a talking to a jay-bird as was a sittin' on his lap. There they was, just as free and sociable as anything you please, a jawin' at each other just like two cherry-bums." Howbeit, whether creeping over the pine-boughs or lying lazily on his back blinking at the leaves above him, to him the birds sang, the squirrels chattered, and the flowers bloomed. Nature was his nurse and playfellow. For him she would let slip between the leaves golden shafts of sunlight that fell just within his grasp; she would send wandering breezes to visit him with the balm of bay and resinous gums; to him the tall red-woods nodded familiarly and sleepily, the bumble-bees buzzed, and the rooks cawed a slumberous accompaniment.

Such was the golden summer of Roaring Camp. They

were "flush times,"—and the luck was with them. The claims had yielded enormously. The camp was jealous of its privileges, and looked suspiciously on strangers. No encouragement was given to immigration, and, to make their seclusion more perfect, the land on either side of the mountain-wall that surrounded the camp they duly pre-empted. This, and a reputation for singular proficiency with the revolver, kept the reserve of Roaring Camp inviolate. The expressman—their only connecting link with the surrounding world—sometimes told wonderful stories of the camp. He would say, "They've a street up there in 'Roaring,' that would lay over any street in Red Dog. They've got vines and flowers round their houses, and they wash themselves twice a day. But they're mighty rough on strangers, and they worship an Ingin baby."

With the prosperity of the camp came a desire for further improvement. It was proposed to build a hotel in the following spring, and to invite one or two decent families to reside there for the sake of "The Luck,"—who might perhaps profit by female companionship. The sacrifice that this concession to the sex cost these men, who were fiercely sceptical in regard to its general virtue and usefulness, can only be accounted for by their affection for Tommy. A few still held out. But the resolve could not be carried into effect for three months, and the minority meekly yielded in the hope that something might turn up to prevent it. And it did.

The winter of 1851 will long be remembered in the foothills. The snow lay deep on the Sierras, and every mountain creek became a river, and every river a lake. Each gorge and gulch was transformed into a tumultuous watercourse that descended the hill-sides, tearing down giant trees, and scattering its drift and débris along the plain. Red Dog had been twice under water, and Roaring Camp had been forewarned. "Water put the gold into them gulches," said Stumpy; "it's been here once and will be here again!" And that night the North Folk suddenly leaped over its banks, and swept up the triangular valley of Roaring Camp.

In the confusion of rushing water, crushing trees, and crackling timber, and the darkness which seemed to flow with the water and blot out the fair valley, but little could be done to collect the scattered camp. When the morning broke, the cabin of Stumpy nearest the river-bank was gone. Higher up the gulch they found the body of its unlucky owner; but the pride, the hope, the joy, the Luck of Roaring Camp had disappeared. They were returning with sad hearts, when a shout from the bank recalled them.

It was a relief-boat from down the river. They had picked up, they said, a man and an infant, nearly exhausted, about two miles below. Did anybody know them, and did they belong here?

It needed but a glance to show them Kentuck lying there, cruelly crushed and bruised, but still holding the Luck of Roaring Camp in his arms. As they bent over the strangely assorted pair, they saw that the child was cold and pulseless. "He is dead," said one. Kentuck opened his eyes. "Dead?" he repeated, feebly. "Yes, my man, and you are dying too." A smile lit the eyes of the expiring Kentuck. "Dying," he repeated, "he's a taking me with him,—tell the boys I've got the Luck with me now;" and the strong man, clinging to the frail babe as a drowning man is said to cling to a straw, drifted away into the shadowy river that flows for ever to the unknown sea.

THE OUTCASTS OF POKER FLAT

As Mr. John Oakhurst, gambler, stepped into the main street of Poker Flat on the morning of the twenty-third of November, 1850, he was conscious of a change in its moral atmosphere since the preceding night. Two or three men, conversing earnestly together, ceased as he approached, and exchanged significant glances. There was a Sabbath lull in the air, which, in a settlement unused to Sabbath influences, looked ominous.

Mr. Oakhurst's calm, handsome face betrayed small concern in these indications. Whether he was conscious of any predisposing cause, was another question. "I reckon they're after somebody," he reflected; "likely it's me." He returned to his pocket the handkerchief with which he had been whipping away the red dust of Poker Flat from his neat boots, and quietly discharged his mind of any further conjecture.

In point of fact, Poker Flat was "after somebody." It had lately suffered the loss of several thousand dollars, two valuable horses, and a prominent citizen. It was experiencing a spasm of virtuous reaction, quite as lawless and ungovernable as any of the acts that had provoked it. A secret committee had determined to rid the town of all improper persons. This was done permanently in regard of two men who were then hanging from the boughs of a sycamore in the gulch, and temporarily in the banishment of certain other objectionable characters. I regret to say that some of these were ladies. It is but due to the sex, however, to state that their impropriety was professional, and it was only in such easily established standards of evil that Poker Flat ventured to sit in judgment.

Mr. Oakhurst was right in supposing that he was included in this category. A few of the committee had urged hanging him as a possible example, and a sure method of reimbursing themselves from his pockets of the sums he had won from them. "It's agin justice," said Jim Wheeler, "to let this yer young man from Roaring Camp—an entire stranger —carry away our money." But a crude sentiment of equity residing in the breasts of those who had been fortunate enough to win from Mr. Oakhurst overruled this narrower local prejudice.

Mr. Oakhurst received his sentence with philosophic calmness, none the less coolly that he was aware of the hesitation of his judges. He was too much of a gambler not to accept

Fate. With him life was at best an uncertain game, and he recognised the usual per-centage in favour of the dealer.

A party of armed men accompanied the deported wickedness of Poker Flat to the outskirts of the settlement. Besides Mr. Oakhurst, who was known to be a coolly desperate man, and for whose intimidation the armed escort was intended, the expatriated party consisted of a young woman familiarly known as "The Duchess;" another, who had bore the title of "Mother Shipton;" and "Uncle Billy," a suspected sluice-robber and confirmed drunkard. The cavalcade provoked no comments from the spectators, nor was any word uttered by the escort. Only when the gulch which marked the uttermost limit of Poker Flat was reached, the leader spoke briefly and to the point. The exiles were forbidden to return at the peril of their lives.

As the escort disappeared, their pent-up feelings found vent in a few hysterical tears from the Duchess, some bad language from Mother Shipton, and a Parthian volley of expletives from Uncle Billy. The philosophic Oakhurst alone remained silent. He listened calmly to Mother Shipton's desire to cut somebody's heart out, to the repeated statements of the Duchess that she would die in the road, and to the alarming oaths that seemed to be bumped out of Uncle Billy as he rode forward. With the easy good-humour characteristic of his class, he insisted upon exchanging his own riding-horse, "Five Spot," for the sorry mule which the Duchess rode. But even this act did not draw the party into any closer sympathy. The young woman readjusted her somewhat draggled plumes with a feeble, faded coquetry; Mother Shipton eyed the possessor of "Five Spot" with malevolence; and Uncle Billy included the whole party in one sweeping anathema.

The road to Sandy Bar—a camp that, not having as yet experienced the regenerating influences of Poker Flat, consequently seemed to offer some invitation to the emigrants— lay over a steep mountain range. It was distant a day's severe travel. In that advanced season, the party soon passed out of the moist, temperate regions of the foot-hills into the dry, cold, bracing air of the Sierras. The trail was narrow and difficult. At noon the Duchess, rolling out of her saddle upon the ground, declared her intention of going no farther, and the party halted.

The spot was singularly wild and impressive. A wooded amphitheatre, surrounded on three sides by precipitous cliffs of naked granite, sloped gently towards the crest of another precipice that overlooked the valley. It was, undoubtedly, the most suitable spot for a camp, had camping been advisable. But Mr. Oakhurst knew that scarcely half the journey to Sandy Bar was accomplished, and the party were not equipped or provisioned for delay. This fact he pointed out to his companions curtly, with a philosophic commentary on the folly of "throwing up their hand before the game was played out." But they were furnished with liquor, which in this emergency stood them in place of food, fuel, rest, and prescience. In spite of his remonstrances, it was not long before they were more or less under its influence. Uncle Billy passed rapidly from a bellicose state into one of stupor, the Duchess became maudlin, and Mother Shipton snored. Mr. Oakhurst alone remained erect, leaning against a rock, calmly surveying them.

Mr. Oakhurst did not drink. It interfered with a profession which required coolness, impassiveness, and presence of mind, and, in his own language, he "couldn't afford it." As he gazed at his recumbent fellow-exiles, the loneliness begotten of his pariah-trade, his habits of life, his very vices, for the first time seriously oppressed him. He bestirred himself in dusting his black clothes, washing his hands and face, and other acts characteristic of his studiously neat habits, and for a moment forgot his annoyance. The thought of deserting his weaker and more pitiable companions never perhaps occurred to him. Yet he could not help feeling the want of that excitement which, singularly enough, was most conducive to that calm equanimity for which he was notorious. He looked at the gloomy walls that rose a thousand feet sheer above the circling pines around him; at the sky, ominously clouded; at the valley below, already deepening into shadow. And, doing so, suddenly he heard his own name called.

A horseman slowly ascended the trail. In the fresh, open face of the new-comer, Mr. Oakhurst recognized Tom Simson, otherwise known as "The Innocent" of Sandy Bar. He had met him some months before over a "little game," and had, with perfect equanimity, won the entire fortune— amounting to some forty dollars—of that guileless youth. After the game was finished, Mr. Oakhurst drew the youthful speculator behind the door, and thus addressed him: "Tommy, you're a good little man, but you can't gamble worth a cent. Don't try it over again." He then handed him his money back, pushed him gently from the room, and so made a devoted slave of Tom Simson.

There was a remembrance of this in his boyish and enthusiastic greeting of Mr. Oakhurst. He had started, he said, to go to Poker Flat to seek his fortune. "Alone?" No, not exactly alone; in fact (a giggle), he had run away with Piney Woods. Didn't Mr. Oakhurst remember Piney? She that used to wait on the table at the Temperance House? They had been engaged a long time, but old Jake Woods had objected, and so they had run away, and were going to Poker Flat to be married; and here they were. And they were tired out, and how lucky it was they had found a place to camp and company. All this the Innocent delivered rapidly, while Piney, a stout, comely damsel of fifteen, emerged from behind the pine-tree, where she had been blushing unseen, and rode to the side of her lover.

Mr. Oakhurst seldom troubled himself with sentiment, still less with propriety; but he had a vague idea that the situation was not fortunate. He retained, however, his presence of mind sufficiently to kick Uncle Billy, who was about to say something, and Uncle Billy was sober enough to recognize in Mr. Oakhurst's kick a superior power that would not bear trifling. He then endeavoured to dissuade Tom Simson from delaying further, but in vain. He even pointed out the fact that there was no provision, nor means of making a camp. But, unluckily, the Innocent met this objection by assuring the party that he was provided with an extra mule loaded with provisions, and by the discovery of a rude attempt at a log-house near the trail. "Piney can stay with Mrs. Oakhurst," said the Innocent, pointing to the Duchess, "and I can shift for myself."

Nothing but Mr. Oakhurst's admonishing foot saved Uncle Billy from bursting into a roar of laughter. As it was, he felt compelled to retire up the cañon until he could recover his gravity. There he confided the joke to the tall pine-trees, with many slaps of his leg, contortions of his face, and the usual profanity. But when he returned to the party, he found them seated by a fire—for the air had grown strangely chill, and the sky overcast—in apparently amicable conversation. Piney was actually talking in an impulsive, girlish fashion to the Duchess, who was listening with an interest and animation she had not shown for many days. The Innocent was holding forth, apparently with equal effect, to Mr. Oakhurst and Mother Shipton, who was actually relaxing into amiability. "Is this yer a d—d pic-nic?" said Uncle Billy, with inward scorn, as he surveyed the sylvan group, the glancing firelight, and the tethered animals in the foreground. Suddenly an idea mingled with the alcoholic fumes that disturbed his brain. It was apparently of a jocular nature, for he felt impelled to slap his leg again and cram his fist into his mouth.

As the shadows crept slowly up the mountain, a slight breeze rocked the tops of the pine-trees, and moaned through their long and gloomy aisles. The ruined cabin, patched and covered with pine-boughs, was set apart for the ladies. As the lovers parted, they unaffectedly exchanged a kiss, so honest and sincere that it might have been heard above the swaying pines. The frail Duchess and the malevolent Mother Shipton were probably too stunned to remark upon this last evidence of simplicity, and so turned without a word to the hut. The fire was replenished, the men lay down before the door, and in a few minutes were asleep.

Mr. Oakhurst was a light sleeper. Toward morning he awoke benumbed and cold. As he stirred the dying fire, the wind, which was now blowing strongly, brought to his cheek that which caused the blood to leave it—snow!

He started to his feet with the intention of awakening the sleepers, for there was no time to lose. But turning to where Uncle Billy had been lying, he found him gone. A suspicion leaped to his brain and a curse to his lips. He ran to the spot where the mules had been tethered; they were no longer there. The tracks were already rapidly disappearing in the snow.

The momentary excitement brought Mr. Oakhurst back to the fire with his usual calm. He did not waken the sleepers. The Innocent slumbered peacefully, with a smile on his good-humoured, freckled face; the virgin Piney slept beside her frailer sisters as sweetly as though attended by celestial guardians, and Mr. Oakhurst, drawing his blanket over his shoulders, stroked his mustaches and waited for the dawn. It came slowly in a whirling mist of snow-flakes, that dazzled and confused the eye. What could be seen of the landscape appeared magically changed. He looked over the valley, and summed up the present and future in two words—"snowed in!"

A careful inventory of the provisions, which, fortunately for the party, had been stored within the hut, and so escaped the felonious fingers of Uncle Billy, disclosed the fact that with care and prudence they might last ten days longer. "That is," said Mr. Oakhurst, *sotto voce* to the Innocent, "if you're willing to board us. If you ain't—and perhaps you'd better not—you can wait till Uncle Billy gets back with provisions." For some occult reason Mr. Oakhurst could not bring himself to disclose Uncle Billy's rascality, and so offered the hypothesis that he had wandered from the camp and had accidentally stampeded the animals. He dropped a warning to the Duchess and Mother Shipton, who of course knew the facts of their associate's defection. "They'll find out the truth about us *all* when they find out anything," he added, significantly, "and there's no good frightening them now."

Tom Simson not only put all his worldly store at the disposal of Mr. Oakhurst, but seemed to enjoy the prospect of their enforced seclusion. "We'll have a good camp for a week, and then the snow'll melt, and we'll all go back together." The cheerful gaiety of the young man, and Mr. Oakhurst's calm infected the others. The Innocent, with the aid of pine-boughs, extemporized a thatch for the roofless cabin, and the Duchess directed Piney in the rearrangement of the interior with a taste and tact that opened the blue eyes of that provincial maiden to their fullest extent. "I reckon now you're used to fine things at Poker Flat," said Piney. The Duchess turned away sharply to conceal something that reddened her cheeks through its professional tint, and Mother Shipton requested Piney not to "chatter." But when Mr. Oakhurst returned from a weary search for the trail, he heard the sound of happy laughter echoed from the rocks. He stopped in some alarm, and his thoughts first naturally reverted to the whiskey, which he had prudently *cachéd*. "And yet it don't somehow sound like whiskey," said the gambler. It was not until he caught sight of the blazing fire through the still blinding storm and the group around it, that he settled to the conviction that it was "square fun."

Whether Mr. Oakhurst had *cachéd* his cards with the whiskey as something debarred the free access of the community, I cannot say. It was certain that, in Mother Shipton's words, he "didn't say cards once" during that evening. Haply the time was beguiled by an accordion, produced somewhat ostentatiously by Tom Simson from his pack. Notwithstanding some difficulties attending the manipulation of this instrument, Piney Woods managed to pluck several reluctant melodies from its keys, to an accompaniment by the Innocent on a pair of bone castanets. But the crowning festivity of the evening was reached in a rude camp-meeting hymn, which the lovers, joining hands, sang with great earnestness and vociferation. I fear that a certain defiant tone and Covenanter's swing to its chorus, rather than any devotional quality, caused it speedily to infect the others, who at last joined in the refrain:—

> "I'm proud to live in the service of the Lord,
> And I'm bound to die in His army."

The pines rocked, the storm eddied and whirled above the miserable group, and the flames of their altar leaped heavenward, as if in token of the vow.

At midnight the storm abated, the rolling clouds parted, and the stars glittered keenly above the sleeping camp. Mr. Oakhurst, whose professional habits had enabled him to live on the smallest possible amount of sleep, in dividing the watch with Tom Simson, somehow managed to take upon himself the greater part of that duty. He excused himself to the Innocent by saying that he had "often been a week without sleep." "Doing what?" asked Tom. "Poker!" replied Oakhurst, sententiously; "when a man gets a streak of luck—nigger-luck—he don't get tired. The luck gives in first. Luck," continued the gambler, reflectively, "is a mighty queer thing. All you know about it for certain is that it's bound to change. And it's finding out when it's going to change that makes you. We've had a streak of bad luck since we left Poker Flat—you come along, and slap you get into it, too. If you can hold your cards right along you're all right. For," added the gambler, with cheerful irrelevance—

> " 'I'm proud to live in the service of the Lord,
> And I'm bound to die in His army.' "

The third day came, and the sun, looking through the white-curtained valley, saw the outcasts divide their slowly decreasing store of provisions for the morning meal. It was one of the peculiarities of that mountain climate that its rays diffused a kindly warmth over the wintry landscape, as if in regretful commiseration of the past. But it revealed drift on drift of snow piled high around the hut—a hopeless, unchartered, trackless sea of white lying below the rocky shores to which the castaways still clung. Through the marvellously clear air the smoke of the pastoral village of Poker Flat rose miles away. Mother Shipton saw it, and from a remote pinnacle of her rocky fastness, hurled in that direction a final malediction. It was her last vituperative attempt, and perhaps for that reason was invested with a certain degree of sublimity. It did her good, she privately informed the Duchess. "Just you go out there and cuss, and see." She then set herself to the task of amusing "the child," as she and the Duchess were pleased to call Piney. Piney was no chicken, but it was a soothing and original theory of the pair thus to account for the fact that she didn't swear and wasn't improper.

When night crept up again through the gorges, the reedy notes of the accordion rose and fell in fitful spasms and long-drawn gasps by the flickering camp-fire. But music failed to fill entirely the aching void left by insufficient food, and a new diversion was proposed by Piney—story-telling. Neither Mr. Oakhurst nor his female companions caring to relate their personal experiences, this plan would have failed, too, but for the Innocent. Some months before he had chanced upon a stray copy of Mr. Pope's ingenious trans- lation of the Iliad. He now proposed to narrate the prin- cipal incidents of that poem—having thoroughly mastered the argument and fairly forgotten the words—in the current vernacular of Sandy Bar. And so for the rest of that night the Homeric demigods again walked the earth. Trojan bully and wily Greek wrestled in the winds, and the great pines in the cañon seemed to bow to the wrath of the son of Peleus. Mr. Oakhurst listened with quiet satisfaction. Most espe- cially was he interested in the fate of "Ash-heels," as the Innocent persisted in denominating the "swift-footed Achilles."

So with small food and much of Homer and the accordion, a week passed over the heads of the outcasts. The sun again forsook them, and again from leaden skies the snow-flakes were sifted over the land. Day by day closer around them drew the snowy circle, until at last they looked from their prison over drifted walls of drizzling white, that towered twenty feet above their heads. It became more and more difficult to replenish their fires, even from the fallen trees beside them, now half hidden in the drifts. And yet no one complained. The lovers turned from the dreary prospect, and looked into each other's eyes, and were happy. Mr. Oakhurst settled himself coolly to the losing game before him. The Duchess, more cheerful than she had been, assumed the care of Piney. Only Mother Shipton—once the strongest of the party—seemed to sicken and fade. At midnight on the tenth day she called Oakhurst to her side. "I'm going," she said, in a voice of querulous weakness, "but don't say anything about it. Don't waken the kids. Take the bundle from under my head and open it." Mr. Oakhurst did so. It contained Mother Shipton's rations for the last week, untouched. "Give 'em to the child," she said, pointing to the sleeping Piney. "You've starved yourself," said the gambler. "That's what they call it," said the woman, querulously, as she lay down again, and, turning her face to the wall, passed quietly away.

The accordion and the bones were put aside that day, and Homer was forgotten. When the body of Mother Shipton had been committed to the snow, Mr. Oakhurst took the Innocent aside, and showed him a pair of snow-shoes, which he had fashioned from the old pack-saddle. "There's one chance in a hundred to save her yet," he said, pointing to Piney; "but it's there," he added, pointing toward Poker Flat. "If you can reach there in two days she's safe." "And you?" asked Tom Simson. "I'll stay here," was the curt reply.

The lovers parted with a long embrace. "You are not going, too?" said the Duchess, as she saw Mr. Oakhurst apparently waiting to accompany him. "As far as the cañon," he replied. He turned suddenly, and kissed the Duchess, leaving her pallid face aflame, and her trembling limbs rigid with amazement.

Night came, but not Mr. Oakhurst. It brought the storm again and the whirling snow. Then the Duchess, feeding the fire, found that some one had quietly piled beside the hut enough fuel to last a few days longer. The tears rose to her eyes, but she hid them from Piney.

The women slept but little. In the morning, looking into each other's faces, they read their fate. Neither spoke; but Piney, accepting the position of the stronger, drew near and placed her arm around the Duchess's waist. They kept this attitude for the rest of the day. That night the storm reached its greatest fury, and, rending asunder the protecting pines, invaded the very hut.

Toward morning they found themselves unable to feed the fire, which gradually died away. As the embers slowly blackened, the Duchess crept closer to Piney, and broke the silence of many hours: "Piney, can you pray?" "No, dear," said Piney, simply. The Duchess, without knowing exactly why, felt relieved, and, putting her head upon Piney's shoulder, spoke no more. And so reclining, the younger and purer pillowing the head of her soiled sister upon her virgin breast, they fell asleep.

The wind lulled as if it feared to waken them. Feathery drifts of snow, shaken from the long pine-boughs, flew like white-winged birds, and settled about them as they slept. The moon through the rifted clouds looked down upon what had been the camp. But all human stain, all trace of earthly travail, was hidden beneath the spotless mantle mercifully flung from above.

They slept all that day and the next, nor did they waken when voices and footsteps broke the silence of the camp. And when pitying fingers brushed the snow from their wan faces, you could scarcely have told, from the equal peace that dwelt upon them, which was she that had sinned. Even the law of Poker Flat recognized this, and turned away, leaving them still locked in each other's arms.

But at the head of the gulch, on one of the largest pine-trees, they found the deuce of clubs pinned to the bark with a bowie-knife. It bore the following, written in pencil, in a firm hand:—

✝

BENEATH THIS TREE
LIES THE BODY
OF
JOHN OAKHURST,
WHO STRUCK A STREAK OF BAD LUCK
ON THE 23RD OF NOVEMBER, 1850,
AND
HANDED IN HIS CHECKS
ON THE 7TH DECEMBER, 1850.

✝

And pulseless and cold, with a Derringer by his side and a bullet in his heart, though still calm as in life, beneath the snow lay he who was at once the strongest and yet the weakest of the outcasts of Poker Flat.

MIGGLES

WE WERE eight, including the driver. We had not spoken during the passage of the last six miles, since the jolting of the heavy vehicle over the roughening road had spoiled the Judge's last poetical quotation. The tall man beside the Judge was asleep, his arm passed through the swaying strap and his head resting upon it—altogether a limp, helpless-looking object, as if he had hanged himself and been cut down too late. The French lady on the back seat was asleep, too, yet in a half-conscious propriety of attitude, shown even in the disposition of the handkerchief which she held to her forehead, and which partially veiled her face. The lady from Virginia City, travelling with her husband,

had long since lost all individuality in a wild confusion of
ribbons, veils, furs, and shawls. There was no sound but the
rattling of wheels and the dash of rain upon the roof. Suddenly the stage stopped, and we became dimly aware of
voices. The driver was evidently in the midst of an exciting
colloquy with some one in the road—a colloquy of which
such fragments as "bridge gone," "twenty feet of water,"
"can't pass," were occasionally distinguishable above the
storm. Then came a lull, and a mysterious voice from the
road shouted the parting adjuration,—

"Try Miggles's."

We caught a glimpse of our leaders as the vehicle slowly
turned, of a horseman vanishing through the rain, and we
were evidently on our way to Miggles's.

Who and where was Miggles? The Judge, our authority,
did not remember the name, and he knew the country thoroughly. The Washoe traveller thought Miggles must keep
a hotel. We only knew that we were stopped by high
water in front and rear, and that Miggles was our rock of
refuge. A ten minutes' splashing through a tangled by-road,
scarcely wide enough for the stage, and we drew up before
a barred and boarded gate in a wide stone wall or fence
about eight feet high. Evidently Miggles's, and evidently
Miggles did not keep a hotel.

The driver got down and tried the gate. It was securely
locked.

"Miggles! O Miggles!"

No answer.

"Migg-ells! You Miggles!" continued the driver, with
rising wrath.

"Migglesy!" joined in the expressman, persuasively. "O
Miggy! Mig!"

But no reply came from the apparently insensate Miggles.
The Judge, who had finally got the window down, put his
head out and propounded a series of questions, which if
answered categorically would have undoubtedly elucidated
the whole mystery, but which the driver evaded by replying

that "if we didn't want to sit in the coach all night, we had better rise up and sing out for Miggles."

So we rose up and called on Miggles in chorus; then separately. And when we had finished, a Hibernian fellow-passenger from the roof called for "Maygells!" whereat we all laughed. While we were laughing, the driver cried "Shoo!"

We listened. To our infinite amazement the chorus of "Miggles" was repeated from the other side of the wall, even to the final and supplemental "Maygells."

"Extraordinary echo," said the Judge.

"Extraordinary d—d skunk!" roared the driver, contemptuously. "Come out of that, Miggles, and show yourself! Be a man, Miggles! Don't hide in the dark; I wouldn't if I were you, Miggles," continued Yuba Bill, now dancing about in an excess of fury.

"Miggles!" continued the voice, "O Miggles!"

"My good man! Mr. Myghail!" said the Judge, softening the asperities of the name as much as possible. "Consider the inhospitality of refusing shelter from the inclemency of the weather to helpless females. Really, my dear sir——" But a succession of "Miggles," ending in a burst of laughter, drowned his voice.

Yuba Bill hesitated no longer. Taking a heavy stone from the road, he battered down the gate, and with the expressman entered the enclosure. We followed. Nobody was to be seen. In the gathering darkness all that we could distinguish was that we were in a garden—from the rosebushes that scattered over us a minute spray from their dripping leaves—and before a long, rambling wooden building.

"Do you know this Miggles?" asked the Judge of Yuba Bill.

"No, nor don't want to," said Bill, shortly, who felt the Pioneer Stage Company insulted in his person by the contumacious Miggles.

"But, my dear sir," expostulated the Judge, as he thought of the barred gate.

"Lookee here," said Yuba Bill, with fine irony, "hadn't you better go back and sit in the coach till yer introduced? I'm going in," and he pushed open the door of the building.

A long room lighted only by the embers of a fire that was dying on the large hearth at its further extremity! the walls curiously papered, and the flickering firelight bringing out its grotesque pattern; somebody sitting in a large arm-chair by the fireplace. All this we saw as we crowded together into the room after the driver and expressman.

"Hello, be you Miggles?" said Yuba Bill to the solitary occupant.

The figure neither spoke nor stirred. Yuba Bill walked wrathfully toward it, and turned the eye of his coach-lantern upon its face. It was a man's face, prematurely old and wrinkled, with very large eyes, in which there was that expression of perfectly gratuitous solemnity which I had sometimes seen in an owl's. The large eyes wandered from Bill's face to the lantern, and finally fixed their gaze on that luminous object, without further recognition.

Bill restrained himself with an effort.

"Miggles! Be you deaf? You ain't dumb anyhow, you know;" and Yuba Bill shook the insensate figure by the shoulder.

To our great dismay, as Bill removed his hand, the venerable stranger apparently collapsed,—sinking into half his size and an undistinguishable heap of clothing.

"Well, dern my skin," said Bill, looking appealingly at us, and hopelessly retiring from the contest.

The Judge now stepped forward, and we lifted the mysterious invertebrate back into his original position. Bill was dismissed with the lantern to reconnoitre outside, for it was evident that from the helplessness of this solitary man there must be attendants near at hand, and we all drew around the fire. The Judge, who had regained his authority, and had never lost his conversational amiability, standing before us with his back to the hearth,—charged us, as an imaginary jury, as follows:—

"It is evident that either our distinguished friend here

has reached that condition described by Shakespeare as 'the sere and yellow leaf,' or has suffered some premature abatement of his mental and physical faculties. Whether he is really the Miggles——"

Here he was interrupted by "Miggles! O Miggles! Migglesy! Mig!" and, in fact, the whole chorus of Miggles in very much the same key as it had once before been delivered unto us.

We gazed at each other for a moment in some alarm. The Judge, in particular, vacated his position quickly, as the voice seemed to come directly over his shoulder. The cause, however, was soon discovered in a large magpie who was perched upon a shelf over the fireplace, and who immediately relapsed into a sepulchral silence, which contrasted singularly with his previous volubility. It was, undoubtedly, his voice which we had heard in the road, and our friend in the chair was not responsible for the discourtesy. Yuba Bill, who re-entered the room after an unsuccessful search, was loath to accept the explanation, and still eyed the helpless sitter with suspicion. He had found a shed in which he had put up his horses, but he came back dripping and sceptical. "Thar ain't nobody but him within ten mile of the shanty, and that 'ar d—d old skeesicks knows it."

But the faith of the majority proved to be securely based. Bill had scarcely ceased growling before we heard a quick step upon the porch, the trailing of a wet skirt; the door was flung open, and, with a flash of white teeth, a sparkle of dark eyes, and an utter absence of ceremony or diffidence, a young woman entered, shut the door, and, panting, leaned back against it.

"Oh, if you please, I'm Miggles!"

And this was Miggles! this bright-eyed, full-throated young woman, whose wet gown of coarse blue stuff could not hide the beauty of the feminine curves to which it clung; from the chestnut crown of whose head, topped by a man's oil-skin sou'wester, to the little feet and ankles, hidden somewhere in the recesses of her boy's brogans, all was grace;—this was Miggles, laughing at us, too, in the most airy, frank, off-hand manner imaginable.

"You see, boys," said she, quite out of breath, and holding one little hand against her side, quite unheeding the speechless discomfiture of our party, or the complete demoralization of Yuba Bill, whose features had relaxed into an expression of gratuitous and imbecile cheerfulness,—"you see, boys, I was mor'n two miles away when you passed down the road. I thought you might pull up here, and so I ran the whole way, knowing nobody was home but Jim,—and—and—I'm out of breath—and—that lets me out."

And here Miggles caught her dripping oil-skin hat from her head, with a mischievous swirl that scattered a shower of rain-drops over us; attempted to put back her hair; dropped two hair-pins in the attempt; laughed and sat down beside Yuba Bill, with her hands crossed lightly on her lap.

The Judge recovered himself first, and essayed an extravagant compliment.

"I'll trouble you for that thar har-pin," said Miggles, gravely. Half a dozen hands were eagerly stretched forward; the missing hair-pin was restored to its fair owner; and Miggles, crossing the room, looked keenly in the face of the invalid. The solemn eyes looked back at hers with an expression we had never seen before. Life and intelligence seemed to struggle back into the rugged face. Miggles laughed again,—it was a singularly eloquent laugh,—and turned her black eyes and white teeth once more towards us.

"This afflicted person is——" hesitated the Judge.

"Jim," said Miggles.

"Your father?"

"No."

"Brother?"

"No."

"Husband?"

Miggles darted a quick, half-defiant glance at the two lady passengers who I had noticed did not participate in the general masculine admiration of Miggles, and said, gravely, "No; it's Jim."

There was an awkward pause. The lady passengers moved closer to each other; the Washoe husband looked abstractedly at the fire; and the tall man apparently turned his eyes inward for self-support at this emergency. But Miggles's laugh, which was very infectious, broke the silence. "Come," she said, briskly, "you must be hungry. Who'll bear a hand to help me to get tea?"

She had no lack of volunteers. In a few moments Yuba Bill was engaged like Caliban in bearing logs for this Miranda; the expressman was grinding coffee on the verandah; to myself the arduous duty of slicing bacon was assigned; and the Judge lent each man his good-humoured and voluble counsel. And when Miggles, assisted by the Judge and our Hibernian "deck passenger," set the table with all the available crockery, we had become quite joyous, in spite of the rain that beat against windows, the wind that whirled down the chimney, the two ladies who whispered together in the corner, or the magpie who uttered a satirical and croaking commentary on their conversation from his perch above. In the now bright, blazing fire, we could see that the walls were papered with illustrated journals, arranged with feminine taste and discrimination. The furniture was extemporized, and adapted from candle-boxes and packing-cases, and covered with gay calico, or the skin of some animal. The arm-chair of the helpless Jim was an ingenious variation of a flour-barrel. There was neatness, and even a taste for the picturesque, to be seen in the few details of the long low room.

The meal was a culinary success. But more, it was a social triumph,—chiefly, I think, owing to the rare tact of Miggles in guiding the conversation, asking all the questions herself, yet bearing throughout a frankness that rejected the idea of any concealment on her own part, so that we talked of ourselves, of our prospects, of the journey, of the weather, of each other,—of everything but our host and hostess. It must be confessed that Miggles's conversation was never elegant, rarely grammatical, and that at times she employed expletives, the use of which had generally been yielded to our sex. But they were delivered with such a lighting up of teeth and eyes, and were usually followed by a laugh—a laugh peculiar to Miggles—so frank and honest that it seemed to clear the moral atmosphere.

Once, during the meal, we heard a noise like the rubbing of a heavy body against the outer walls of the house. This was shortly followed by a scratching and sniffling at the door. "That's Joaquin," said Miggles, in reply to our questioning glances; "would you like to see him?" Before we could answer she had opened the door, and disclosed a half-grown grizzly, who instantly raised himself on his haunches, with his forepaws hanging down in the popular attitude of mendicancy, and looked admiringly at Miggles, with a very singular resemblance in his manner to Yuba Bill. "That's my watch-dog," said Miggles, in explanation, "Oh, he don't bite," she added, as the two lady passengers fluttered into a corner. "Does he, old Toppy?" (the latter remark being addressed directly to the sagacious Joaquin). "I tell you what, boys," continued Miggles, after she had fed and closed the door on *Ursa Minor*, "you were in big luck that Joaquin wasn't hanging round when you dropped in tonight." "Where was he?" asked the Judge. "With me," said Miggles. "Lord love you; he trots round with me nights like as if he was a man."

We were silent for a few moments, and listened to the wind. Perhaps we all had the same picture before us,—of Miggles walking through the rainy woods, with her savage guardian at her side. The Judge, I remember, said something about Una and her lion; but Miggles received it as she did other compliments, with quiet gravity. Whether she was altogether unconscious of the admiration she excited—she could hardly have been oblivious of Yuba Bill's adoration—I know not; but her very frankness suggested a perfect sexual equality that was cruelly humiliating to the younger members of our party.

The incident of the bear did not add anything in Miggles's

favour to the opinions of those of her own sex who were
present. In fact, the repast over, a chillness radiated from
the two lady passengers that no pine-boughs brought in by
Yuba Bill and cast as a sacrifice upon the hearth could
wholly overcome. Miggles felt it; and, suddenly declaring
that it was time to "turn in," offered to show the ladies to
their bed in an adjoining room. "You, boys, will have to
camp out here by the fire as well as you can," she added,
"for thar ain't but the one room."

Our sex—by which, my dear sir, I allude of course to the
stronger portion of humanity—has been generally relieved
from the imputation of curiosity, or a fondness for gossip.
Yet I am constrained to say, that hardly had the door
closed on Miggles than we crowded together, whispering,
snickering, smiling, and exchanging suspicions, surmises, and
a thousand speculations in regard to our pretty hostess and
her singular companion. I fear that we even hustled that
imbecile paralytic, who sat like a voiceless Memnon in our
midst, gazing with the serene indifference of the Past in his
passionless eyes upon our wordy counsels. In the midst of
an exciting discussion the door opened again and Miggles
re-entered.

But not, apparently, the same Miggles who a few hours
before had flashed upon us. Her eyes were downcast, and
as she hesitated for a moment on the threshold, with a
blanket on her arm, she seemed to have left behind her the
frank fearlessness which had charmed us a moment before.
Coming into the room, she drew a low stool beside the
paralytic's chair, sat down, drew the blanket over her
shoulders, and saying, "If it's all the same to you, boys, as
we're rather crowded, I'll stop here to-night," took the invalid's withered hand in her own, and turned her eyes upon
the dying fire. An instinctive feeling that this was only
premonitory to more confidential relations, and perhaps
some shame at our previous curiosity kept us silent. The
rain still beat upon the roof, wandering gusts of wind stirred
the embers into momentary brightness, until, in a lull of the
elements, Miggles suddenly lifted up her head, and throw-

ing her hair over her shoulder, turned her face upon the group and asked,—

"Is there any of you that knows me?"

There was no reply.

"Think again! I lived at Marysville in '53. Everybody knew me there, and everybody had the right to know me. I kept the Polka Saloon until I came to live with Jim. That's six years ago. Perhaps I've changed some."

The absence of recognition may have disconcerted her. She turned her head to the fire again, and it was some seconds before she again spoke, and then more rapidly,—

"Well, you see, I thought some of you must have known me. There's no great harm done, anyway. What I was going to say was this: Jim here"—she took his hand in both of hers as she spoke—"used to know me, if you didn't, and spent a heap of money upon me. I reckon he spent all he had. And one day—it's six years ago—Jim came into my back room, sat down on my sofy, like as you see him in that chair, and never moved again without help. He was struck all of a heap, and never seemed to know what ailed him. The doctors came and said as how it was caused all along of his way of life—for Jim was mighty free and wild like—and that he would never get better, and couldn't last long anyway. They advised me to send him to Frisco, to the hospital for he was no good to any one and would be a baby all his life. Perhaps it was something in Jim's eye, perhaps it was that I never had a baby, but I said 'No.' I was rich then, for I was popular with everybody—gentlemen like yourself, sir, came to see me—and I sold out my business and bought this yer place, because it was sort of out of the way of travel, you see, and I brought my baby here."

With a woman's intuitive tact and poetry, she had, as she spoke, slowly shifted her position so as to bring the mute figure of the ruined man between her and her audience, hiding in the shadow behind it, as if she offered it as a tacit apology for her actions. Silent and expressionless, it yet spoke for her; helpless, crushed, and smitten with the

Divine thunderbolt, it still stretched an invisible arm around her.

Hidden in the darkness, but still holding his hand, she went on,—

"It was a long time before I could get the hang of things about yer, for I was used to company and excitement. I couldn't get any woman to help me, and a man I dursent trust; but what with the Indians hereabout, who'd do odd jobs for me, and having everything sent from the North Fork, Jim and I managed to worry through. The Doctor would run up from Sacramento once in a while. He'd ask to see 'Miggles's baby,' as he called Jim, and when he'd go away, he'd say, 'Miggles, you're a trump, God bless you!' and it didn't seem so lonely after that. But the last time he was here, he said, as he opened the door to go, 'Do you know, Miggles, your baby will grow up to be a man yet and an honour to his mother; but not here, Miggles, not here!' And I thought he went away sad—and—and—" and here Miggles's voice and head were somehow both lost completely in the shadow.

"The folks about here are very kind," said Miggles, after a pause, coming a little into the light again. "The men from the fork used to hang around here, until they found they wasn't wanted, and the women are kind—and don't call. I was pretty lonely until I picked up Joaquin in the woods yonder one day, when he wasn't so high, and taught him to beg for his dinner; and then thar's Polly—that's the magpie—she knows no end of tricks, and makes it quite sociable of evenings with her talk, and so I don't feel like as I was the only living being about the ranch. And Jim here," said Miggles, with her old laugh again, and coming out quite into the firelight, "Jim—why, boys, you would admire to see how much he knows for a man like him. Sometimes I bring him flowers, and he looks at 'em just as natural as if he knew 'em; and times, when we're sitting alone, I read him those things on the wall. Why, Lord!" said Miggles, with her frank laugh, "I've read him that whole side of the house this winter. There never was such a man for reading as Jim."

"Why," asked the Judge, "do you not marry this man to whom you have devoted your youthful life?"

"Well, you see," said Miggles, "it would be playing it rather low down on Jim, to take advantage of his being so helpless. And then, too, if we were man and wife, now, we'd both know that I was *bound* to do what I do now of my own accord."

"But you are young yet and attractive——"

"It's getting late," said Miggles, gravely, "and you'd better all turn in. Good-night, boys;" and, throwing the blanket over her head, Miggles laid herself down beside Jim's chair, her head pillowed on the low stool that held his feet, and spoke no more. The fire slowly faded from the hearth; we each sought our blankets in silence; and presently there was no sound in the long room but the pattering of the rain upon the roof, and the heavy breathing of the sleepers.

It was nearly morning when I awoke from a troubled dream. The storm had passed, the stars were shining, and through the shutterless window the full moon, lifting itself over the solemn pines without, looked into the room. It touched the lonely figure in the chair with an infinite compassion, and seemed to baptize with a shining flood the lowly head of the woman whose hair, as in the sweet old story, bathed the feet of him she loved. It even lent a kindly poetry to the rugged outline of Yuba Bill, half reclining on his elbow between them and his passengers, with savagely patient eyes keeping watch and ward. And then I fell asleep and only woke at broad day, with Yuba Bill standing over me, and "All aboard" ringing in my ears.

Coffee was waiting for us on the table, but Miggles was gone. We wandered about the house and lingered long after the horses were harnessed, but she did not return. It was evident that she wished to avoid a formal leave-taking, and had so left us to depart as we had come. After we had helped the ladies into the coach, we returned to the house and solemnly shook hands with the paralytic Jim, as solemnly settling him back into position after each handshake. Then we looked for the last time around the long low room, at the stool where Miggles had sat, and slowly took our seats in the waiting coach. The whip cracked, and we were off!

But as we reached the high-road, Bill's dexterous hand laid the six horses back on their haunches, and the stage stopped with a jerk. For there, on a little eminence beside the road, stood Miggles, her hair flying, her eyes sparkling, her white handkerchief waving, and her white teeth flashing a last "good-by." We waved our hats in return. And then Yuba Bill, as if fearful of further fascination, madly lashed his horses forward, and we sank back in our seats. We exchanged not a word until we reached the North Fork and the stage drew up at the Independence House. Then, the Judge leading, we walked into the bar-room and took our places gravely at the bar.

"Are your glasses charged, gentlemen?" said the Judge, solemnly taking off his white hat.

They were.

"Well, then, here's to *Miggles*, GOD BLESS HER!"

Perhaps He had. Who knows?

TENNESSEE'S PARTNER

I DO not think that we ever knew his real name. Our ignorance of it certainly never gave us any social inconvenience, for at Sandy Bar in 1854 most men were christened anew. Sometimes these appellatives were derived from some distinctiveness of dress, as in the case of "Dungaree Jack;" or from some peculiarity of habit, as shown in "Saleratus Bill," so called from an undue proportion of that chemical in his daily bread; or from some unlucky slip, as exhibited in "The Iron Pirate," a mild, inoffensive man, who earned that baleful title by his unfortunate mispronunciation of the term "iron pyrites." Perhaps this may have been the beginning of a rude heraldry; but I am constrained to think that it was because a man's real name in that day rested solely upon his own unsupported statement. "Call yourself Clifford, do you?" said Boston, addressing a timid new-comer with infinite scorn; "hell is full of such Cliffords!" He then introduced the unfortunate man, whose name happened to be really Clifford, as "Jay-bird Charley," —an unhallowed inspiration of the moment, that clung to him ever after.

But to return to Tennessee's Partner, whom we never knew by any other than this relative title; that he had ever existed as a separate and distinct individuality we only learned later. It seems that in 1853 he left Poker Flat to go to San Francisco, ostensibly to procure a wife. He never got any father than Stockton. At that place he was attracted by a young person who waited upon the table at the hotel where he took his meals. One morning he said something to her which caused her to smile not unkindly, to somewhat coquettishly break a plate of toast over his upturned, serious, simple face, and to retreat to the kitchen. He followed her, and emerged a few moments later, covered with more toast and victory. That day week they were married by a Justice of the Peace, and returned to Poker Flat. I am aware that something more might be made of this episode, but I prefer to tell it as it was current at Sandy Bar—in the gulches and bar rooms—where all sentiment was modified by a strong sense of humour.

Of their married felicity but little is known, perhaps for the reason that Tennessee, then living with his partner, one day took occasion to say something to the bride on his own account, at which, it is said, she smiled not unkindly and chastely retreated,—this time as far as Marysville, where Tennessee followed her, and where they went to housekeeping without the aid of a Justice of the Peace. Tennessee's Partner took the loss of his wife simply and seriously, as was his fashion. But to everybody's surprise, when Tennessee one day returned from Marysville, without his partner's wife,—she having smiled and retreated with somebody else,—Tennessee's Partner was the first man to shake his hand and greet him with affection. The boys who had gathered in the cañon to see the shooting were naturally indignant. Their indignation might have found vent in sarcasm but for a certain look in Tennessee's Partner's eye that indicated a lack of humourous appreciation. In fact, he was a grave man, with a steady application to practical detail which was unpleasant in a difficulty.

Meanwhile a popular feeling against Tennessee had grown up on the Bar. He was known to be a gambler; he was suspected to be a thief. In these suspicions Tennessee's Partner was equally compromised; his continued intimacy with Tennessee after the affair above quoted could only be accounted for on the hypothesis of a copartnership of crime. At last Tennessee's guilt became flagrant. One day he overtook a stranger on his way to Red Dog. The stranger afterward related that Tennessee beguiled the time with interesting anecdote and reminiscence, but illogically concluded the interview in the following words: "And now, young man, I'll trouble you for your knife, your pistols, and your money. You see your weppings might get you into trouble at Red Dog, and your money's a temptation to the evilly disposed. I think you said your address was San Francisco. I shall endeavour to call." It may be stated here that Tennessee had a fine flow of humour, which no business preoccupation could wholly subdue.

This exploit was his last. Red Dog and Sandy Bar made common cause against the highwayman. Tennessee was hunted in very much the same fashion as his prototype, the grizzly. As the toils closed around him, he made a desperate dash through the Bar, emptying his revolver at the crowd before the Arcade Saloon, and so on up Grizzly Cañon; but at its farther extremity he was stopped by a small man on a gray horse. The men looked at each other a moment in silence. Both were fearless, both self-possessed and independent; and both types of a civilization that in the seventeenth century would have been called heroic, but, in the

nineteenth, simply "reckless." "What have you got there?
—I call," said Tennessee, quietly. "Two bowers and an
ace," said the stranger, as quietly, showing two revolvers
and a bowie knife. "That takes me," returned Tennessee;
and with this gambler's epigram, he threw away his useless
pistol, and rode back with his captor.

It was a warm night. The cool breeze which usually
sprang up with the going down of the sun behind the *cha-
parral*-crested mountain was that evening withheld from
Sandy Bar. The little cañon was stifling with heated
resinous odours, and the decaying drift-wood on the Bar
sent forth faint, sickening exhalations. The feverishness of
day, and its fierce passions, still filled the camp. Lights
moved restlessly along the bank of the river, striking no answering reflection from its tawny current. Against the
blackness of the pines the windows of the old loft above the
express-office stood out staringly bright; and through their
curtainless panes the loungers below could see the forms of
those who were even then deciding the fate of Tennessee.
And above all this, etched on the dark firmament, rose the
Sierra, remote and passionless, crowned with remoter passionless stars.

The trial of Tennessee was conducted as fairly as was consistent with a judge and jury who felt themselves to some
extent obliged to justify, in their verdict, the previous ir-
regularities of arrest and indictment. The law of Sandy
Bar was implacable, but not vengeful. The excitement and
personal feeling of the chase were over; with Tennessee safe
in their hands they were ready to listen patiently to any
defence, which they were already satisfied was insufficient.
There being no doubt in their own minds, they were willing
to give the prisoner the benefit of any that might exist.
Secure in the hypothesis that he ought to be hanged, on
general principles, they indulged him with more latitude of
defence than his reckless hardihood seemed to ask. The
Judge appeared to be more anxious than the prisoner, who,
otherwise unconcerned, evidently took a grim pleasure in the

responsibility he had created. "I don't take any hand in this yer game," had been his invariable, but good-humoured reply to all questions. The Judge—who was also his captor—for a moment vaguely regretted that he had not shot him "on sight," that morning, but presently dismissed this human weakness as unworthy of the judicial mind. Nevertheless, when there was a tap at the door, and it was said that Tennessee's Partner was there on behalf of the prisoner, he was admitted at once without question. Perhaps the younger members of the jury, to whom the proceedings were becoming irksomely thoughtful, hailed him as a relief.

For he was not, certainly, an imposing figure. Short and stout, with a square face, sunburned into a preternatural redness, clad in a loose duck "jumper," and trousers streaked and splashed with red soil, his aspect under any circumstances would have been quaint, and was now even ridiculous. As he stooped to deposit at his feet a heavy carpet-bag he was carrying, it became obvious, from partially developed regions and inscriptions, that the material with which his trousers had been patched had been originally intended for a less ambitious covering. Yet he advanced with great gravity, and after having shaken the hand of each person in the room with laboured cordiality, he wiped his serious, perplexed face on a red bandanna handkerchief, a shade lighter than his complexion, laid his powerful hand upon the table to steady himself, and thus addressed the Judge:—

"I was passin' by," he began, by way of apology, "and I thought I'd just step in and see how things was gittin' on with Tennessee thar—my pardner. It's a hot night. I disremember any sich weather before on the Bar."

He paused a moment, but nobody volunteering any other meteorological recollection, he again had recourse to his pocket-handkerchief, and for some moments mopped his face diligently.

"Have you anything to say in behalf of the prisoner?" said the Judge, finally.

"Thet's it," said Tennessee's Partner, in a tone of relief. "I come yar as Tennessee's pardner—knowing him nigh on four years, off and on, wet and dry, in luck and out o' luck. His ways ain't allers my ways, but thar ain't any p'ints in that young man, thar ain't any liveliness as he's been up to, as I don't know. And you sez to me, sez you—confidential-like, and between man and man—sez you, 'Do you know anything in his behalf?' and I sez to you, sez I—confidential-like, as between man and man—'What should a man know of his pardner?'"

"Is this all you have to say?" asked the Judge, impatiently, feeling, perhaps, that a dangerous sympathy of humour was beginning to humanize the Court.

"Thet's so," continued Tennessee's Partner. "It ain't for me to say anything agin' him. And now what's the case? Here's Tennessee wants money, wants it bad, and doesn't like to ask it of his old pardner. Well, what does Tennessee do? He lays for a stranger, and he fetches that stranger. And you lays for *him*, and you fetches *him*; and the honours is easy. And I put it to you, bein' a far-minded man, and to you, gentlemen, all, as far-minded men, ef this isn't so."

"Prisoner," said the Judge, interrupting, "have you any questions to ask this man?"

"No! no!" continued Tennessee's Partner, hastily. "I play this yer hand alone. To come down to the bed-rock, it's just this: Tennessee, thar, has played it pretty rough and expensive-like on a stranger, and on this yer camp. And now, what's the fair thing? Some would say more; some would say less. Here's seventeen hundred dollars in coarse gold and a watch,—it's about all my pile,—and call it square!" And before a hand could be raised to prevent him, he had emptied the contents of the carpet-bag upon the table.

For a moment his life was in jeopardy. One or two men sprang to their feet, several hands groped for hidden weapons, and a suggestion to "throw him from the window" was only overridden by a gesture from the Judge. Tennessee laughed. And apparently oblivious of the excitement, Tennessee's Partner improved the opportunity to mop his face again with his handkerchief.

When order was restored, and the man was made to understand, by the use of forcible figures and rhetoric, that Tennessee's offence could not be condoned by money, his face took a more serious and sanguinary hue, and those who were nearest to him noticed that his rough hand trembled slightly on the table. He hesitated a moment as he slowly returned the gold to the carpet-bag, as if he had not yet entirely caught the elevated sense of justice which swayed the tribunal, and was perplexed with the belief that he had not offered enough. Then he turned to the Judge, and saying, "This yer is a lone hand, played alone, and without my pardner," he bowed to the jury and was about to withdraw, when the Judge called him back. "If you have anything to say to Tennessee, you had better say it now." For the first time that evening the eyes of the prisoner and his strange advocate met. Tennessee smiled, showed his white teeth, and saying, "Euchred, old man!" held out his hand. Tennessee's Partner took it in his own, and saying, "I just dropped in as I was passin' to see how things was gettin' on," let the hand passively fall, and adding that "it was a warm night," again mopped his face with his handkerchief, and without another word withdrew.

The two men never again met each other alive. For the unparalleled insult of a bribe offered to Judge Lynch—who, whether bigoted, weak, or narrow, was at least incorruptible —firmly fixed in the mind of that mythical personage any wavering determination of Tennessee's fate; and at the break of day he was marched, closely guarded, to meet it at the top of Marley's Hill.

How he met it, how cool he was, how he refused to say anything, how perfect were the arrangements of the committee, were all duly reported, with the addition of a warning moral and example to all future evil-doers, in the Red Dog Clarion, by its editor, who was present, and to whose vigorous English I cheerfully refer the reader. But the beauty of that midsummer morning, the blessed amity of

earth and air and sky, the awakened life of the free woods
and hills, the joyous renewal and promise of Nature, and
above all, the infinite Serenity that thrilled through each,
was not reported, as not being a part of the social lesson.
And yet, when the weak and foolish deed was done, and a
life, with its possibilities and responsibilities, had passed out
of the misshapen thing that dangled between earth and sky,
the birds sang, the flowers bloomed, the sun shone, as
cheerily as before; and possibly the Red Dog Clarion was
right.

Tennessee's Partner was not in the group that surrounded
the ominous tree. But as they turned to disperse, attention was drawn to the singular appearance of a motionless
donkey-cart halted at the side of the road. As they approached, they at once recognised the venerable "Jenny"
and the two-wheeled cart as the property of Tennessee's
Partner,—used by him in carrying dirt from his claim; and
a few paces distant the owner of the equipage himself, sit-
ing under a buckeye-tree, wiping the perspiration from his
glowing face. In answer to an inquiry, he said he had come
for the body of the "diseased" "if it was all the same to the
committee." He didn't wish to "hurry anything;" he could
"wait." He was not working that day; and when the
gentlemen were done with the "diseased," he would take
him. "Ef thar is any present," he added, in his simple,
serious way, "as would care to jine in the fun'l, they kin
come." Perhaps it was from a sense of humour, which I
have already intimated was a feature of Sandy Bar,—perhaps it was from something even better than that; but two-
thirds of the loungers accepted the invitation at once.

It was noon when the body of Tennessee was delivered
into the hands of his partner. As the cart drew up to the
fatal tree, we noticed that it contained a rough oblong box,
apparently made from a section of sluicing,—and half filled
with bark and the tassels of pine. The cart was further
decorated with slips of willow, and made fragrant with
buckeye-blossoms. When the body was deposited in the
box, Tennessee's Partner drew over it a piece of tarred

canvas, and gravely mounting the narrow seat in front, with his feet upon the shafts, urged the little donkey forward. The equipage moved slowly on, at that decorous pace which was habitual with "Jenny," even under less solemn circumstances. The men—half-curiously, half-jestingly, but all good-humouredly—strolled along beside the cart; some in advance, some a little in the rear of the homely catafalque. But, whether from the narrowing of the road or some present sense of decorum, as the cart passed on the company fell to the rear in couples, keeping step, and otherwise assuming the external show of a formal procession. Jack Folinsbee, who had at the outset played a funeral march in dumb show upon an imaginary trombone, desisted, from a lack of sympathy and appreciation,—not having, perhaps, your true humourist's capacity to be content with the enjoyment of his own fun.

The way led through Grizzly Cañon—by this time clothed in funereal drapery and shadows. The red-woods, burying their moccasined feet in the red soil, stood in Indian file along the track, trailing an uncouth benediction from their bending boughs upon the passing bier. A hare, surprised into helpless activity, sat upright and pulsating in the ferns by the roadside as the *cortége* went by. Squirrels hastened to gain a secure outlook from higher boughs; and the blue-jays, spreading their wings, fluttered before them like outriders, until the outskirts of Sandy Bar were reached, and the solitary cabin of Tennessee's Partner.

Viewed under more favourable circumstances, it would not have been a cheerful place. The unpicturesque site, the rude and unlovely outlines, the unsavoury details, which distinguish the nest-building of the California miner, were all here, with the dreariness of decay superadded. A few paces from the cabin there was a rough enclosure, which, in the brief days of Tennessee's Partner's matrimonial felicity, had been used as a garden, but was now overgrown with fern. As we approached it, we were surprised to find that what we had taken for a recent attempt at cultivation was the broken soil about an open grave.

The cart was halted before the enclosure; and rejecting the offers of assistance with the same air of simple self-reliance he had displayed throughout, Tennessee's Partner lifted the rough coffin on his back, and deposited it, unaided, within the shallow grave. He then nailed down the board which served as a lid; and mounting the little mound of earth beside it, took off his hat, and slowly mopped his face with his handkerchief. This the crowd felt was a preliminary to speech; and they disposed themselves variously on stumps and boulders, and sat expectant.

"When a man," began Tennessee's Partner, slowly, "has been running free all day, what's the natural thing for him to do? Why, to come home. And if he ain't in a condition to go home, what can his best friend do? Why, bring him home! And here's Tennessee has been running free, and we brings him home from his wardering." He paused, and picked up a fragment of quartz, rubbed it thoughtfully on his sleeve, and went on: "It ain't the first time that I've packed him on my back, as you see'd me now. It ain't the first time that I brought him to this yer cabin when he couldn't help himself; it ain't the first time that I and 'Jinny' have waited for him on yon hill, and picked him up and so fetched him home, when he couldn't speak, and didn't know me. And now that it's the last time, why——" he paused, and rubbed the quartz gently on his sleeve—"you see it's a sort of rough on his partner. And now, gentlemen," he added, abruptly, picking up his long-handled shovel, "the fun'l's over; and my thanks, and Tennessee's thanks to you for your trouble."

Resisting any proffers of assistance, he began to fill in the grave, turning his back upon the crowd, that after a few moments' hesitation gradually withdrew. As they crossed the little ridge that hid Sandy Bar from view, some, looking back, thought they could see Tennessee's Partner, his work done, sitting upon the grave, his shovel between his knees, and his face buried in his red bandanna handkerchief. But it was argued by others that you couldn't tell his face from his handkerchief at that distance; and this point remained undecided.

In the reaction that followed the feverish excitement of that day, Tennessee's Partner was not forgotten. A secret investigation had cleared him of any complicity in Tennessee's guilt, and left only a suspicion of his general sanity. Sandy Bar made a point of calling on him, and proffering various uncouth, but well-meant kindnesses. But from that day this rude health and great strength seemed visibly to decline; and when the rainy season fairly set in, and the tiny grass-blades were beginning to peep from the rocky mound above Tennessee's grave, he took to his bed.

One night, when the pines beside the cabin were swaying in the storm, and trailing their slender fingers over the roof, and the roar and rush of the swollen river were heard below, Tennessee's Partner lifted his head from the pillow, saying, "It is time to go for Tennessee; I must put 'Jinny' in the cart;" and would have risen from his bed but for the restraint of his attendant. Struggling, he still pursued his singular fancy: "There, now, steady, 'Jinny,'—steady, old girl. How dark it is! Look out for the ruts,—and look out for him, too, old gal. Sometimes, you know, when he's blind drunk, he drops down right in the trail. Keep on straight up to the pine on the top of the hill. Thar—I told you so!—thar he is,—coming this way, too,—all by himself, sober, and his face a-shining. Tennessee! Pardner!"

And so they met.

THE IDYL OF RED GULCH

SANDY was very drunk. He was lying under an azalea-bush, in pretty much the same attitude in which he had fallen some hours before. How long he had been lying there he could not tell, and didn't care; how long he should lie there was a matter equally indefinite and unconsidered. A tran-

quil philosophy, born of his physical condition, suffused and
saturated his moral being.

The spectacle of a drunken man, and of this drunken man
in particular, was not, I grieve to say, of sufficient novelty
in Red Gulch to attract attention. Earlier in the day some
local satirist had erected a temporary tombstone at Sandy's
head, bearing the inscription,—"Effects of McCorkle's
whiskey,—kills at forty rods," with a hand pointing to Mc-
Corkle's saloon. But this, I imagine, was, like most local
satire, personal; and was a reflection upon the unfairness of
the process rather than a commentary upon the impropriety
of the result. With this facetious exception, Sandy had
been undisturbed. A wandering mule, released from his
pack, had cropped the scant herbage beside him, and sniffed
curiously at the prostrate man; a vagabond dog, with that
deep sympathy which the species have for drunken men,
had licked his dusty boots, and curled himself up at his feet,
and lay there, blinking one eye in the sunlight, with a simu-
lation of dissipation that was ingenious and dog-like in its
implied flattery of the unconscious man beside him.

Meanwhile the shadows of the pine-trees had slowly
swung around until they crossed the road, and their trunks
barred the open meadow with gigantic parallels of black
and yellow. Little puffs of red dust, lifted by the plunging
hoofs of passing teams, dispersed in a grimy shower upon
the recumbent man. The sun sank lower and lower; and
still Sandy stirred not. And then the repose of this philosopher was disturbed, as other philosophers have been, by
the intrusion of an unphilosophical sex.

"Miss Mary," as she was known to the little flock that
she had just dismissed from the log school-house beyond the
pines, was taking her afternoon walk. Observing an unusually fine cluster of blossoms on the azalea-bush opposite, she
crossed the road to pluck it,—picking her way through the
red dust, not without certain fierce little shivers of disgust,
and some feline circumlocution. And then she came suddenly upon Sandy!

Of course she uttered the little *staccato* cry of her sex.

But when she had paid that tribute to her physical weakness she became overbold, and halted for a moment,—at least six feet from this prostrate monster,—with her white skirts gathered in her hand, ready for flight. But neither sound nor motion came from the bush. With one little foot she then overturned the satirical head-board, and muttered, "Beasts!"—an epithet which probably, at that moment, conveniently classified in her mind the entire male population of Red Gulch. For Miss Mary, being possessed of certain rigid notions of her own, had not, perhaps, properly appreciated the demonstrative gallantry for which the Californian has been so justly celebrated by his brother Californians, and had, as a new-comer, perhaps, fairly earned the reputation of being "stuck up."

As she stood there she noticed, also, that the slant sunbeams were heating Sandy's head to what she judged to be an unhealthy temperature, and that his hat was lying uselessly at his side. To pick it up and to place it over his face was a work requiring some courage, particularly as his eyes were open. Yet she did it and made good her retreat. But she was somewhat concerned, on looking back, to see that the hat was removed, and that Sandy was sitting up and saying something.

The truth was, that in the calm depths of Sandy's mind he was satisfied that the rays of the sun were beneficial and healthful; that from childhood he had objected to lying down in a hat; that no people but condemned fools, past redemption, ever wore hats; and that his right to dispense with them when he pleased was inalienable. This was the statement of his inner consciousness. Unfortunately, its outward expression was vague, being limited to a repetition of the following formula,—"Su'shine all ri'! Wasser maär, eh? Wass up, su'shine?"

Miss Mary stopped, and, taking fresh courage from her vantage of distance, asked him if there was anything that he wanted.

"Wass up? Wasser maär?" continued Sandy, in a very high key.

"Get up, you horrid man!" said Miss Mary, now thoroughly incensed; "get up, and go home."

Sandy staggered to his feet. He was six feet high, and Miss Mary trembled. He started forward a few paces and then stopped.

"Wass I go home for?" he suddenly asked, with great gravity.

"Go and take a bath," replied Miss Mary, eyeing his grimy person with great disfavour.

To her infinite dismay, Sandy suddenly pulled off his coat and vest, threw them on the ground, kicked off his boots, and, plunging wildly forward, darted headlong over the hill, in the direction of the river.

"Goodness Heavens!—the man will be drowned!" said Miss Mary; and then, with feminine inconsistency, she ran back to the school-house, and locked herself in.

That night, while seated at supper with her hostess, the blacksmith's wife, it came to Miss Mary to ask, demurely, if her husband ever got drunk. "Abner," responded Mrs. Stidger, reflectively, "let's see: Abner hasn't been tight since last 'lection." Miss Mary would have liked to ask if he preferred lying in the sun on these occasions, and if a cold bath would have hurt him; but this would have involved an explanation, which she did not then care to give. So she contented herself with opening her gray eyes widely at the red-cheeked Mrs. Stidger,—a fine specimen of South-western efflorescence,—and then dismissed the subject altogether. The next day she wrote to her dearest friend, in Boston: "I think I find the intoxicated portion of this community the least objectionable. I refer, my dear, to the men, of course. I do not know anything that could make the women tolerable."

In less than a week Miss Mary had forgotten this episode, except that her afternoon walks took thereafter, almost unconsciously, another direction. She noticed, however, that every morning a fresh cluster of azalea-blossoms appeared among the flowers on her desk. This was not strange, as her little flock were aware of her fondness for flowers, and invariably kept her desk bright with anemones, syringas, and lupines; but, on questioning them, they, one and all, professed ignorance of the azaleas. A few days later, Master Johnny Stidger, whose desk was nearest to the window, was suddenly taken with spasms of apparently gratuitous laughter, that threatened the discipline of the school. All that Miss Mary could get from him was that some one had been "looking in the winder." Irate and indignant, she sallied from her hive to do battle with the intruder. As she turned the corner of the school house she came plump upon the quondam drunkard, now perfectly sober, and inexpressibly sheepish and guilty-looking.

These facts Miss Mary was not slow to take a feminine advantage of, in her present humour. But it was somewhat confusing to observe, also, that the beast, despite some faint signs of past dissipation, was amiable-looking,—in fact, a kind of blond Samson, whose corn-coloured, silken beard apparently had never yet known the touch of barber's razor or Delilah's shears. So that the cutting speech which quivered on her ready tongue died upon her lips, and she contented herself with receiving his stammering apology with supercilious eyelids, and the gathered skirts of uncontamination. When she re-entered the school-room, her eyes fell upon the azaleas with a new sense of revelation. And then she laughed, and the little people all laughed, and they were all unconsciously very happy.

It was on a hot day—and not long after this—that two short-legged boys came to grief on the threshold of the school with a pail of water, which they had laboriously brought from the spring, and that Miss Mary compassionately seized the pail and started for the spring herself. At the foot of the hill a shadow crossed her path, and a blue-shirted arm dexterously, but gently, relieved her of her burden. Miss Mary was both embarrassed and angry. "If you carried more of that for yourself," she said, spitefully, to the blue arm, without deigning to raise her lashes to its owner, "you'd do better." In the submissive silence that followed she regretted the speech, and thanked him so sweetly at the door that he stumbled, which caused the children to laugh again,—a laugh in which Miss Mary joined, until the colour came faintly into her pale cheeks. The next day a barrel was mysteriously placed beside the door, and as mysteriously filled with fresh spring-water every morning.

Nor was this superior young person without other quiet attentions. "Profane Bill," driver of the Slumgullion Stage, widely known in the newspapers for his "gallantry" in invariably offering the box-seat to the fair sex, had excepted Miss Mary from this attention, on the ground that he had a habit of "cussin' on up grades," and gave her half the coach to herself. Jack Hamlin, a gambler, having once silently ridden with her in the same coach, afterwards threw a decanter at the head of a confederate for mentioning her name in a bar-room. The over-dressed mother of a pupil whose paternity was doubtful, had often lingered near this astute Vestal's temple, never daring to enter its sacred precincts, but content to worship the priestess from afar.

With such unconscious intervals the monotonous procession of blue skies, glittering sunshine, brief twilights, and starlit nights passed over Red Gulch. Miss Mary grew fond of walking in the sedate and proper woods. Perhaps she believed, with Mrs. Stidger, that the balsamic odours of the firs "did her chest good," for certainly her slight cough was less frequent and her step was firmer; perhaps she had learned the unending lesson which the patient pines are never weary of repeating to heedful or listless ears. And so, one day, she planned a pic-nic on Buck-eye Hill, and took the children with her. Away from the dusty road, the straggling shanties, the yellow ditches, the clamour of restless engines, the cheap finery of shop-windows, the deeper glitter of paint and coloured glass, and the thin veneering which barbarism takes upon itself in such localities—what infinite relief was theirs! The last heap of ragged rock and clay passed, the last unsightly chasm crossed,—how the waiting woods opened their long files to receive them! How the children—perhaps because they had not yet grown quite away from the breast of the bounteous Mother—threw themselves face downward on her brown bosom with uncouth caresses, filling the air with their laughter; and how Miss Mary herself—felinely fastidious and intrenched as she was in the purity of spotless skirts, collar, and cuffs—forgot all, and ran like a crested quail at the head of her brood, until, romping, laughing, and panting, with a loosened braid of brown hair, a hat hanging by a knotted ribbon from her throat, she came suddenly and violently, in the heart of the forest, upon—the luckless Sandy!

The explanation, apologies, and not overwise conversation that ensued, need not be indicated here. It would seem, however, that Miss Mary had already established some acquaintance with this ex-drunkard. Enough that he was soon accepted as one of the party; that the children, with that quick intelligence which Providence gives the helpless, recognized a friend, and played with his blond beard, and long silken mustache, and took other liberties,—as the helpless are apt to do. And when he had built a fire against a tree, and had shown them other mysteries of wood-craft, their admiration knew no bounds. At the close of two such foolish, idle, happy hours he found himself lying at the feet of the schoolmistress, gazing dreamily in her face, as she sat upon the sloping hill-side, weaving wreaths of laurel and syringa, in very much the same attitude as he had lain when first they met. Nor was the similitude greatly forced. The weakness of an easy, sensuous nature, that had found a dreamy exaltation in liquor, it is to be feared was now finding an equal intoxication in love.

I think that Sandy was dimly conscious of this himself. I know that he longed to be doing something,—slaying a grizzly, scalping a savage, or sacrificing himself in some way for the sake of this sallow-faced, gray-eyed schoolmistress. As I should like to present him in a heroic attitude, I stay my hand with great difficulty at this moment, being only withheld from introducing such an episode by a strong conviction that it does not usually occur at such times. And I trust that my fairest reader, who remembers that, in a real crisis, it is always some uninteresting stranger or unromantic policeman, and not Adolphus, who rescues, will forgive the omission.

So they sat there, undisturbed—the woodpeckers chattering overhead, and the voices of the children coming pleasantly from the hollow below. What they said matters little. What they thought—which might have been interesting—did not transpire. The woodpeckers only learned how Miss Mary was an orphan; how she left her uncle's house, to come to California, for the sake of health and independence; how Sandy was an orphan, too; how he came to California for excitement; how he had lived a wild life, and how he was trying to reform; and other details, which, from a woodpecker's view-point, undoubtedly must have seemed stupid, and a waste of time. But even in such trifles was the afternoon spent; and when the children were again gathered, and Sandy, with a delicacy which the schoolmistress well understood, took leave of them quietly at the outskirts of the settlement, it had seemed the shortest day of her weary life.

As the long, dry summer withered to its roots, the school term of Red Gulch—to use a local euphuism—"dried up" also. In another day Miss Mary would be free; and for a season, at least, Red Gulch would know her no more. She was seated alone in the school-house, her cheek resting on her hand, her eyes half closed in one of those day-dreams in which Miss Mary—I fear, to the danger of school discipline—was lately in the habit of indulging. Her lap was full of mosses, ferns, and other woodland memories. She was so pre-occupied with these and her own thoughts that a gentle tapping at the door passed unheard, or translated itself into the remembrance of far-off woodpeckers. When at last it asserted itself more distinctly, she started up with a flushed cheek and opened the door. On the threshold stood a woman, the self-assertion and audacity of whose dress were in singular contrast to her timid, irresolute bearing.

Miss Mary recognised at a glance the dubious mother of

her anonymous pupil. Perhaps she was disappointed, perhaps she was only fastidious; but as she coldly invited her to enter, she half-unconsciously settled her white cuffs and collar, and gathered closer her own chaste skirts. It was, perhaps, for this reason that the embarrassed stranger, after a moment's hesitation, left her gorgeous parasol open and sticking in the dust beside the door, and then sat down at the farther end of a long bench. Her voice was husky as she began,—

"I heerd tell that you were goin' down to the Bay tomorrow, and I couldn't let you go until I came to thank you for your kindness to my Tommy."

Tommy, Miss Mary said, was a good boy, and deserved more than the poor attention she could give him.

"Thank you, miss; thank ye!" cried the stranger, brightening even through the colour which Red Gulch knew facetiously as her "war paint," and striving, in her embarrassment, to drag the long bench nearer the schoolmistress. "I thank you, miss, for that; and if I am his mother, there ain't a sweeter, dearer, better boy lives than him. And if I ain't much as says it, thar ain't a sweeter dearer, angeler teacher lives than he's got."

Miss Mary, sitting primly behind her desk, with a ruler over her shoulder, opened her gray eyes widely at this, but said nothing.

"It ain't for you to be complimented by the like of me, I know," she went on, hurriedly. "It ain't for me to be comin' here, in broad day, to do it, either; but I come to ask a favour,—not for me, miss,—not for me, but for the darling boy."

Encouraged by a look in the young schoolmistress's eye, and putting her lilac-gloved hands together, the fingers downward, between her knees, she went on, in a low voice,—

"You see, miss, there's no one the boy has any claim on but me, and I ain't the proper person to bring him up. I thought some, last year, of sending him away to 'Frisco to school, but when they talked of bringing a schoolma'am here, I waited till I saw you, and then I knew it was all right, and I could keep my boy a little longer. And O, miss, he loves you so much; and if you could hear him talk about you, in his pretty way, and if he could ask you what I ask you now, you couldn't refuse him.

"It is natural," she went on rapidly, in a voice that trembled strangely between pride and humility,—"it's natural that he should take to you, miss, for his father, when I first knew him, was a gentleman,—and the boy must forget me, sooner or later,—and so I ain't a-goin' to cry about that. For I come to ask you to take my Tommy,—God bless him for the bestest, sweetest boy that lives!—to—to—take him with you."

She had risen and caught the young girl's hand in her own, and had fallen on her knees beside her.

"I've money plenty, and it's all yours and his. Put him in some good school, where you can go and see him, and help him to—to—forget his mother. Do with him what you like. The worst you can do will be kindness to what he will learn with me. Only take him out of this wicked life, this cruel place, this home of shame and sorrow. You will; I know you will,—won't you? You will,—you must not, you cannot say no! You will make him as pure, as gentle as yourself; and when he has grown up, you will tell him his father's name,—the name that hasn't passed my lips for years,—the name of Alexander Morton, whom they call here Sandy! Miss Mary!—do not take your hand away! Miss Mary, speak to me! You will take my boy! Do not put your face from me. I know it ought not to look on such as me. Miss Mary!—my God, be merciful!—she is leaving me!"

Miss Mary had risen, and, in the gathering twilight, had felt her way to the open window. She stood there, leaning against the casement, her eyes fixed on the last rosy tints that were fading from the western sky. There was still some of its light on her pure young forehead, on her white collar. on her clasped white hands, but all fading slowly away. The suppliant had dragged herself, still on her knees, beside her.

"I know it takes time to consider. I will wait here all night; but I cannot go until you speak. Do not deny me now. You will!—I see it in your sweet face,—such a face as I have seen in my dreams. I see it in your eyes, Miss Mary!—you will take my boy!"

The last red beam crept higher, suffused Miss Mary's eyes with something of its glory, flickered, and faded, and went out. The sun had set on Red Gulch. In the twilight and silence Miss Mary's voice sounded pleasantly.

"I will take the boy. Send him to me to-night."

The happy mother raised the hem of Miss Mary's skirts to her lips. She would have buried her hot face in its virgin folds, but she dared not. She rose to her feet.

"Does—this man—know of your intention?" asked Miss Mary, suddenly.

"No; nor cares. He has never even seen the child to know it."

"Go to him at once,—to-night,—now. Tell him what you have done. Tell him I have taken his child, and tell him—he must never see—see—the child again. Wherever it may be, he must not come; wherever I may take it, he must not follow! There, go now, please—I'm weary, and— have much yet to do!"

They walked together to the door. On the threshold the woman turned.

"Good night."

She would have fallen at Miss Mary's feet. But at the same moment the young girl reached out her arms, caught the sinful woman to her own pure breast for one brief moment, and then closed and locked the door.

It was with a sudden sense of great responsibility that Profane Bill took the reins of the Slumgullion Stage the next morning, for the schoolmistress was one of his passengers. As he entered the high road, in obedience to a pleasant voice from the "inside," he suddenly reined up his

and inspiring. Certainly not the blue heron standing mid-leg deep in the water, obviously catching cold in a reckless disregard of wet feet and consequences; nor the mournful curlew, the dejected plover, or the low-spirited snipe, who saw fit to join him in his suicidal contemplation; nor the impassive king-fisher—an ornithological Marius—reviewing the desolate expanse; nor the black raven that went to and fro over the face of the marsh continually, but evidently couldn't make up his mind whether the waters had subsided, and felt low-spirited in the reflection that, after all this trouble, he wouldn't be able to give a definite answer. On the contrary, it was evident at a glance that the dreary expanse of Dedlow Marsh told unpleasantly on the birds, and that the season of migration was looked forward to with a feeling of relief and satisfaction by the full-grown, and of extravagant anticipation by the callow, brood. But if Dedlow Marsh was cheerless at the slack of the low tide, you should have seen it when the tide was strong and full. When the damp air blew chilly over the cold, glittering expanse, and came to the faces of those who looked seaward like another tide; when a steel-like glint marked the low hollows and the sinuous line of slough; when the great shell-incrusted trunks of fallen trees arose again, and went forth on their dreary, purposeless wanderings, drifting hither and thither, but getting no farther toward any goal at the falling tide or the day's decline than the cursed Hebrew in the legend; when the glossy ducks swung silently, making neither ripple nor furrow on the simmering surface; when the fog came in with the tide and shut out the blue above, even as the green below had been obliterated; when boatmen, lost in that fog, paddling about in a hopeless way, started at what seemed the brushing of mermen's fingers on the boat's keel, or shrank from the tufts of grass spreading around like the floating hair of a corpse, and knew by these signs that they were lost upon Dedlow Marsh, and must make a night of it, and a gloomy one at that,—then you might know something of Dedlow Marsh at high water.

Let me recall a story connected with this latter view,

which never failed to recur to my mind in my long gunning excursions upon Dedlow Marsh. Although the event was briefly recorded in the county paper, I had the story, in all its eloquent detail, from the lips of the principal actor. I cannot hope to catch the varying emphasis and peculiar colouring of feminine delineation, for my narrator was a woman; but I'll try to give at least its substance.

She lived midway of the great slough of Dedlow Marsh and a good-sized river, which debouched four miles beyond into an estuary formed by the Pacific Ocean, on the long sandy peninsula which constituted the south-western boundary of a noble bay. The house in which she lived was a small frame cabin, raised from the marsh a few feet by stout piles, and was three miles distant from the settlements upon the river. Her husband was a logger,—a profitable business in a county where the principal occupation was the manufacture of lumber.

It was the season of early spring, when her husband left on the ebb of a high tide, with a raft of logs for the usual transportation to the lower end of the bay. As she stood by the door of the little cabin when the voyagers departed, she noticed a cold look in the south-eastern sky, and she remembered hearing her husband say to his companions that they must endeavour to complete their voyage before the coming of the south-westerly gale which he saw brewing. And that night it began to storm and blow harder than she had ever before experienced, and some great trees fell in the forest by the river, and the house rocked like her baby's cradle.

But however the storm might roar about the little cabin, she knew that one she trusted had driven bolt and bar with his own strong hand, and that had he feared for her he would not have left her. This, and her domestic duties, and the care of her little sickly baby, helped to keep her mind from dwelling on the weather, except, of course, to hope that he was safely harboured with the logs at Utopia in the dreary distance. But she noticed that day, when she went out to feed the chickens and look after the cow, that the tide was up to the little fence of their garden patch, and the roar of the surf on the south beach, though miles away, she could hear distinctly. And she began to think that she would like to have some one to talk with about matters, and she believed that if it had not been so far and so stormy, and the trail so impassable, she would have taken the baby, and have gone over to Ryckman's, her nearest neighbour. But then, you see, he might have returned in the storm, all wet with no one to see to him; and it was a long exposure for baby, who was croupy and ailing.

But that night, she never could tell why, she didn't feel like sleeping or even lying down. The storm had somewhat abated, but she still "sat and sat," and even tried to read. I don't know whether it was a Bible or some profane magazine that this poor woman read, but most probably the latter, for the words all ran together and made such sad nonsense that she was forced at last to put the book down and turn to that dearer volume which lay before her in the cradle, with its white initial leaf as yet unsoiled, and try to look forward to its mysterious future. And, rocking the cradle, she thought of everything and everybody, but still was wide awake as ever.

It was nearly twelve o'clock when she at last lay down in her clothes. How long she slept she could not remember, but she awoke with a dreadful choking in her throat, and found herself standing, trembling all over, in the middle of the room, with her baby clasped to her breast, and she was "saying something." The baby cried and sobbed, and she walked up and down trying to hush it, when she heard a scratching at the door. She opened it fearfully, and was glad to see it was only old Pete, their dog, who crawled, dripping with water, into the room. She would like to have looked out, not in the faint hope of her husband's coming, but to see how things looked; but the wind shook the door so savagely that she could hardly hold it. Then she sat down a little while, and then walked up and down a little while, and then she lay down again a little while. Lying close by the wall of the little cabin, she thought she heard once or twice something scrape slowly against the clap-boards, like the scraping of branches. Then there was a little gurgling sound, "like the baby made when it was swallowing;" then something went "click-click" and "cluck-cluck," so that she sat up in bed. When she did so she was attracted by something else that seemed creeping from the back door towards the centre of the room. It wasn't much wider than her little finger, but soon it swelled to the width of her hand, and began spreading all over the floor. It was water.

She ran to the front door and threw it wide open, and saw nothing but water. She ran to the back door and threw it open, and saw nothing but water. She ran to the side window, and, throwing that open, she saw nothing but water. Then she remembered hearing her husband once say that there was no danger in the tide, for that fell regularly, and people could calculate on it, and that he would rather live near the bay than the river, whose banks might overflow at any time. But was it the tide? So she ran again to the back door, and threw out a stick of wood. It drifted away towards the bay. She scooped up some of the water and put it eagerly to her lips. It was fresh and sweet. It was the river, and not the tide!

It was then—O God be praised for his goodness! she did neither faint nor fall; it was then—blessed be the Saviour, for it was his merciful hand that touched and strengthened her in this awful moment—that fear dropped from her like a garment, and her trembling ceased. It was then and thereafter that she never lost her self-command, through all the trials of that gloomy night.

She drew the bedstead towards the middle of the room, and placed a table upon it, and on that she put the cradle. The water on the floor was already over her ankles, and the house once or twice moved so perceptibly, and seemed to be racked so, that the closet doors all flew open. Then she heard the same rasping and thumping against the wall, and, looking out, saw that a large uprooted tree, which had lain near the road at the upper end of the pasture, had floated down to the house. Luckily its long roots dragged in the soil and kept it from moving as rapidly as the current, for had it struck the house in its full career, even the strong nails and bolts in the piles could not have withstood the shock. The hound had leaped upon its knotty surface, and crouched near the roots shivering and whining. A ray of hope flashed across her mind. She drew a heavy blanket from the bed, and, wrapping it about the babe, waded in the deepening waters to the door. As the tree swung again, broadside on, making the little cabin creak and tremble, she leaped on to its trunk. By God's mercy she succeeded in obtaining a footing on its slippery surface, and, twining an arm about its roots, she held in the other a moaning child. Then something cracked near the front porch, and the whole front of the house she had just quitted fell forward, just as cattle fall on their knees before they lie down,—and at the same moment the great redwood tree swung round and drifted away with its living cargo into the black night.

For all the excitement and danger, for all her soothing of her crying babe, for all the whistling of the wind, for all the uncertainty of her situation, she still turned to look at the deserted and water-swept cabin. She remembered even then, and she wonders how foolish she was to think of it at that time, that she wished she had put on another dress and the baby's best clothes; and she kept praying that the house would be spared so that he, when he returned, would have something to come to, and it wouldn't be quite so desolate, and—how could he ever know what had become of her and baby? And at the thought she grew sick and faint. But she had something else to do besides worrying, for whenever the long roots of her ark struck an obstacle, the whole trunk made half a revolution, and twice dipped her in the black water. The hound, who kept distracting her by running up and down the tree and howling, at last fell off at one of these collisions. He swam for some time beside her, and she tried to get the poor beast upon the tree, but he "acted silly" and wild, and at last she lost sight of him for ever. Then she and her baby were left alone. The light which had burned for a few minutes in the deserted cabin was quenched suddenly. She could not then tell whither she was drifting. The outline of the white dunes on the peninsula showed dimly ahead, and she judged the tree was moving in a line with the river. It must be about slack water, and she had probably reached the eddy formed by the confluence of the tide and the overflowing waters of the river. Unless the tide fell soon, there was present danger of her drifting to its channel, and being carried out to sea or crushed in the floating drift. That peril averted, if she were carried out on the ebb toward the bay, she might hope to strike one of the wooded promontories of the peninsula, and rest till daylight. Sometimes she thought she heard voices and shouts from the river, and the bellowing of cattle and bleating of sheep. Then again it was only the ringing in her ears and throbbing of her heart. She found at about this time that she was so chilled and stiffened in her cramped position that she could scarcely move, and the baby cried so when she put it to her breast that she noticed the milk refused to flow; and she was so frightened at that, that she put her head under her shawl and for the first time cried bitterly.

When she raised her head again, the boom of the surf was behind her, and she knew that her ark had again swung round. She dipped up the water to cool her parched throat, and found that it was salt as her tears. There was a relief, though, for by this sign she knew she was drifting with the tide. It was then the wind went down, and the great and awful silence oppressed her. There was scarcely a ripple against the furrowed sides of the great trunk on which she rested, and around her all was black gloom and quiet. She spoke to the baby just to hear herself speak, and to know that she had not lost her voice. She thought then—it was queer, but she could not help thinking it—how awful must have been the night when the great ship swung over the Asiatic peak, and the sounds of creation were blotted out from the world. She thought, too, of mariners clinging to spars, and of poor women who were lashed to rafts, and beaten to death by the cruel sea. She tried to thank God that she was thus spared, and lifted her eyes from the baby who had fallen into a fretful sleep. Suddenly, away to the southward, a great light lifted itself out of the gloom, and flashed and flickered, and flickered and flashed again. Her heart fluttered quickly against the baby's cold cheek. It was the lighthouse at the entrance of the bay. As she was yet wondering, the tree suddenly rolled a little, dragged a little, and then seemed to lie quiet and still. She put out her hand and the current gurgled against it. The tree was aground, and, by the position of the light and the noise of the surf, aground upon the Dedlow Marsh.

Had it not been for her baby, who was ailing and croupy, had it not been for the sudden drying up of that sensitive fountain, she would have felt safe and relieved. Perhaps it was this which tended to make all her impressions mournful and gloomy. As the tide rapidly fell, a great flock of black brent fluttered by her, screaming and crying. Then the plover flew up and piped mournfully, as they wheeled around the trunk, and at last fearlessly lit upon it like a gray cloud. Then the heron flew over and around her, shrieking and protesting, and at last dropped its gaunt legs only a few yards from her. But, strangest of all, a pretty white bird, larger than a dove, like a pelican, but not a pelican, circled around and around her. At last it lit upon a rootlet of the tree, quite over her shoulder. She put out her hand and stroked its beautiful white neck, and it never appeared to move. It stayed there so long that she thought she would lift up the baby to see it, and try to attract her attention. But when she did so, the child was so chilled and cold, and had such a blue look under the little lashes, which it didn't raise at all, that she screamed aloud, and the bird flew away, and she fainted.

Well, that was the worst of it, and perhaps it was not so much, after all, to any but herself. For when she recovered her senses it was bright sunlight, and dead low water.

There was a confused noise of guttural voices about her, and an old squaw, singing an Indian "hushaby," and rocking herself from side to side before a fire built on the marsh, before which she, the recovered wife and mother, lay weak and weary. Her first thought was for her baby, and she was about to speak, when a young squaw, who must have been a mother herself, fathomed her thought, and brought her the "mowitch," pale but living, in such a queer little willow cradle all bound up, just like the squaw's own young one, that she laughed and cried together, and the young squaw and the old squaw showed their big white teeth and glinted their black eyes and said, "Plenty get well, skeena mowitch," "wagee man come plenty soon," and she could have kissed their brown faces in her joy. And then she found that they had been gathering berries on the marsh in their queer, comical baskets, and saw the skirt of her gown fluttering on the tree from afar, and the old squaw couldn't resist the temptation of procuring a new garment, and came down and discovered the "wagee" woman and child. And of course she gave the garment to the old squaw, as you may imagine, and when *he* came at last and rushed up to her, looking about ten years older in his anxiety, she felt so faint again that they had to carry her to the canoe. For, you see, he knew nothing about the flood until he met the Indians at Utopia, and knew by the signs that the poor woman was his wife. And at the next high-tide he towed the tree away back home, although it wasn't worth the trouble, and built another house, using the old tree for the foundation and props, and called it after her, "Mary's Ark!" But you may guess the next house was built above high water mark. And that's all.

Not much, perhaps, considering the malevolent capacity of the Dedlow Marsh. But you must tramp over it at low water, or paddle over it at high tide, or get lost upon it once or twice in the fog, as I have, to understand properly Mary's adventure, or to appreciate duly the blessings of living beyond High Water Mark.

A LONELY RIDE

As I stepped into the Slumgullion stage I saw that it was a
dark night, a lonely road, and that I was the only passenger.
Let me assure the reader that I have no ulterior design in
making this assertion. A long course of light reading has
forewarned me what every experienced intelligence must
confidently look for from such a statement. The story-
teller who wilfully tempts Fate by such obvious beginnings;
who is to the expectant reader in danger of being robbed
or half-murdered, or frightened by an escaped lunatic, or
introduced to his lady-love for the first time, deserves to be
detected. I am relieved to say that none of these things
occurred to me. The road from Wingdam to Slumgullion
knew no other banditti than the regularly licensed hotel-
keepers; lunatics had not yet reached such depth of imbecility as to ride of their own free-will in Californian
stages; and my Laura, amiable and long-suffering as she always is, could not, I fear, have borne up against these
depressing circumstances long enough to have made the
slightest impression on me.

I stood with my shawl and carpet-bag in hand, gazing
doubtingly on the vehicle. Even in the darkness the red
dust of Wingdam was visible on its roof and sides, and the
red slime of Slumgullion clung tenaciously to its wheels. I
opened the door; the stage creaked uneasily, and in the
gloomy abyss the swaying straps beckoned me, like ghostly
hands, to come in now, and have my sufferings out at once.

I must not omit to mention the occurrence of a circumstance which struck me as appalling and mysterious. A
lounger on the steps of the hotel, whom I had reason to
suppose was not in any way connected with the stage company, gravely descended, and, walking towards the convey-
ance, tried the handle of the door, opened it, expectorated
in the carriage, and returned to the hotel with a serious demeanour. Hardly had he resumed his position, when another individual, equally disinterested, impassively walked
down the steps, proceeded to the back of the stage, lifted it,

expectorated carefully on the axle, and returned slowly and pensively to the hotel. A third spectator wearily disengaged himself from one of the Ionic columns of the portico and walked to the box, remained for a moment in serious and expectorative contemplation of the boot, and then returned to his column. There was something so weird in this baptism that I grew quite nervous.

Perhaps I was out of spirits. A number of infinitesimal annoyances, winding up with the resolute persistency of the clerk at the stage-office to enter my name misspelt on the way-bill, had not predisposed me to cheerfulness. The inmates of the Eureka House, from a social view-point, were not attractive. There was the prevailing opinion—so common to many honest people—that a serious style of deportment and conduct toward a stranger indicates high gentility and elevated station. Obeying this principle, all hilarity ceased on my entrance to supper, and general remark merged into the safer and uncompromising chronicle of several bad cases of diphtheria, then epidemic at Wingdam. When I left the dining-room, with an odd feeling that I had been supping exclusively on mustard and tea-leaves, I stopped a moment at the parlour door. A piano, harmoniously related to the dinner-bell, tinkled responsive to a diffident and uncertain touch. On the white wall the shadow of an old and sharp profile was bending over several symmetrical and shadowy curls. "I sez to Mariar, Mariar, sez I, 'Praise to the face is open disgrace.'" I heard no more. Dreading some susceptibility to sincere expression on the subject of female loveliness, I walked away, checking the compliment that otherwise might have risen unbidden to my lips, and have brought shame and sorrow to the household.

It was with the memory of these experiences resting heavily upon me, that I stood hesitatingly before the stage door. The driver, about to mount, was for a moment illuminated by the open door of the hotel. He had the wearied look which was the distinguishing expression of Wingdam. Satisfied that I was properly way-billed and receipted for, he took no further notice of me. I looked longingly at the box-seat, but he did not respond to the appeal. I flung my carpet-bag into the chasm, dived recklessly after it, and—before I was fairly seated—with a great sigh, a creaking of unwilling springs, complaining bolts, and harshly expostulating axle, we moved away. Rather the hotel door slipped behind, the sound of the piano sank to rest, and the night and its shadows moved solemnly upon us.

To say it was dark expressed but faintly the pitchy obscurity that encompassed the vehicle. The roadside trees were scarcely distinguishable as deeper masses of shadow; I knew them only by the peculiar sodden odour that from time to time sluggishly flowed in at the open window as we rolled by. We proceeded slowly; so leisurely that, leaning from the carriage, I more than once detected the fragrant sigh of some astonished cow, whose ruminating repose upon the highway we had ruthlessly disturbed. But in the darkness our progress, more the guidance of some mysterious instinct than any apparent volition of our own, gave an indefinable charm of security to our journey, that a moment's hesitation or indecision on the part of the driver would have destroyed.

I had indulged a hope that in the empty vehicle I might obtain that rest so often denied me in its crowded condition. It was a weak delusion. When I stretched out my limbs it was only to find that the ordinary conveniences for making several people distinctly uncomfortable were distributed throughout my individual frame. At last, resting my arms on the straps, by dint of much gymnastic effort I became sufficiently composed to be aware of a more refined species of torture. The springs of the stage, rising and falling regularly, produced a rhythmical beat, which began to painfully absorb my attention. Slowly this thumping merged into a senseless echo of the mysterious female of the hotel parlour, and shaped itself into this awful and benumbing axiom,—"Praise-to-the-face-is-open-disgrace. Praise-to-the-face-is-open-disgrace." Inequalities of the road only quickened its utterance or drawled it to an exasperating length.

It was of no use to seriously consider the statement. It was of no use to except to it indignantly. It was of no use to recall the many instances where praise to the face had redounded to the everlasting honour of praiser and be-praised; of no use to dwell sentimentally on modest genius and courage lifted up and strengthened by open commen-dation; of no use to except to the mysterious female,—to picture her as rearing a thin-blooded generation on selfish and mechanically-repeated axioms,—all this failed to coun-teract the monotonous repetition of this sentence. There was nothing to do but to give in, and I was about to accept it weakly, as we too often treat other illusions of darkness and necessity, for the time being, when I became aware of some other annoyance that had been forcing itself upon me for the last few moments. How quiet the driver was!

Was there any driver? Had I any reason to suppose that he was not lying, gagged and bound on the roadside, and the highwayman, with blackened face, who did the thing so quietly, driving me—whither? The thing is perfectly feasible. And what is this fancy now being jolted out of me? A story? It's of no use to keep it back, particularly in this abysmal vehicle, and here it comes: I am a Marquis —a French Marquis; French, because the peerage is not so well known, and the country is better adapted to romantic incident—a Marquis, because the democratic reader delights in the nobility. My name is something *ligny*. I am coming from Paris to my country seat at St. Germain. It is a dark night, and I fall asleep and tell my honest coachman André not to disturb me, and dream of an angel. The carriage at last stops at the château. It is so dark that, when I alight, I do not recognize the face of the footman who holds the carriage-door. But what of that?—*peste!* I am heavy with sleep. The same obscurity also hides the old familiar indecencies of the statues on the terrace; but there is a door, and it opens and shuts behind me smartly. Then I find myself in a trap, in the presence of the brigand who has quietly gagged poor André and conducted the carriage thither. There is nothing for me to do, as a gallant French

Marquis, but to say, *"Parbleu!"* draw my rapier, and die valorously! I am found, a week or two after, outside a deserted *cabaret* near the barrier, with a hole through my ruffled linen, and my pockets stripped. No; on second thoughts, I am rescued,—rescued by the angel I have been dreaming of, who is the assumed daughter of the brigand, but the real daughter of an intimate friend.

Looking from the window again, in the vain hope of distinguishing the driver, I found my eyes were growing accustomed to the darkness. I could see the distant horizon, defined by India-inky woods, relieving a lighter sky. A few stars, widely spaced in this picture, glimmered sadly. I noticed again the infinite depth of patient sorrow in their serene faces; and I hope that the Vandal who first applied the flippant "twinkle" to them may not be driven melancholy mad by their reproachful eyes. I noticed again the mystic charm of space, that imparts a sense of individual solitude to each integer of the densest constellation, involving the smallest star with immeasurable loneliness. Something of this calm and solitude crept over me, and I dozed in my gloomy cavern. When I awoke the full moon was rising. Seen from my window, it had an indescribably unreal and theatrical effect. It was the full moon of Norma—that remarkable celestial phenomenon which rises so palpably to a hushed audience and a sublime *andante* chorus, until the *Casta Diva* is sung—the "inconstant moon" that then and thereafter remains fixed in the heavens as though it were a part of the solar system inaugurated by Joshua. Again the white-robed Druids filed past me, again I saw that improbable mistletoe cut from that impossible oak, and again cold chills ran down my back with the first strain of the recitative. The thumping springs essayed to beat time, and the private box-like obscurity of the vehicle lent a cheap enchantment to the view. But it was a vast improvement upon my past experience, and I hugged the fond delusion.

My fears for the driver were dissipated with the rising moon. A familiar sound had assured me of his presence in the full possession of at least one of his most important func-

tions. Frequent and full expectoration convinced me that
his lips were as yet not sealed by the gag of highwaymen,
and soothed my anxious ear. With this load lifted from my
mind, and assisted by the mild presence of Diana, who left,
as when she visited Endymion, much of her splendour outside my cavern,—I looked around the empty vehicle. On
the forward seat lay a woman's hair-pin. I picked it up
with an interest that, however, soon abated. There was no
scent of the roses to cling to it still, not even of hair-oil.
No bend or twist in its rigid angles betrayed any trait of
its wearer's character. I tried to think that it might have
been "Mariar's." I tried to imagine that, confining the
symmetrical curls of that girl, it might have heard the soft
compliments whispered in her ears, which provoked the
wrath of the aged female. But in vain. It was reticent
and unswerving in its upright fidelity, and at last slipped
listlessly through my fingers.

I had dozed repeatedly,—waked on the threshold of obli-
vion by contact with some of the angles of the coach, and
feeling that I was unconsciously assuming, in imitation of a
humble insect of my childish recollection, that spherical
shape which could best resist those impressions, when I per-
ceived that the moon, riding high in the heavens, had begun
to separate the formless masses of the shadowy landscape.
Trees isolated, in clumps and assemblages, changed places
before my window. The sharp outlines of the distant hills
came back, as in daylight, but little softened in the dry,
cold, dewless air of a California summer night. I was wondering how late it was, and thinking that if the horses of the
night travelled as slowly as the team before us, Faustus
might have been spared his agonizing prayer, when a sudden
spasm of activity attacked my driver. A succession of
whip-snappings, like a pack of Chinese crackers, broke from
the box before me. The stage leaped forward, and when I
could pick myself from under the seat, a long white building had in some mysterious way rolled before my window.
It must be Slumgullion! As I descended from the stage I
addressed the driver:—

"I thought you changed horses on the road?"

"So we did. Two hours ago."

"That's odd. I didn't notice it."

"Must have been asleep, sir. Hope you had a pleasant nap. Bully place for a nice quiet snooze—empty stage, sir!"

THE MAN OF NO ACCOUNT

His name was Fagg—David Fagg. He came to California in '52 with us, in the "Skyscraper." I don't think he did it in an adventurous way. He probably had no other place to go to. When a knot of us young fellows would recite what splendid opportunities we resigned to go, and how sorry our friends were to have us leave, and show daguerreo-types and locks of hair, and talk of Mary and Susan, the man of no account used to sit by and listen with a pained, mortified expression on his plain face, and say nothing. I think he had nothing to say. He had no associates, except when we patronized him; and, in point of fact, he was a good deal of sport to us. He was always sea-sick whenever we had a capful of wind. He never got his sea-legs on either. And I never shall forget how we all laughed when Rattler took him the piece of pork on a string, and—— But you know that time-honoured joke. And then we had such a splendid lark with him. Miss Fanny Twinkler couldn't bear the sight of him, and we used to make Fagg think that she had taken a fancy to him, and send him little delicacies and books from the cabin. You ought to have witnessed the rich scene that took place when he came up, stammering and very sick, to thank her! Didn't she flash up grandly and beautifully and scornfully? So like "Medora," Rattler said,—Rattler knew Byron by heart,—and wasn't old Fagg awfully cut up? But he got over it, and when Rattler fell sick at Valparaiso, old Fagg used to nurse him. You see he was a good sort of fellow, but he lacked manliness and spirit.

He had absolutely no idea of poetry. I've seen him sit stolidly by, mending his old clothes, when Rattler delivered that stirring apostrophe of Byron's to the ocean. He asked Rattler once, quite seriously, if he thought Byron was ever sea-sick. I don't remember Rattler's reply, but I know we all laughed very much, and I have no doubt it was something good, for Rattler was smart.

When the "Skyscraper" arrived at San Francisco, we had a grand "feed." We agreed to meet every year and perpetuate the occasion. Of course we didn't invite Fagg. Fagg was a steerage passenger, and it was necessary, you see, now we were ashore, to exercise a little discretion. But Old Fagg, as we called him,—he was only about twenty-five years old, by the way,—was the source of immense amusement to us that day. It appeared that he had conceived the idea that he could walk to Sacramento, and actually started off afoot. We had a good time, and shook hands with one another all around, and so parted. Ah me! only eight years ago, and yet some of those hands then clasped in amity have been clenched at each other, or have dipped furtively in one another's pockets. I know that we didn't dine together the next year, because young Barker swore he wouldn't put his feet under the same mahogany with such a very contemptible scoundrel as that Mixer; and Nibbles, who borrowed money at Valparaiso of young Stubbs, who was then a waiter in a restaurant, didn't like to meet such people.

When I bought a number of shares in the Coyote Tunnel at Mugginsville, in '54, I thought I'd take a run up there and see it. I stopped at the Empire Hotel, and after dinner I got a horse and rode round the town and out to the claim. One of those individuals whom newspaper correspondents call "our intelligent informant," and to whom in all small communities the right of answering questions is tacitly yielded, was quietly pointed out to me. Habit had enabled him to work and talk at the same time, and he never pretermitted either. He gave me a history of the claim, and added: "You see, stranger" (he addressed the bank before him), "gold is sure to come out 'er that theer claim (he put in a comma with his pick), but the old pro-pri-e-tor (he wriggled out the word and the point of his pick) warn't of much account (a long stroke of the pick for a period). He was green, and let the boys about here jump him,"—and the rest of his sentence was confided to his hat, which he had removed to wipe his manly brow with his red bandanna.

I asked him who was the original proprietor

"His name war Fagg."

I went to see him. He looked a little older and plainer. He had worked hard, he said, and was getting on "so, so." I took quite a liking to him, and patronized him to some extent. Whether I did so because I was beginning to have a distrust for such fellows as Rattler and Mixer is not necessary for me to state.

You remember how the Coyote Tunnel went in, and how awfully we shareholders were done! Well, the next thing I heard was that Rattler, who was one of the heaviest shareholders, was up in Mugginsville keeping bar for the proprietor of the Mugginsville Hotel, and that old Fagg had struck it rich, and didn't know what to do with his money. All this was told me by Mixer, who had been there, settling up matters, and likewise that Fagg was sweet upon the daughter of the proprietor of the aforesaid hotel. And so by hearsay and letter I eventually gathered that old Robins, the hotel man, was trying to get up a match between Nellie Robins and Fagg. Nellie was a pretty, plump, and foolish little thing, and would do just as her father wished. I thought it would be a good thing for Fagg if he should marry and settle down; that as a married man he might be of some account. So I ran up to Mugginsville one day to look after things.

It did me an immense deal of good to make Rattler mix my drinks for me,—Rattler? the gay, brilliant, and unconquerable Rattler, who had tried to snub me two years ago. I talked to him about old Fagg and Nellie, particularly as I thought the subject was distasteful. He never liked Fagg, and he was sure, he said, that Nellie didn't. Did Nellie

like anybody else? He turned around to the mirror behind
the bar and brushed up his hair; I understood the con-
ceited wretch. I thought I'd put Fagg on his guard and
get him to hurry up matters. I had a long talk with him.
You could see by the way the poor fellow acted that he was
badly struck. He sighed, and promised to pluck up courage
to hurry matters to a crisis. Nellie was a good girl, and I
think had a sort of quiet respect for old Fagg's unobtrusive-
ness. But her fancy was already taken captive by Rattler's
superficial qualities, which were obvious and pleasing. I
don't think Nellie was any worse than you or I. We are
more apt to take acquaintances at their apparent value than
their intrinsic worth. It's less trouble, and, except when we
want to trust them, quite as convenient. The difficulty with
women is that their feelings are apt to get interested sooner
than ours, and then, you know, reasoning is out of the question. This is what old Fagg would have known had he been
of any account. But he wasn't. So much the worse for
him.

It was a few months afterward, and I was sitting in my
office, when in walked old Fagg. I was surprised to see
him down, but we talked over the current topics in that
mechanical manner of people who know that they have
something else to say, but are obliged to get at it in that
formal way. After an interval Fagg in his natural manner
said,—

"I'm going home!"

"Going home?"

"Yes,—that is, I think I'll take a trip to the Atlantic
States. I came to see you, as you know I have some little
property, and I have executed a power of attorney for you
to manage my affairs. I have some papers I'd like to leave
with you. Will you take charge of them?"

"Yes," I said. "But what of Nellie?"

His face fell. He tried to smile, and the combination
resulted in one of the most startling and grotesque effects I
ever beheld. At length he said,—

"I shall not marry Nellie,—that is,"—he seemed to

apologize internally for the positive form of expression,—"I think that I had better not."

"David Fagg," I said with sudden severity, "you're of no account!"

To my astonishment his face brightened. "Yes," said he, "that's it!—I'm of no account! But I always knew it. You see I thought Rattler loved that girl as well as I did, and I knew she liked him better than she did me, and would be happier I dare say with him. But then I knew that old Robins would have preferred me to him, as I was better off,—and the girl would do as he said,—and, you see, I thought I was kinder in the way,—and so I left. But," he continued, as I was about to interrupt him, "for fear the old man might object to Rattler, I've lent him enough to set him up in business for himself in Dogtown. A pushing, active, brilliant fellow, you know, like Rattler, can get along, and will soon be in his old position again,—and you needn't be hard on him, you know, if he doesn't. Good by."

I was too much disgusted with his treatment of that Rattler to be at all amiable, but as his business was profitable, I promised to attend to it, and he left. A few weeks passed. The return steamer arrived, and a terrible incident occupied the papers for days afterward. People in all parts of the State conned eagerly the details of an awful shipwreck, and those who had friends aboard went away by themselves, and read the long list of the lost under their breath. I read of the gifted, the gallant, the noble, and loved ones who had perished, and among them I think I was the first to read the name of David Fagg. For the "man of no account" had "gone home!"

MLISS

CHAPTER I

JUST where the Sierra Nevada begins to subside in gentler undulations, and the rivers grow less rapid and yellow, on the side of a great red mountain, stands "Smith's Pocket."

Seen from the red road at sunset, in the red light and the red dust, its white houses look like the outcroppings of quartz on the mountain-side. The red stage topped with red-shirted passengers is lost to view half a dozen times in the tortuous descent, turning up unexpectedly in out-of-the-way places, and vanishing altogether within a hundred yards of the town. It is probably owing to this sudden twist in the road that the advent of a stranger at Smith's Pocket is usually attended with a peculiar circumstance. Dismounting from the vehicle at the stage office, the too confident traveller is apt to walk straight out of town under the impression that it lies in quite another direction. It is related that one of the tunnel-men, two miles from town, met one of these self-reliant passengers with a carpet-bag, umbrella, Harper's Magazine, and other evidences of "Civilization and Refinement," plodding along over the road he had just ridden, vainly endeavouring to find the settlement of Smith's Pocket.

An observant traveller might have found some compensation for his disappointment in the weird aspect of that vicinity. There were huge fissures on the hillside, and displacements of the red soil, resembling more the chaos of some primary elemental upheaval than the work of man; while, half-way down, a long flume straddled its narrow body and disproportionate legs over the chasm, like an enormous fossil of some forgotten antediluvian. At every step smaller ditches crossed the road, hiding in their sallow depths unlovely streams that crept away to a clandestine union with the great yellow torrent below, and here and there were the ruins of some cabin with the chimney alone left intact and the hearthstone open to the skies.

The settlement of Smith's Pocket owed its origin to the finding of a "pocket" on its site by a veritable Smith. Five thousand dollars were taken out of it in one half-hour by Smith. Three thousand dollars were expended by Smith and others in erecting a flume and in tunnelling. And then Smith's Pocket was found to be only a pocket, and subject like other pockets to depletion. Although Smith pierced the bowels of the great red mountain, that five thousand dollars was the first and last return of his labour. The mountain grew reticent of its golden secrets, and the flume steadily ebbed away the remainder of Smith's fortune. Then Smith went into quartz-mining; then into quartz-milling; then into hydraulics and ditching, and then by easy degrees into saloon-keeping. Presently it was whispered that Smith was drinking a great deal; then it was known that Smith was a habitual drunkard, and then people began to think, as they are apt to, that he had never been anything else. But the settlement of Smith's Pocket, like that of most discoveries, was happily not dependent on the fortune of its pioneer, and other parties projected tunnels and found pockets. So Smith's Pocket became a settlement with its two fancy stores, its two hotels, its one express-office, and its two first families. Occasionally its one long straggling street was overawed by the assumption of the latest San Francisco fashions, imported per express, exclusively to the first families; making outraged Nature, in the ragged outline of her furrowed surface, look still more homely, and putting personal insult on that greater portion of the population to whom the Sabbath, with a change of linen, brought merely the necessity of cleanliness, without the luxury of adornment. Then there was a Methodist Church, and hard by a Monte Bank, and a little beyond, on the mountain-side, a graveyard; and then a little school-house.

"The Master," as he was known to his little flock, sat alone one night in the school-house, with some open copybooks before him, carefully making those bold and full characters which are supposed to combine the extremes of chirographical and moral excellence, and had got as far as "Riches are deceitful," and was elaborating the noun with an insincerity of flourish that was quite in the spirit of his text, when he heard a gentle tapping. The woodpeckers had been busy about the roof during the day, and the noise did not disturb his work. But the opening of the door, and the tapping continuing from the inside, caused him to look up. He was slightly startled by the figure of a young girl, dirty and shabbily clad. Still, her great black eyes, her coarse, uncombed, lustreless black hair falling over her sunburned face, her red arms and feet streaked with the red soil, were all familiar to him. It was Melissa Smith,— Smith's motherless child.

"What can she want here?" thought the master. Everybody knew "Mliss," as she was called, throughout the length and height of Red Mountain. Everybody knew her as an incorrigible girl. Her fierce, ungovernable disposition, her mad freaks and lawless character, were, in their way, as proverbial as the story of her father's weaknesses, and as philosophically accepted by the townsfolk. She wrangled with and fought the school-boys with keener invective and quite as powerful arm. She followed the trails with a woodman's craft, and the master had met her before, miles away, shoeless, stockingless, and bareheaded on the mountain road. The miners' camps along the stream supplied her with subsistence during these voluntary pilgrimages, in freely offered alms. Not but that a larger protection had been previously extended to Mliss. The Rev. Joshua McSnagley, "stated" preacher, had placed her in the hotel as servant, by way of preliminary refinement, and had introduced her to his scholars at Sunday-school. But she threw plates occasionally at the landlord, and quickly retorted to the cheap witticisms of the guests, and created in the Sabbath-school a sensation that was so inimical to the orthodox dulness and placidity of that institution, that, with a decent regard for the starched frocks and unblemished morals of the two pink-and-white-faced children of the first families, the reverend gentleman had her ignominiously expelled. Such were the antecedents, and such the character of Mliss, as she stood before the master. It was shown in the ragged dress, the unkempt hair, and bleeding feet, and asked his pity. It flashed from her black, fearless eyes, and commanded his respect.

"I come here to-night," she said rapidly and boldly, keeping her hard glance on his, "because I knew you was alone. I wouldn't come here when them gals was here. I

hate 'em and they hates me. That's why. You keep school,
don't you? I want to be teached!"

If to the shabbiness of her apparel and uncomeliness of
her tangled hair and dirty face she had added the humility
of tears, the master would have extended to her the usual
moiety of pity, and nothing more. But with the natural,
though illogical instincts of his species, her boldness
awakened in him something of that respect which all original
natures pay unconsciously to one another in any grade.
And he gazed at her the more fixedly as she went on still
rapidly, her hand on that door-latch and her eyes on his:—

"My name's Mliss,—Mliss Smith! You can bet your
life on that. My father's Old Smith,—Old Bummer Smith,
—that's what's the matter with him. Mliss Smith,—and
I'm coming to school."

"Well?" said the master.

Accustomed to be thwarted and opposed, often wantonly
and cruelly, for no other purpose than to excite the violent
impulses of her nature, the master's phlegm evidently took
her by surprise. She stopped; she began to twist a lock of
her hair between her fingers; and the rigid line of upper
lip, drawn over the wicked little teeth, relaxed and quivered
slightly. Then her eyes dropped, and something like a
blush struggled up to her cheek, and tried to assert itself
through the splashes of redder soil, and the sunburn of
years. Suddenly she threw herself forward, calling on God
to strike her dead, and fell quite weak and helpless, with
her face on the master's desk, crying and sobbing as if her
heart would break.

The master lifted her gently and waited for the paroxysm
to pass. When with face still averted, she was repeating
between her sobs the *mea culpa* of childish penitence,—that
"she'd be good, she didn't mean to," &c., it came to him to
ask her why she had left Sabbath-school.

Why had she left the Sabbath-school?—why? O yes.
What did he (McSnagley) want to tell her she was wicked
for? What did he tell her that God hated her for? If God
hated her, what did she want to go to Sabbath-school for?

She didn't want to be "beholden" to anybody who hated her.

Had she told McSnagley this?

Yes she had.

The master laughed. It was a hearty laugh, and echoed so oddly in the little school-house, and seemed so inconsistent and discordant with the sighing of the pines without, that he shortly corrected himself with a sigh. The sigh was quite as sincere in its way, however, and after a moment of serious silence he asked her about her father.

Her father? What father? Whose father? What had he ever done for her? Why did the girls hate her? Come now! what made the folks say, "Old Bummer Smith's Mliss!" when she passed? Yes; O yes. She wished he was dead,—she was dead,—everybody was dead; and her sobs broke forth anew.

The master, then leaning over her, told her as well as he could what you or I might have said after hearing such unnatural theories from childish lips; only bearing in mind perhaps better than you or I the unnatural facts of her ragged dress, her bleeding feet, and the omnipresent shadow of her drunken father. Then, raising her to her feet, he wrapped his shawl around her, and, bidding her come early in the morning, he walked with her down the road. There he bade her "good night." The moon shone brightly on the narrow path before them. He stood and watched the bent little figure as it staggered down the road, and waited until it had passed the little graveyard and reached the curve of the hill, where it turned and stood for a moment, a mere atom of suffering outlined against the far-off patient stars. Then he went back to his work. But the lines of the copy-book thereafter faded into long parallels of never-ending road, over which childish figures seemed to pass sobbing and crying into the night. Then, the little school-house seeming lonelier than before, he shut the door and went home.

The next morning Mliss came to school. Her face had been washed, and her coarse black hair bore evidence of recent struggles with the comb, in which both had evidently

suffered. The old defiant look shone occasionally in her
eyes, but her manner was tamer and more subdued. Then
began a series of little trials and self-sacrifices, in which
master and pupil bore an equal part, and which increased
the confidence and sympathy between them. Although
obedient under the master's eye, at times during the recess,
if thwarted or stung by a fancied slight, Mliss would rage
in ungovernable fury, and many a palpitating young savage, finding himself matched with his own weapons of torment, would seek the master with torn jacket and scratched
face, and complaints of the dreadful Mliss. There was a
serious division among the townspeople on the subject; some
threatening to withdraw their children from such evil companionship, and others as warmly upholding the course of
the master in his work of reclamation. Meanwhile, with a
steady persistence that seemed quite astonishing to him on
looking back afterward, the master drew Mliss gradually
out of the shadow of her past life, as though it were but her
natural progress down the narrow path on which he had set
her feet the moonlit night of their first meeting. Remembering the experience of the evangelical McSnagley, he carefully avoided that Rock of Ages on which that unskilful
pilot had shipwrecked her young faith. But if, in the course
of her reading, she chanced to stumble upon those few words
which have lifted such as she above the level of the older,
the wiser, and the more prudent,—if she learned something
of a faith that is symbolized by suffering, and the old light
softened in her eyes, it did not take the shape of a lesson.
A few of the plainer people had made up a little sum by
which the ragged Mliss was enabled to assume the garments
of respect and civilisation; and often a rough shake of the
hand, and words of homely commendation from a red-
shirted and burly figure, sent a glow to the cheek of the
young master, and set him to thinking if it was altogether
deserved.

Three months had passed from the time of their first
meeting, and the master was sitting late one evening over
the moral and sententious copies, when there came a tap at

the door, and again Mliss stood before him. She was neatly clad and clean-faced, and there was nothing, perhaps, but the long black hair and bright black eyes to remind him of his former apparition. "Are you busy?" she asked; "can you come with me?" And on his signifying his readiness, in her old wilful way she said, "Come, then, quick."

They passed out of the door together, and into the dark road. As they entered the town the master asked her whither she was going. She replied, "To see my father."

It was the first time he had heard her call him by that filial title, or indeed anything more than "Old Smith," or the "Old Man." It was the first time in three months that she had spoken of him at all, and the master knew she had kept resolutely aloof from him since her great change. Satisfied from her manner that it was fruitless to question her purpose, he passively followed. In out-of-the-way places, low groggeries, restaurants, and saloons; in gambling-halls and dance-houses, the master, preceded by Mliss, came and went. In the reeking smoke and blasphemous outcries of low dens, the child, holding the master's hand, stood and anxiously gazed, seemingly unconscious of all in the one absorbing nature of her pursuit. Some of the revellers, recognising Mliss, called to the child to sing and dance for them, and would have forced liquor upon her but for the interference of the master. Others, recognising him mutely, made way for them to pass. So an hour slipped by. Then the child whispered in his ear that there was a cabin on the other side of the creek, crossed by the long flume, where she thought he still might be. Thither they crossed,—a toilsome half-hour's walk, but in vain. They were returning by the ditch at the abutment of the flume, gazing at the lights of the town on the opposite bank, when suddenly, sharply, a quick report rang out on the clear night air. The echoes caught it, and carried it round and round Red Mountain, and set the dogs to barking all along the streams. Lights seemed to dance and move quickly on the outskirts of the town for a few moments, the stream rippled quite audibly beside them, a few stones loosened themselves from the hill-side, and splashed into the stream, a heavy wind seemed to surge the branches of the funereal pines, and then the silence seemed to fall thicker, heavier, and deadlier. The master turned towards Mliss with an unconscious gesture of protection, but the child had gone. Oppressed by a strange fear, he ran quickly down the trail to the river's bed, and, jumping from boulder to boulder, reached the base of Red Mountain and the outskirts of the village. Midway of the crossings he looked up and held his breath in awe. For high above him, on the narrow flume, he saw the fluttering little figure of his late companion crossing swiftly in the darkness.

He climbed the bank, and, guided by a few lights moving about a central point on the mountain, soon found himself breathless among a crowd of awe-stricken and sorrowful men. Out from among them the child appeared, and, taking the master's hand, led him silently before what seemed a ragged hole in the mountain. Her face was quite white, but her excited manner gone, and her look that of one to whom some long-expected event had at last happened,—an expression that, to the master in his bewilderment, seemed almost like relief. The walls of the cavern were partly propped by decaying timbers. The child pointed to what appeared to be some ragged cast-off clothes left in the hole by the late occupant. The master approached nearer with his flaming dip, and bent over them. It was Smith, already cold, with a pistol in his hand, and a bullet in his heart, lying beside his empty pocket.

CHAPTER II

THE opinion which McSnagley expressed in reference to a "change of heart" supposed to be experienced by Mliss was more forcibly described in the gulches and tunnels. It was thought there that Mliss had "struck a good lead." So when there was a new grave added to the little enclosure, and at the expense of the master a little board and inscription put above it, the Red Mountain Banner came out quite handsomely, and did the fair thing to the memory of one of "our oldest Pioneers," alluding gracefully to that "bane of noble intellects," and otherwise genteelly shelving our dear brother with the past. "He leaves an only child to mourn his loss," says the Banner, "who is now an exemplary scholar, thanks to the efforts of the Rev. Mr. McSnagley." The Rev. McSnagley, in fact, made a strong point of Mliss's conversion, and indirectly attributing to the unfortunate child the suicide of her father, made affecting allusions in Sunday-school to the beneficial effects of the "silent tomb," and in this cheerful contemplation drove most of the children into speechless horror, and caused the pink-and-white scions of the first families to howl dismally and refuse to be comforted.

The long dry summer came. As each fierce day burned itself out in little whiffs of pearl-gray smoke on the mountain summits, and the upspringing breeze scattered its red embers over the landscape, the green wave which in early spring upheaved above Smith's grave grew sere, and dry, and hard. In those days the master, strolling in the little churchyard of a Sabbath afternoon, was sometimes surprised to find a few wild flowers plucked from the damp pine forest scattered there, and oftener rude wreaths hung upon the little pine cross. Most of these wreaths were formed of a sweet-scented grass, which the children loved to keep in their desks, intertwined with the plumes of the buckeye, the syringa, and the wood anemone; and here and there the master noticed the dark blue cowl of the monk's-hood, or deadly aconite. There was something in the odd association of this noxious plant with these memorials which occasioned a painful sensation to the master deeper than his esthetic sense. One day, during a long walk, in crossing a wooded ridge, he came upon Mliss in the heart of the forest, perched upon a prostrate pine, on a fantastic throne formed by the hanging plumes of lifeless branches, her lap full of grasses and pine-burrs, and crooning to herself one of the negro melodies of her younger life. Recognizing him at a distance, she made room for him on her elevated throne,

and with a grave assumption of hospitality and patronage
that would have been ridiculous had it not been so terribly
earnest, she fed him with pine nuts and crab-apples. The
master took that opportunity to point out to her the noxious and deadly qualities of the monk's-hood, whose dark
blossoms he saw in her lap, and extorted from her a promise
not to meddle with it as long as she remained his pupil.
This done,—as the master had tested her integrity before,—
he rested satisfied, and the strange feeling which had overcome him on seeing them died away.

Of the homes that were offered Mliss when her conversion
became known, the master preferred that of Mrs. Morpher,
a womanly and kind-hearted specimen of south-western
efflorescence, known in her maidenhood as the "Per-rairie
Rose." Being one of those who contend resolutely against
their own natures, Mrs. Morpher, by a long series of self-
sacrifices and struggles, had at last subjugated her naturally
careless disposition to principles of "order," which she considered, in common with Mr. Pope, as "Heaven's first law."
But she could not entirely govern the orbits of her satellites,
however regular her own movements, and even her own
"Jeemes" sometimes collided with her. Again her old nature asserted itself in her children. Lycurgus dipped into
the cupboard "between meals," and Aristides came home
from school without shoes, leaving those important articles
on the threshold, for the delight of a bare-footed walk down
the ditches. Octavia and Cassandra were "keerless" of their
clothes. So with but one exception, however much the
"Prairie Rose" might have trimmed and pruned and trained
her own matured luxuriance, the little shoots came up de-
fiantly wild and straggling. That one exception was Clytemnestra Morpher, aged fifteen. She was the realization
of her mother's immaculate conception,—neat, orderly, and
dull.

It was an amiable weakness of Mrs. Morpher to imagine
that "Clytie" was a consolation and model for Mliss.
Following this fallacy, Mrs. Morpher threw Clytie at the
head of Mliss when she was "bad," and set her up before

the child for adoration in her penitential moments. It was not, therefore, surprising to the master to hear that Clytie was coming to school, obviously as a favour to the master and as an example for Mliss and others. For "Clytie" was quite a young lady. Inheriting her mother's physical peculiarities, and in obedience to the climatic laws of the Red Mountain region, she was an early bloomer. The youth of "Smith's Pocket," to whom this kind of flower was rare, sighed for her in April and languished in May. Enamoured swains haunted the school-house at the hour of dismissal. A few were jealous of the master.

Perhaps it was this latter circumstance that opened the master's eyes to another. He could not help noticing that Clytie was romantic; that in school she required a great deal of attention; that her pens were uniformly bad and wanted fixing; that she usually accompanied the request with a certain expectation in her eye that was somewhat disproportionate to the quality of service she verbally required; that she sometimes allowed the curves of a round, plump white arm to rest on his when he was writing her copies; that she always blushed and flung back her blond curls when she did so. I don't remember whether I have stated that the master was a young man,—it's of little consequence, however; he had been severely educated in the school in which Clytie was taking her first lesson, and, on the whole, withstood the flexible curves and facetious glance like the fine young Spartan that he was. Perhaps an insufficient quality of food may have tended to this asceticism. He generally avoided Clytie; but one evening when she returned to the school-house after something she had forgotten, and did not find it until the master walked home with her I hear that he endeavoured to make himself particularly agreeable,—partly from the fact, I imagine, that his conduct was adding gall and bitterness to the already overcharged hearts of Clytemnestra's admirers.

The morning after this affecting episode Mliss did not come to school. Noon came, but not Mliss. Questioning

Clytie on the subject, it appeared that they had left for school together, but the wilful Mliss had taken another road. The afternoon brought her not. In the evening he called on Mrs. Morpher, whose motherly heart was really alarmed. Mr. Morpher had spent all day in search of her, without discovering a trace that might lead to her discovery. Aristides was summoned as a probable accomplice, but that equitable infant succeeded in impressing the household with his innocence. Mrs. Morpher entertained a vivid impression that the child would yet be found drowned in a ditch, or, what was almost as terrible, muddied and soiled beyond the redemption of soap and water. Sick at heart, the master returned to the school-house. As he lit his lamp and seated himself at his desk, he found a note lying before him addressed to himself, in Mliss's handwriting. It seemed to be written on a leaf torn from some old memorandum-book, and to prevent sacrilegious trifling, had been sealed with six broken wafers. Opening it almost tenderly, the master read as follows:—

RESPECTED SIR,—When you read this, I am run away. Never to come back. *Never*, NEVER, NEVER. You can give my beeds to Mary Jennings, and my Amerika's Pride [a highly coloured lithograph from a tobacco-box] to Sally Flanders. But don't you give anything to Clytie Morpher. Don't you dare to. Do you know what my opinion is of her, it is this, she is perfekly disgustin. That is all and no more at present from

Yours respectfully,
MELISSA SMITH.

The master sat pondering on this strange epistle till the moon lifted its bright face above the distant hills, and illuminated the trail that led to the school-house, beaten quite hard with the coming and going of little feet. Then, more satisfied in mind, he tore the missive into fragments and scattered them along the road.

At sunrise the next morning he was picking his way through the palm-like fern and thick underbrush of the pine-forest, starting the hare from its form, and awakening a querulous protest from a few dissipated crows, who had evidently been making a night of it, and so came to the wooded ridge where he had once found Mliss. There he found the prostrate pine and tasselled branches, but the throne was vacant. As he drew nearer, what might have been some frightened animal started through the crackling limbs. It ran up the tossed arms of the fallen monarch, and sheltered itself in some friendly foliage. The master, reaching the old seat, found the nest still warm; looking up in the intertwining branches, he met the black eyes of the errant Mliss. They gazed at each other without speaking. She was the first to break the silence.

"What do you want?" she asked curtly.

The master had decided on a course of action. "I want some crab-apples," he said, humbly.

"Shan't have 'em; go away. Why don't you get 'em of Clytemnerestera?" (It seemed to be a relief to Mliss to express her contempt in additional syllables to that classical young woman's already long-drawn title.) "O you wicked thing!"

"I am hungry, Lizzy. I have eaten nothing since dinner yesterday. I am famished!" and the young man, in a state of remarkable exhaustion, leaned against the tree.

Melissa's heart was touched. In the bitter days of her gipsy life she had known the sensation he so artfully simulated. Overcome by his heart-broken tone, but not entirely divested of suspicion, she said,—

"Dig under the tree near the roots, and you'll find lots; but mind you don't tell," for Mliss had *her* hoards as well as the rats and squirrels.

But the master, of course, was unable to find them; the effects of hunger probably blinding his senses. Mliss grew uneasy. At length she peered at him through the leaves in an elfish way, and questioned,—

"If I come down and give you some, you'll promise you won't touch me?"

The master promised.

"Hope you'll die if you do!"

The master accepted instant dissolution as a forfeit. Mliss slid down the tree. For a few moments nothing transpired but the munching of the pine-nuts. "Do you feel better?" she asked, with some solicitude. The master confessed to a recuperated feeling, and then, gravely thanking her, proceeded to retrace his steps. As he expected, he had not gone far before she called him. He turned. She was standing there quite white, with tears in her widely opened orbs. The master felt that the right moment had come. Going up to her, he took both her hands, and, looking in her tearful eyes, said, gravely, "Lissy, do you remember the first evening you came to see me?"

Lissy remembered.

"You asked me if you might come to school, for you wanted to learn something and be better, and I said——"

"Come," responded the child, promptly.

"What would *you* say if the master now came to you and said that he was lonely without his little scholar, and that he wanted her to come and teach him to be better?"

The child hung her head for a few moments in silence. The master waited patiently. Tempted by the quiet, a hare ran close to the couple, and raising her bright eyes and velvet forepaws, sat and gazed at them. A squirrel ran half-way down the furrowed bark of the fallen tree, and there stopped.

"We are waiting, Lissy," said the master, in a whisper, and the child smiled. Stirred by a passing breeze, the tree-tops rocked, and a long pencil of light stole through their interlaced boughs full on the doubting face and irresolute little figure. Suddenly she took the master's hand in her quick way. What she said was scarcely audible, but the master, putting the black hair back from her forehead, kissed her; and so, hand in hand, they passed out of the damp aisles and forest odours into the open sunlit road.

CHAPTER III

SOMEWHAT less spiteful in her intercourse with other scholars, Mliss still retained an offensive attitude in regard to Clytemnestra. Perhaps the jealous element was not entirely lulled in her passionate little breast. Perhaps it was only that the round curves and plump outline offered more extended pinching surface. But while such ebullitions were under the master's control, her enmity occasionally took a new and irrepressible form.

The master in his first estimate of the child's character could not conceive that she had ever possessed a doll. But the master, like many other professed readers of character, was safer in *à posteriori* than *à priori* reasoning. Mliss had a doll, but then it was emphatically Mliss's doll,—a smaller copy of herself. Its unhappy existence had been a secret discovered accidentally by Mrs. Morpher. It had been the old-time companion of Mliss's wanderings, and bore evident marks of suffering. Its original complexion was long since washed away by the weather and anointed by the slime of ditches. It looked very much as Mliss had in days past. Its one gown of faded stuff was dirty and ragged as hers had been. Mliss had never been known to apply to it any childish term of endearment. She never exhibited it in the presence of other children. It was put severely to bed in a hollow tree near the school-house, and only allowed exercise during Mliss's rambles. Fulfilling a stern duty to her doll, as she would to herself, it knew no luxuries.

Now Mrs. Morpher, obeying a commendable impulse, bought another doll and gave it to Mliss. The child received it gravely and curiously. The master, on looking at it one day, fancied he saw a slight resemblance in its round red cheeks and mild blue eyes to Clytemnestra. It became evident before long that Mliss had also noticed the same resemblance. Accordingly she hammered its waxen head on the rocks when she was alone, and sometimes dragged it with a string round its neck to and from school. At other times, setting it up on her desk, she made a pin-cushion of its patient and inoffensive body. Whether this was done in revenge of what she considered a second figurative obtrusion of Clytie's excellences upon her, or whether she had an intuitive appreciation of the rites of certain other heathens, and, indulging in that "Fetish," ceremony, imagined that the original of her wax model would pine away and finally die, is a metaphysical question I shall not now consider.

In spite of these moral vagaries, the master could not help noticing in her different tasks the working of a quick, restless, and vigorous perception. She knew neither the hesitancy nor the doubts of childhood. Her answers in class were always slightly dashed with audacity. Of course she was not infallible. But her courage and daring in passing beyond her own depth and that of the floundering little swimmers around her, in their minds outweighed all errors of judgment. Children are not better than grown people in this respect, I fancy; and whenever the little red hand flashed above her desk, there was a wondering silence, and even the master was sometimes oppressed with a doubt of his own experience and judgment.

Nevertheless, certain attributes which at first amused and entertained his fancy began to afflict him with grave doubts. He could not but see that Mliss was revengeful, irreverent, and wilful. That there was but one better quality which pertained to her semi-savage disposition,—the faculty of physical fortitude and self-sacrifice, and another, though not always an attribute of the noble savage,—Truth. Mliss was both fearless and sincere; perhaps in such a character the adjectives were synonymous.

The master had been doing some hard thinking on this subject, and had arrived at that conclusion quite common to all who think sincerely, that he was generally the slave of his own prejudices, when he determined to call on the Rev. McSnagley for advice. This decision was somewhat humiliating to his pride, as he and McSnagley were not friends. But he thought of Mliss, and the evening of their first meeting; and perhaps with a pardonable superstition that it was not chance alone that had guided her wilful

feet to the school-house, and perhaps with a complacent
consciousness of the rare magnanimity of the act, he choked
back his dislike and went to McSnagley.

The reverend gentleman was glad to see him. Moreover,
he observed that the master was looking "peartish," and
hoped he had got over the "neuralgy" and "rheumatiz."
He himself had been troubled with a dumb "ager" since
last conference. But he had learned to "rastle and pray."
Pausing a moment to enable the master to write his
certain method of curing the dumb "ager" upon the book
and volume of his brain, Mr. McSnagley proceeded to in-
quire after Sister Morpher. "She is an adornment to
Christewanity, and has a likely growin' young family,"
added Mr. McSnagley; "and there's that mannerly young
gal,—so well behaved,—Miss Clytie." In fact, Clytie's per-
fections seemed to affect him to such an extent that he
dwelt for several minutes upon them. The master was
doubly embarrassed. In the first place, there was an enforced contrast with poor Mliss in all this praise of Clytie.
Secondly, there was something unpleasantly confidential in
his tone of speaking of Mrs. Morpher's earliest born. So
that the master, after a few futile efforts to say something
natural, found it convenient to recall another engagement,
and left without asking the information required, but in his
after reflections somewhat unjustly giving the Rev. Mr.
McSnagley the full benefit of having refused it.

Perhaps this rebuff placed the master and pupil once
more in the close communion of old. The child seemed to
notice the change in the master's manner, which had of late
been constrained, and in one of their long post-prandial
walks she stopped suddenly, and, mounting a stump, looked
full in his face with big, searching eyes. "You ain't
mad?" said she, with an interrogative shake of the black
braids. "No." "Nor bothered?" "No." "Nor hungry?"
(Hunger was to Mliss a sickness that might attack a person
at any moment.) "No." "Nor thinking of her?" "Of
whom, Lissy?" "That white girl." (This was the latest
epithet invented by Mliss, who was a very dark brunette, to

express Clytemnestra.) "No." "Upon your word?" (A substitute for "Hope you'll die!" proposed by the master.) "Yes." "And sacred honour?" "Yes." Then Mliss gave him a fierce little kiss, and, hopping down, fluttered off. For two or three days after that she condescended to appear more like other children, and be, as she expressed it, "good."

Two years had passed since the master's advent at Smith's Pocket, and as his salary was not large, and the prospects of Smith's Pocket eventually becoming the capital of the State not entirely definite, he contemplated a change. He had informed the school trustees privately of his intentions, but, educated young men of unblemished moral character being scarce at that time, he consented to continue his school term through the winter to early spring. None else knew of his intention except his one friend, a Dr. Duchesne, a young Creole physician known to the people of Wingdam as "Duchesny." He never mentioned it to Mrs. Morpher, Clytie, or any of his scholars. His reticence was partly the result of a constitutional indisposition to fuss, partly a desire to be spared the questions and surmises of vulgar curiosity, and partly that he never really believed he was going to do anything before it was done.

He did not like to think of Mliss. It was a selfish instinct, perhaps, which made him try to fancy his feeling for the child was foolish, romantic, and unpractical. He even tried to imagine that she would do better under the control of an older and sterner teacher. Then she was nearly eleven, and in a few years, by the rules of Red Mountain, would be a woman. He had done his duty. After Smith's death he addressed letters to Smith's relatives, and received one answer from a sister of Melissa's mother. Thanking the master, she stated her intention of leaving the Atlantic States for California with her husband in a few months. This was a slight superstructure for the airy castle which the master pictured for Mliss's house, but it was easy to fancy that some loving sympathetic woman, with the claims of kindred, might better guide her wayward nature.

Yet, when the master had read the letter, Mliss listened to it carelessly, received it submissively, and afterwards cut figures out of it with her scissors, supposed to represent Clytemnestra, labelled "the white girl," to prevent mistakes, and impaled them upon the outer walls of the school-house.

When the summer was about spent, and the last harvest had been gathered in the valleys, the master bethought him of gathering in a few ripened shoots of the young idea, and of having his Harvest-Home, or Examination. So the savants and professionals of Smith's Pocket were gathered to witness that time-honoured custom of placing timid children in a constrained position, and bullying them as in a witness-box. As usual in such cases, the most audacious and self-possessed were the lucky recipients of the honours. The reader will imagine that in the present instance Mliss and Clytie were pre-eminent, and divided public attention; Mliss with her clearness of material perception and self-reliance, Clytie with her placid self-esteem and saint-like correctness of deportment. The other little ones were timid and blundering. Mliss's readiness and brilliancy, of course, captivated the greatest number and provoked the greatest applause. Mliss's antecedents had unconsciously awakened the strongest sympathies of a class whose athletic forms were ranged against the walls, or whose handsome bearded faces looked in at the windows. But Mliss's popularity was overthrown by an unexpected circumstance.

McSnagley had invited himself, and had been going through the pleasing entertainment of frightening the more timid pupils by the vaguest and most ambiguous questions delivered in an impressive funereal tone; and Mliss had soared into Astronomy, and was tracking the course of our spotted ball through space, and keeping time with the music of the spheres, and defining the tethered orbits of the planets, when McSnagley impressively arose. "Meelissy! ye were speaking of the revolutions of this yere yearth and the move-*ments* of the sun, and I think ye said it had been a-doing of it since the creashun, eh?" Mliss nodded a scornful affirmative. "Well, war that the truth?" said

McSnagley, folding his arms. "Yes," said Mliss, shutting up her little red lips tightly. The handsome outlines at the windows peered further in the school-room, and a saintly Raphael-face, with blond beard and soft blue eyes, belonging to the biggest scamp in the diggings, turned toward the child and whispered, "Stick to it Mliss!" The reverend gentleman heaved a deep sigh, and cast a compassionate glance at the master, then at the children, and then rested his look on Clytie. That young woman softly elevated her round, white arm. Its seductive curves were enhanced by a gorgeous and massive specimen bracelet, the gift of one of her humblest worshippers, worn in honour of the occasion. There was a momentary silence. Clytie's round cheeks were very pink and soft. Clytie's big eyes were very bright and blue. Clytie's low-necked white book-muslin rested softly on Clytie's white, plump shoulders. Clytie looked at the master, and the master nodded. Then Clytie spoke softly:—

"Joshua commanded the sun to stand still, and it obeyed him!" There was a low hum of applause in the school-room, a triumphant expression on McSnagley's face, a grave shadow on the master's, and a comical look of disappointment reflected from the windows. Mliss skimmed rapidly over her Astronomy, and then shut the book with a loud snap. A groan burst from McSnagley, an expression of astonishment from the school-room, a yell from the windows, as Mliss brought her red fist down on the desk, with the emphatic declaration,

"It's a d—n lie. I don't believe it!"

CHAPTER IV

THE long wet season had drawn near its close. Signs of spring were visible in the swelling buds and rushing torrents. The pine-forests exhaled the fresher spicery. The azaleas were already budding, the Ceanothus getting ready its lilac livery for spring. On the green upland which climbed Red Mountain at its southern aspect the long

spike of the monk's-hood shot up from its broad-leaved
stool, and once more shook its dark-blue bells. Again the
billow above Smith's grave was soft and green, its crest
just tossed with the foam of daisies and buttercups. The
little graveyard had gathered a few new dwellers in the
past year, and the mounds were placed two by two by the
little paling until they reached Smith's grave, and there
there was but one. General superstition had shunned it,
and the plot beside Smith was vacant.

There had been several placards posted about the town,
intimating that, at a certain period, a celebrated dramatic
company would perform, for a few days, a series of "side-
splitting" and "screaming farces;" that, alternating pleasantly with this, there would be some melodrama and a
grand divertisement, which would include singing, dancing,
&c. These announcements occasioned a great fluttering
among the little folk, and were the theme of much excitement and great speculation among the master's scholars.
The master had promised Mliss, to whom this sort of thing
was sacred and rare, that she should go, and on that momentous evening the master and Mliss "assisted."

The performance was the prevalent style of heavy medioc-
rity; the melodrama was not bad enough to laugh at nor
good enough to excite. But the master, turning wearily to
the child, was astonished, and felt something like self-accusation in noticing the peculiar effect upon her excitable
nature. The red blood flushed in her cheeks at each stroke
of her panting little heart. Her small passionate lips were
slightly parted to give vent to her hurried breath. Her
widely opened lids threw up and arched her black eyebrows. She did not laugh at the dismal comicalities of
the funny man, for Mliss seldom laughed. Nor was she
discreetly affected to the delicate extremes of the corner of
a white handkerchief, as was the tender-hearted "Clytie,"
who was talking with her "feller" and ogling the master
at the same moment. But when the performance was
over, and the green curtain fell on the little stage, Mliss
drew a long deep breath, and turned to the master's grave,

face with a half-apologetic smile and wearied gesture. Then she said, "Now take me home!" and dropped the lids of her black eyes, as if to dwell once more in fancy on the mimic stage.

On their way to Mrs. Morpher's, the master thought proper to ridicule the whole performance. Now he shouldn't wonder if Mliss thought that the young lady who acted so beautifully was really in earnest, and in love with the gentleman who wore such fine clothes. Well, if she were in love with him, it was a very unfortunate thing! "Why?" said Mliss, with an upward sweep of the drooping lid. "Oh! well, he couldn't support his wife at his present salary, and pay so much a week for his fine clothes, and then they wouldn't receive as much wages if they were married as if they were merely lovers—that is," added the master, "if they are not already married to somebody else; but I think the husband of the pretty young countess takes the tickets at the door, or pulls up the curtain, or snuffs the candles, or does something equally refined and elegant. As to the young man with nice clothes, which are really nice now, and must cost at least two and a half or three dollars, not to speak of that mantle of red drugget which I happen to know the price of, for I bought some of it for my room once; as to this young man, Lissy, he is a pretty good fellow, and if he does drink occasionally, I don't think people ought to take advantage of it and give him black eyes and throw him in the mud. Do you? I am sure he might owe me two dollars and a half a long time, before I would throw it up in his face, as the fellow did the other night at Wingdam."

Mliss had taken his hand in both of hers and was trying to look in his eyes, which the young man kept as resolutely averted. Mliss had a faint idea of irony, indulging herself sometimes in a species of sardonic humour, which was equally visible in her actions and her speech. But the young man continued in this strain until they had reached Mrs. Morpher's, and he had deposited Mliss in her maternal charge Waiving the invitation of Mrs. Morpher to refreshment and rest, and shading his eyes with his hand to keep out the blue-eyed Clytemnestra's siren glances, he excused himself, and went home.

For two or three days after the advent of the dramatic company, Mliss was late at school, and the master's usual Friday afternoon ramble was for once omitted, owing to the absence of his trustworthy guide. As he was putting away his books and preparing to leave the school-house, a small voice piped at his side, "Please, sir?" The master turned, and there stood Aristides Morpher.

"Well, my little man," said the master, impatiently, "what is it? quick!"

"Please, sir, me and 'Kerg' thinks that Mliss is going to run away agin."

"What's that, sir?" said the master, with that unjust testiness with which we always receive disagreeable news.

"Why, sir, she don't stay home any more, and 'Kerg' and me see her talking with one of those actor fellers, and she's with him now; and please, sir, yesterday she told 'Kerg' and me she could make a speech as well as Miss Cellerstina Montmoressy, and she spouted right off by heart," and the little fellow paused in a collapsed condition.

"What actor?" asked the master.

"Him as wears the shiny hat. And hair. And gold pin. And gold chain," said the just Aristides, putting periods for commas to eke out his breath.

The master put on his gloves and hat, feeling an unpleasant tightness in his chest and thorax, and walked out in the road. Aristides trotted along by his side, endeavouring to keep pace with his short legs to the master's strides, when the master stopped suddenly, and Aristides bumped up against him. "Where were they talking?" asked the master, as if continuing the conversation.

"At the Arcade," said Aristides.

When they reached the main street the master paused. "Run down home," said he to the boy. "If Mliss is there, come to the Arcade and tell me. If she isn't there, stay home: run!" And off trotted the short-legged Aristides.

The Arcade was just across the way—a long rambling building, containing a bar-room, billiard-room, and restaurant. As the young man crossed the plaza he noticed that two or three of the passers-by turned and looked after him. He looked at his clothes, took out his handkerchief and wiped his face, before he entered the bar-room. It contained the usual number of loungers, who stared at him as he entered. One of them looked at him so fixedly and with such a strange expression, that the master stopped and looked again, and then saw it was only his own reflection in a large mirror. This made the master think that perhaps he was a little excited, and so he took up a copy of the Red Mountain Banner from one of the tables, and tried to recover his composure by reading the column of advertisements.

He then walked through the bar-room, through the restaurant, and into the billiard-room. The child was not there. In the latter apartment a person was standing by one of the tables with a broad-brimmed glazed hat on his head. The master recognized him as the agent of the dramatic company; he had taken a dislike to him at their first meeting, from the peculiar fashion of wearing his beard and hair. Satisfied that the object of his search was not there, he turned to the man with a glazed hat. He had noticed the master, but tried that common trick of unconsciousness, in which vulgar natures always fail. Balancing a billiard cue in his hand, he pretended to play with a ball in the centre of the table. The master stood opposite to him until he raised his eyes; when their glances met, the master walked up to him.

He had intended to avoid a scene or quarrel, but when he began to speak, something kept rising in his throat and retarded his utterance, and his own voice frightened him, it sounded so distant, low, and resonant. "I understand," he began, "that Melissa Smith, an orphan, and one of my scholars, has talked with you about adopting your profession. Is that so?"

The man with the glazed hat leaned over the table, and

made an imaginary shot, that sent the ball spinning round the cushions. Then walking round the table he recovered the ball, and placed it upon the spot. This duty discharged, getting ready for another shot, he said,—

"S'pose she has?"

The master choked up again, but, squeezing the cushion of the table in his gloved hand, he went on:—

"If you are a gentleman, I have only to tell you that I am her guardian, and responsible for her career. You know as well as I do the kind of life you offer her. As you may learn of any one here, I have already brought her out of an existence worse than death,—out of the streets and the contamination of vice. I am trying to do so again. Let us talk like men. She has neither father, mother, sister, or brother. Are you seeking to give her an equivalent for these?"

The man with the glazed hat examined the point of his cue, and then looked around for somebody to enjoy the joke with him.

"I know that she is a strange, wilful girl," continued the master, "but she is better than she was. I believe that I have some influence over her still. I beg and hope, therefore, that you will take no further steps in this matter, but as a man, as a gentleman, leave her to me. I am willing——" But here something rose again in the master's throat, and the sentence remained unfinished.

The man with the glazed hat, mistaking the master's silence, raised his head with a coarse, brutal laugh, and said in a loud voice,—

"Want her yourself, do you? That cock won't fight here, young man!"

The insult was more in the tone than the words, more in the glance than tone, and more in the man's instinctive nature than all these. The best appreciable rhetoric to this kind of animal is a blow. The master felt this, and with his pent-up, nervous energy finding expression in the one act, he struck the brute full in his grinning face. The blow sent the glazed hat one way and the cue another, and tore the glove and skin from the master's hand from knuckle to joint. It opened up the corners of the fellow's mouth, and spoilt the peculiar shape of his beard for some time to come.

There was a shout, an imprecation, a scuffle, and the trampling of many feet. Then the crowd parted right and left, and two sharp quick reports followed each other in rapid succession. Then they closed again about his opponent, and the master was standing alone. He remembered picking bits of burning wadding from his coat-sleeve with his left hand. Some one was holding his other hand. Looking at it, he saw it was still bleeding from the blow, but his fingers were clenched around the handle of a glittering knife. He could not remember when or how he got it.

The man who was holding his hand was Mr. Morpher. He hurried the master to the door, but the master held back, and tried to tell him as well as he could with his parched throat about "Mliss." "It's all right, my boy," said Mr. Morpher. "She's home!" And they passed out into the street together. As they walked along Mr. Morpher said that Mliss had come running into the house a few moments before, and had dragged him out, saying that somebody was trying to kill the master at the Arcade. Wishing to be alone, the master promised Mr. Morpher that he would not seek the Agent again that night, and parted from him, taking the road toward the school-house. He was surprised in nearing it to find the door open,—still more surprised to find Mliss sitting there.

The master's nature, as I have hinted before, had, like most sensitive organizations, a selfish basis. The brutal taunt thrown out by his late adversary still rankled in his heart. It was possible, he thought, that such a construction might be put upon his affection for the child, which at best was foolish and Quixotic. Besides, had she not voluntarily abnegated his authority and affection? And what had everybody else said about her? Why should he alone combat the opinion of all, and be at last obliged tacitly to confess the truth of all they had predicted? And he had been a participant in a low bar-room fight with a common boor, and risked his life, to prove what? What had he proved? Nothing! What would the people say? What would his friends say? What would McSnagley say?

In his self-accusation the last person he should have wished to meet was Mliss. He entered the door, and, going up to his desk told the child, in a few cold words, that he was busy, and wished to be alone. As she rose he took her vacant seat, and sitting down, buried his head in his hands. When he looked up again she was still standing there. She was looking at his face with an anxious expression.

"Did you kill him?" she asked.

"No!" said the master.

"That's what I gave you the knife for!" said the child, quickly.

"Gave me the knife?" repeated the master, in bewilderment.

"Yes, gave you the knife. I was there under the bar. Saw you hit him. Saw you both fall. He dropped his old knife. I gave it to you. Why didn't you stick him?" said Mliss, rapidly, with an expressive twinkle of the black eyes and a gesture of the little red hand.

The master could only look his astonishment.

"Yes," said Mliss. "If you'd asked me, I'd told you I was off with the play-actors. Why was I off with the play-actors? Because you wouldn't tell me you was going away. I knew it. I heard you tell the Doctor so. I wasn't a-going to stay here alone with those Morpher's. I'd rather die first."

With a dramatic gesture which was perfectly consistent with her character, she drew from her bosom a few limp green leaves, and, holding them out at arm's length, said in her quick vivid way, and in the queer pronunciation of her old life, which she fell into when unduly excited,—

"That's the poison plant you said would kill me. I'll go with the play-actors, or I'll eat this and die here. I don't care which. I won't stay here, where they hate and despise me! Neither would you let me, if you didn't hate and despise me too!"

The passionate little breast heaved, and two big tears peeped over the edge of Mliss's eyelids, but she whisked them away with the corner of her apron as if they had been wasps.

"If you lock me up in jail," said Mliss fiercely, "to keep me from the play-actors, I'll poison myself. Father killed himself,—why shouldn't I? You said a mouthful of that root would kill me, and I always carry it here," and she struck her breast with her clenched fist.

The master thought of the vacant plot beside Smith's grave, and of the passionate little figure before him. Seizing her hands in his and looking full into her truthful eyes, he said,—

"Lissy, will you go with *me?*"

The child put her arms around his neck, and said, joyfully, "Yes."

"But now—to-night?"

"To-night."

And, hand in hand, they passed into the road,—the narrow road that had once brought her weary feet to the master's door, and which it seemed she should not tread again alone. The stars glittered brightly above them. For good or ill the lesson had been learned, and behind them the school of Red Mountain closed upon them for ever.

THE RIGHT EYE OF THE COMMANDER

THE year of grace 1797 passed away on the coast of California in a south-westerly gale. The little bay of San Carlos, albeit sheltered by the headlands of the blessed Trinity, was rough and turbulent; its foam clung quivering to the seaward wall of the Mission garden; the air was filled with flying sand and spume, and as the Señor Commandante, Hermenegildo Salvatierra, looked from the deep embrasured window of the Presidio guard room, he felt the salt breath of the distant sea buffet a colour into his smoke-dried cheeks.

The Commander, I have said, was gazing thoughtfully from the window of the guard-room. He may have been reviewing the events of the year now about to pass away. But, like the garrison at the Presidio, there was little to review; the year, like its predecessors, had been uneventful,—the days had slipped by in a delicious monotony of simple duties, unbroken by incident or interruption. The regularly recurring feasts and saints' days, the half-yearly courier from San Diego, the rare transport-ship and rarer foreign vessel, were the mere details of his patriarchal life. If there was no achievement, there was certainly no failure. Abundant harvests and patient industry amply supplied the wants of Presidio and Mission. Isolated from the family of nations, the wars which shook the world concerned them not so much as the latest earthquake; the struggle that emancipated their sister colonies on the other side of the continent to them had no suggestiveness. In short, it was that glorious Indian summer of California history, around which so much poetical haze still lingers,—that bland, indolent autumn of Spanish rule, so soon to be followed by the wintry storms of Mexican independence and the reviving spring of American conquest.

The Commander turned from the window and walked toward the fire that burned brightly on the deep oven-like hearth. A pile of copy-books, the work of the Presidio school, lay on the table. As he turned over the leaves with a paternal interest, and surveyed the fair round Scripture-text,—the first pious pot-hooks of the pupils of San Carlos,—an audible commentary fell from his lips: "'Abimelech took her from Abraham'—ah, little one, excellent!—'Jacob sent to see his brother'—body of Christ! that up-stroke of thine, Paquita, is marvellous; the Governor shall see it!" A film of honest pride dimmed the Commander's left eye,—the right, alas! twenty years before had been sealed by an Indian arrow. He rubbed it softly with the

sleeve of his leather jacket, and continued: " 'The Ish-
maelites having arrived——' "

He stopped, for there was a step in the court-yard, a foot
upon the threshold, and a stranger entered. With the instinct of an old soldier, the Commander, after one glance
at the intruder, turned quickly toward the wall, where his
trusty Toledo hung, or should have been hanging. But it
was not there, and as he recalled the last time he had seen
that weapon it was being ridden up and down the gallery
by Pepito, the infant son of Bautista, the tortilio-maker, he
blushed and then contented himself with frowning upon the
intruder.

But the stranger's air, though irreverent, was decidedly
peaceful. He was unarmed, and wore the ordinary cape of
tarpaulin and sea-boots of a mariner. Except a villanous
smell of codfish, there was little about him that was peculiar.

His name, as he informed the Commander, in Spanish
that was more fluent than elegant or precise,—his name was
Peleg Scudder. He was master of the schooner *General
Court*, of the port of Salem, in Massachusetts, on a trading
voyage to the South Seas, but now driven by stress of
weather into the bay of San Carlos. He begged permission
to ride out the gale under the headlands of the blessed
Trinity, and no more. Water he did not need, having taken
in a supply at Bodega. He knew the strict surveillance of
the Spanish port regulations in regard to foreign vessels, and
would do nothing against the severe discipline and good
order of the settlement. There was a slight tinge of sarcasm
in his tone as he glanced toward the desolate parade-ground
of the Presidio and the open unguarded gate. The fact was
that the sentry, Felipe Gomez, had discreetly retired to
shelter at the beginning of the storm, and was then sound
asleep in the corridor.

The Commander hesitated. The port regulations were
severe, but he was accustomed to exercise individual authority, and beyond an old order issued ten years before,
regarding the American ship *Columbia*, there was no prece-
dent to guide him. The storm was severe, and a sentiment

of humanity urged him to grant the stranger's request. It is but just to the Commander to say, that his inability to enforce a refusal did not weigh with his decision. He would have denied with equal disregard of consequences that right to a seventy-four gun ship which he now yielded so gracefully to this Yankee trading schooner. He stipulated only, that there should be no communication between the ship and shore. "For yourself, Señor Captain," he continued, "accept my hospitality. The fort is yours as long as you shall grace it with your distinguished presence;" and with old-fashioned courtesy, he made the semblance of withdrawing from the guard-room.

Master Peleg Scudder smiled as he thought of the half-dismantled fort, the two mouldy brass cannon, cast in Manila a century previous, and the shiftless garrison. A wild thought of accepting the Commander's offer literally, conceived in the reckless spirit of a man who never let slip an offer for trade, for a moment filled his brain, but a timely reflection of the commercial unimportance of the transaction checked him. He only took a capacious quid of tobacco, as the Commander gravely drew a settle before the fire, and in honour of his guest untied the black silk handkerchief that bound his grizzled brows.

What passed between Salvatierra and his guest that night it becomes me not, as a grave chronicler of the salient points of history, to relate. I have said that Master Peleg Scudder was a fluent talker, and under the influence of divers strong waters, furnished by his host, he became still more loquacious. And think of a man with a twenty years' budget of gossip! The Commander learned, for the first time, how Great Britain lost her colonies; of the French Revolution; of the great Napoleon, whose achievements, perhaps, Peleg coloured more highly than the Commander's superiors would have liked. And when Peleg turned questioner, the Commander was at his mercy. He gradually made himself master of the gossip of the Mission and Presidio, the "small-beer" chronicles of the pastoral age, the conversion of the heathen, the Presidio schools, and even asked the Commander how he had lost his eye! It is said that at this point of the conversation Master Peleg produced from about his person divers small trinkets, kick-shaws and new-fangled trifles, and even forced some of them upon his host. It is further alleged that under the malign influence of Peleg and several glasses of *aguardiente*, the Commander lost somewhat of his decorum, and behaved in a manner unseemly for one in his position, reciting high-flown Spanish poetry, and even piping in a thin, high voice, divers madrigals and heathen canzonets of an amorous complexion; chiefly in regard to a "little one" who was his, the Commander's, "soul!" These allegations, perhaps unworthy the notice of a serious chronicler, should be received with great caution, and are introduced here as simple hearsay. That the Commander, however, took a handkerchief, and attempted to show his guest the mysteries of the *sembi cuacua*, capering in an agile but indecorous manner about the apartment, has been denied. Enough for the purposes of this narrative, that at midnight Peleg assisted his host to bed with many protestations of undying friendship, and then, as the gale had abated, took his leave of the Presidio and hurried aboard the *General Court*. When the day broke the ship was gone.

I know not if Peleg kept his word with his host. It is said that the holy fathers at the Mission that night heard a loud chanting in the plaza, as of the heathens singing psalms through their noses; that for many days after an odour of salt codfish prevailed in the settlement; that a dozen hard nutmegs, which were unfit for spice or seed, were found in the possession of the wife of the baker, and that several bushels of shoe-pegs, which bore a pleasing resemblance to oats, but were quite inadequate to the purposes of provender, were discovered in the stable of the blacksmith. But when the reader reflects upon the sacredness of a Yankee trader's word, the stringent discipline of the Spanish port regulations, and the proverbial indisposition of my countrymen to impose upon the confidence of a simple people, he will at once reject this part of the story.

A roll of drums, ushering in the year 1798, awoke the Commander. The sun was shining brightly, and the storm had ceased. He sat up in bed, and through the force of habit rubbed his left eye. As the remembrance of the previous night came back to him, he jumped from his couch and ran to the window. There was no ship in the bay. A sudden thought seemed to strike him, and he rubbed both of his eyes. Not content with this, he consulted the metallic mirror which hung beside his crucifix. There was no mistake; the Commander had a visible second eye,—a right one,—as good, save for the purposes of vision, as the left.

Whatever might have been the true secret of this transformation, but one opinion prevailed at San Carlos. It was one of those rare miracles vouchsafed a pious Catholic community as an evidence to the heathen, through the intercession of the blessed San Carlos himself. That their beloved Commander, the temporal defender of the Faith, should be the recipient of this miraculous manifestation was most fit and seemly. The Commander himself was reticent; he could not tell a falsehood,—he dared not tell the truth. After all, if the good folk of San Carlos believed that the powers of his right eye were actually restored, was it wise and discreet for him to undeceive them? For the first time in his life the Commander thought of policy,—for the first time he quoted that text which has been the lure of so many well-meaning but easy Christians, of being "all things to all men." Infelix Hermenegildo Salvatierra!

For by degrees an ominous whisper crept through the little settlement. The Right Eye of the Commander, although miraculous, seemed to exercise a baleful effect upon the beholder. No one could look at it without winking. It was cold, hard, relentless, and unflinching. More than that, it seemed to be endowed with a dreadful prescience,—a faculty of seeing through and into the inarticulate thoughts of those it looked upon. The soldiers of the garrison obeyed the eye rather than the voice of their commander, and answered his glance rather than his lips in questioning. The servants could not evade the ever watchful but cold atten-

tion that seemed to pursue them. The children of the
Presidio School smirched their copy-books under the awful
supervision, and poor Paquita, the prize pupil, failed utterly
in that marvellous up-stroke when her patron stood beside
her. Gradually distrust, suspicion, self-accusation, and
timidity took the place of trust, confidence, and security
throughout San Carlos. Wherever the Right Eye of the
Commander fell, a shadow fell with it.

Nor was Salvatierra entirely free from the baleful influence of his miraculous acquisition. Unconscious of its effect
upon others, he only saw in their actions evidence of certain
things that the crafty Peleg had hinted on that eventful
New Year's eve. His most trusty retainers stammered,
blushed, and faltered before him. Self-accusations, confes-
sions of minor faults and delinquencies, or extravagant ex-
cuses and apologies met his mildest inquiries. The very
children that he loved—his pet pupil, Paquita—seemed to
be conscious of some hidden sin. The result of this constant
irritation showed itself more plainly. For the first half-year
the Commander's voice and eye were at variance. He was
still kind, tender, and thoughtful in speech. Gradually,
however, his voice took upon itself the hardness of his
glance and its sceptical impassive quality, and as the year
again neared its close, it was plain that the Commander had
fitted himself to the eye, and not the eye to the Commander.

It may be surmised that these changes did not escape the
watchful solicitude of the Fathers. Indeed, the few who
were first to ascribe the right eye of Salvatierra to miraculous origin, and the special grace of the blessed San Carlos,
now talked openly of witchcraft and the agency of Luzbel,
the evil one. It would have fared ill with Hermenegildo
Salvatierra had he been aught but Commander or amenable
to local authority. But the reverend father, Friar Manuel
de Cortes, had no power over the political executive, and all
attempts at spiritual advice failed signally. He retired
baffled and confused from his first interview with the Commander, who seemed now to take a grim satisfaction in the

fateful power of his glance. The holy father contradicted himself, exposed the fallacies of his own arguments, and even, it is asserted, committed himself to several undoubted heresies. When the Commander stood up at mass, if the officiating priest caught that sceptical and searching eye, the service was inevitably ruined. Even the power of the Holy Church seemed to be lost, and the last hold upon the affections of the people and the good order of the settlement departed from San Carlos.

As the long dry summer passed, the low hills that surrounded the white walls of the Presidio grew more and more to resemble in hue the leathern jacket of the Commander, and Nature herself seemed to have borrowed his dry, hard glare. The earth was cracked and seamed with drought; a blight had fallen upon the orchards and vineyards, and the rain, long delayed and ardently prayed for, came not. The sky was as tearless as the right eye of the Commander. Murmurs of discontent, insubordination, and plotting among the Indians reached his ears; he only set his teeth the more firmly, tightened the knot of his black silk handkerchief, and looked up his Toledo.

The last day of the year 1798 found the Commander sitting, at the hour of evening prayers, alone in the guard-room. He no longer attended the services of the Holy Church, but crept away at such times to some solitary spot, where he spent the interval in silent meditation. The firelight played upon the low beams and rafters, but left the bowed figure of Salvatierra in darkness. Sitting thus, he felt a small hand touch his arm, and, looking down, saw the figure of Paquita, his little Indian pupil, at his knee. "Ah, littlest of all," said the Commander, with something of his old tenderness, lingering over the endearing diminutives of his native speech,—"sweet one, what doest thou here? Art thou not afraid of him whom every one shuns and fears?"

"No," said the little Indian, readily, "not in the dark. hear your voice,—the old voice; I feel your touch,—the old touch; but I see not your eye, Señor Commandante. That only I fear,—and that, O Señor, O my father," said the child, lifting her little arms toward his, "that I know is not thine own!"

The Commander shuddered and turned away. Then, recovering himself, he kissed Paquita gravely on the forehead and bade her retire. A few hours later, when silence had fallen upon the Precidio, he sought his own couch and slept peacefully.

At about the middle watch of the night a dusky figure crept through the low embrasure of the Commander's apartment. Other figures were flitting through the parade-ground, which the Commander might have seen had he not slept so quietly. The intruder stepped noiselessly to the couch and listened to the sleeper's deep-drawn inspiration. Something glittered in the firelight as the savage lifted his arm; another moment and the sore perplexities of Hermenegildo Salvatierra would have been over, when suddenly the savage started, and fell back in a paroxysm of terror. The Commander slept peacefully, but his right eye, widely opened, fixed and unaltered, glared coldly on the would-be assassin. The man fell to the earth in a fit, and the noise awoke the sleeper.

To rise to his feet, grasp his sword, and deal blows thick and fast upon the mutinous savages who now thronged the room, was the work of a moment. Help opportunely arrived, and the undisciplined Indians were speedily driven beyond the walls, but in the scuffle the Commander received a blow upon his right eye, and, lifting his hand to that mysterious organ, it was gone. Never again was it found, and never again, for bale or bliss, did it adorn the right orbit of the Commander.

With it passed away the spell that had fallen upon San Carlos. The rain returned to invigorate the languid soil, harmony was restored between priest and soldier, the green grass presently waved over the sere hillsides, the children flocked again to the side of their martial preceptor, a *Te Deum* was sung in the Mission Church, and pastoral content once more smiled upon the gentle valleys of San Carlos. And far southward crept the *General Court* with its master,

Peleg Scudder, trafficking in beads and peltries with the Indians, and offering glass eyes, wooden legs, and other Boston notions to the chiefs.

NOTES BY FLOOD AND FIELD

PART I—IN THE FIELD

It was near the close of an October day that I began to be disagreeably conscious of the Sacramento Valley. I had been riding since sunrise, and my course, through the depressing monotony of the long level landscape, affected me more like a dull dyspeptic dream than a business journey, performed under that sincerest of natural phenomena,—a California sky. The recurring stretches of brown and baked fields, the gaping fissures in the dusty trail, the hard outline of the distant hills, and the herds of slowly moving cattle, seemed like features of some glittering stereoscopic picture that never changed. Active exercise might have removed this feeling, but my horse by some subtle instinct had long since given up all ambitious effort, and had lapsed into a dogged trot.

It was autumn, but not the season suggested to the Atlantic reader under that title. The sharply defined boundaries of the wet and dry seasons were prefigured in the clear outlines of the distant hills. In the dry atmosphere the decay of vegetation was too rapid for the slow hectic which overtakes an Eastern landscape, or else Nature was too practical for such thin disguises. She merely turned the Hippocratic face to the spectator, with the old diagnosis of Death in her sharp, contracted features.

In the contemplation of such a prospect there was little to excite any but a morbid fancy. There were no clouds in the flinty blue heavens, and the setting of the sun was accompanied with as little ostentation as was consistent with the dryly practical atmosphere. Darkness soon followed,

with a rising wind, which increased as the shadows deepened
on the plain. The fringe of alder by the watercourse began
to loom up as I urged my horse forward. A half-hour's
active spurring brought me to a *corral*, and a little beyond a
house, so low and broad it seemed at first sight to be half
buried in the earth.

My second impression was that it had grown out of the
soil, like some monstrous vegetable, its dreary proportions
were so in keeping with the vast prospect. There were no
recesses along its roughly boarded walls for vagrant and un-
profitable shadows to lurk in the daily sunshine. No pro-
jection for the wind by night to grow musical over, to wail,
whistle, or whisper to; only a long wooden shelf containing
a chilly-looking tin basin, and a bar of soap. Its uncur-
tained windows were red with the sinking sun, as though
bloodshot and inflamed from a too long unlidded existence.
The tracks of cattle led to its front door, firmly closed
against the rattling wind.

To avoid being confounded with this familiar element, I
walked to the rear of the house, which was connected with
a smaller building by a slight platform. A grizzled, hard-
faced old man was standing there, and met my salutation
with a look of inquiry, and without speaking, led the way
to the principal room. As I entered, four young men, who
were reclining by the fire, slightly altered their attitudes of
perfect repose, but beyond that betrayed neither curiosity
nor interest. A hound started from a dark corner with a
growl, but was immediately kicked by the old man into
obscurity, and silenced again. I can't tell why, but I instantly received the impression that for a long time the
group by the fire had not uttered a word or moved a muscle.
Taking a seat, I briefly stated my business.

Was a United States surveyor. Had come on account of
the Espíritu Santo Rancho. Wanted to correct the exterior
boundaries of township lines, so as to connect with the near
exteriors of private grants. There had been some intervention to the old survey by a Mr. Tryan who had pre-
empted adjacent—"settled land warrants," interrupted the

old man. "Ah, yes! Land Warrants,—and then this was
Mr. Tryan?"

I had spoken mechanically, for I was preoccupied in connecting other public lines with private surveys, as I looked
in his face. It was certainly a hard face, and reminded me
of the singular effect of that mining operation known as
"ground sluicing;" the harder lines of underlying character
were exposed, and what were once plastic curves and soft
outlines were obliterated by some powerful agency.

There was a dryness in his voice not unlike the prevailing
atmosphere of the valley, as he launched into an *ex parte*
statement of the contest, with a fluency, which, like the
wind without, showed frequent and unrestrained expression.
He told me—what I had already learned—that the boundary line of the old Spanish grant was a creek, described in
the loose phraseology of the *deseno* as beginning in the
valda or skirt of the hill, its precise location long the subject of litigation. I listened and answered with little interest, for my mind was still distracted by the wind which
swept violently by the house, as well as by his odd face,
which was again reflected in the resemblance that the silent
group by the fire bore toward him. He was still talking,
and the wind was yet blowing, when my confused attention
was aroused by a remark addressed to the recumbent
figures.

"Now, then, which on ye'll see the stranger up the creek
to Altascar's, to-morrow!"

There was a general movement of opposition in the group,
but no decided answer.

"Kin you go, Kerg?"

"Who's to look up stock in Strarberry per-ar-ie?"

This seemed to imply a negative, and the old man turned
to another hopeful, who was pulling the fur from a mangy
bear-skin on which he was lying, with an expression as
though it were somebody's hair.

"Well, Tom, wot's to hinder you from goin'?"

"Mam's goin' to Brown's store at sun-up, and I s'pose
I've got to pack her and the baby agin."

I think the expression of scorn this unfortunate youth exhibited for the filial duty into which he had been evidently beguiled, was one of the finest things I had ever seen.

"Wise?"

Wise deigned no verbal reply, but figuratively thrust a worn and patched boot into the discourse. The old man flushed quickly.

"I told you to get Brown to give you a pair the last time you war down the river."

"Said he wouldn't without'en order. Said it was like pulling gum-teeth to get the money from you even then."

There was a grim smile at this local hit at the old man's parsimony, and Wise, who was clearly the privileged wit of the family, sank back in honourable retirement.

"Well, Joe, ef your boots are new, and you aren't pestered with wimmin and children, p'r'aps you'll go," said Tryan, with a nervous twitching, intended for a smile, about a mouth not remarkably mirthful.

Joe lifted a pair of bushy eyebrows, and said shortly,—

"Got no saddle."

"Wot's gone of your saddle?"

"Kerg, there,"—indicating his brother with a look such as Cain might have worn at the sacrifice.

"You lie," returned Kerg, cheerfully.

Tryan sprang to his feet, seizing the chair, flourishing it around his head and gazing furiously in the hard young faces which fearlessly met his own. But it was only for a moment; his arm soon dropped by his side, and a look of hopeless fatality crossed his face. He allowed me to take the chair from his hand, and I was trying to pacify him by the assurance that I required no guide, when the irrepressible Wise again lifted his voice:—

"There's George comin'? why don't ye ask him? He'll go and introduce you to Don Fernandy's darter, too, ef you ain't partickler."

The laugh which followed this joke, which evidently had some domestic allusion (the general tendency of rural pleasantry), was followed by a light step on the platform, and the young man entered. Seeing a stranger present, he stopped and coloured; made a shy salute and coloured again, and then, drawing a box from the corner, sat down, his hands clasped lightly together and his very handsome bright blue eyes turned frankly on mine.

Perhaps I was in a condition to receive the romantic impression he made upon me, and I took it upon myself to ask his company as guide, and he cheerfully assented. But some domestic duty called him presently away.

The fire gleamed brightly on the hearth, and no longer resisting the prevailing influence, I silently watched the spirting flame, listening to the wind which continually shook the tenement. Besides the one chair which had acquired a new importance in my eyes, I presently discovered a crazy table in one corner, with an ink-bottle and pen; the latter in that greasy state of decomposition peculiar to country taverns and farm-houses. A goodly array of rifles and double barrelled guns stocked the corner; half a dozen saddles and blankets lay near, with a mild flavour of the horse about them. Some deer and bear skins completed the inventory. As I sat there, with the silent group around me, the shadowy gloom within and the dominant wind without, I found it difficult to believe I had ever known a different existence. My profession had often led me to wilder scenes, but rarely among those whose unrestrained habits and easy unconsciousness made me feel so lonely and uncomfortable. I shrank closer to myself, not without grave doubts—which I think occur naturally to people in like situations—that this was the general rule of humanity, and I was a solitary and somewhat gratuitous exception.

It was a relief when a laconic announcement of supper by a weak-eyed girl caused a general movement in the family. We walked across the dark platform, which led to another low-ceiled room. Its entire length was occupied by a table, at the farther end of which a weak-eyed woman was already taking her repast, as she, at the same time, gave nourishment to a weak-eyed baby. As the formalities of introduction had been dispensed with, and as she took no notice of me, I was enabled to slip into a seat without discomposing or interrupting her. Tryan extemporized a grace, and the attention of the family became absorbed in bacon, potatoes, and dried apples.

The meal was a sincere one. Gentle gurglings at the upper end of the table often betrayed the presence of the "well-spring of pleasure." The conversation generally referred to the labours of the day, and comparing notes as to the whereabouts of missing stock. Yet the supper was such a vast improvement upon the previous intellectual feast, that when a chance allusion of mine to the business of my visit brought out the elder Tryan, the interest grew quite exciting. I remember he inveighed bitterly against the system of ranch-holding by the "greasers," as he was pleased to term the native Californians. As the same ideas have been sometimes advanced under more pretentious circumstances, they may be worthy of record.

"Look at 'em holdin' the finest grazin' land that ever lay outer doors? Whar's the papers for it? Was it grants? Mighty fine grants,—most of 'em made arter the 'Merrikans got possession. More fools the 'Merrikans for lettin' 'em hold 'em. Wot paid for 'em? 'Merrikan blood and money.

"Didn't they oughter have suthin out of their native country? Wot for? Did they ever improve? Got a lot of yaller-skinned diggers, not so sensible as niggers to look arter stock, and they a-sittin' home and smokin'. With their gold and silver candlesticks, and missions, and crucifixens, priests and graven idols, and sich? Them sort things wurent allowed in Mizzoori."

At the mention of improvements, I involuntarily lifted my eyes, and met the half-laughing, half-embarrassed look of George. The act did not escape detection, and I had at once the satisfaction of seeing that the rest of the family had formed an offensive alliance against us.

"It was agin Nater, and agin God," added Tryan. "God never intended gold in the rocks to be made into heathen candlesticks and crucifixens. That's why he sent 'Merrikans here. Nater never intended such a climate for lazy lopers.

She never gin six months' sunshine to be slept and smoked away."

How long he continued, and with what further illustration, I could not say, for I took an early opportunity to escape to the sitting-room. I was soon followed by George, who called me to an open door leading to a smaller room, and pointed to a bed.

"You'd better sleep there to-night," he said; "you'll be more comfortable, and I'll call you early."

I thanked him, and would have asked him several questions which were then troubling me, but he shily slipped to the door and vanished.

A shadow seemed to fall on the room when he had gone. The "boys" returned, one by one, and shuffled to their old places. A larger log was thrown on the fire, and the huge chimney glowed like a furnace, but it did not seem to melt or subdue a single line of the hard faces that it lit. In half an hour later, the furs which had served as chairs by day undertook the nightly office of mattresses, and each received its owner's full-length figure. Mr. Tryan had not returned, and I missed George. I sat there until, wakeful and nervous, I saw the fire fall and shadows mount the wall. There was no sound but the rushing of the wind and the snoring of the sleepers. At last, feeling the place insupportable, I seized my hat and, opening the door, ran out briskly into the night.

The acceleration of my torpid pulse in the keen fight with the wind, whose violence was almost equal to that of a tornado, and the familiar faces of the bright stars above me, I felt as a blessed relief. I ran not knowing whither, and when I halted, the square outline of the house was lost in the alder-bushes. An uninterrupted plain stretched before me, like a vast sea beaten flat by the force of the gale. As I kept on I noticed a slight elevation toward the horizon, and presently my progress was impeded by the ascent of an Indian mound. It struck me forcibly as resembling an island in the sea. Its height gave me a better view of the expanding plain. But even here I found no rest. The ridiculous interpretation Tryan had given the climate was somehow sung in my ears, and echoed in my throbbing pulse, as, guided by the star, I sought the house again.

But I felt fresher and more natural as I stepped upon the platform. The door of the lower building was open, and the old man was sitting beside the table, thumbing the leaves of a Bible with a look in his face as though he were hunting up prophecies against the "Greaser." I turned to enter, but my attention was attracted by a blanketed figure lying beside the house, on the platform. The broad chest heaving with healthy slumber, and the open, honest face were familiar. It was George, who had given up his bed to the stranger among his people. I was about to wake him, but he lay so peaceful and quiet, I felt awed and hushed. And I went to bed with a pleasant impression of his handsome face and tranquil figure soothing me to sleep.

I was awakened the next morning from a sense of lulled repose and grateful silence by the cheery voice of George, who stood beside my bed, ostentatiously twirling a "riata," as if to recall the duties of the day to my sleep-bewildered eyes. I looked around me. The wind had been magically laid, and the sun shone warmly through the windows. A dash of cold water, with an extra chill on from the tin basin, helped to brighten me. It was still early, but the family had already breakfasted and dispersed, and a waggon winding far in the distance showed that the unfortunate Tom had already "packed" his relatives away. I felt more cheerful,—there are few troubles Youth cannot distance with a start of a good night's rest. After a substantial breakfast prepared by George, in a few moments we were mounted and dashing down the plain.

We followed the line of alder that defined the creek, now dry and baked with summer's heat, but which in winter, George told me, overflowed its banks. I still retain a vivid impression of that morning's ride, the far-off mountains, like *silhouettes*, against the steel-blue sky, the crisp dry air, and the expanding track before me, animated often by the well-knit figure of George Tryan, musical with jingling spurs, and picturesque with flying "riata." He rode a powerful native roan, wild-eyed, untiring in stride and unbroken in nature. Alas! the curves of beauty were concealed by the cumbrous *machillas* of the Spanish saddle, which levels all equine distinctions. The single rein lay loosely on the cruel bit that can gripe, and, if need be, crush the jaw it controls.

Again the illimitable freedom of the valley rises before me, as we again bear down into sunlit space. Can this be "Chu-Chu," staid and respectable filly of American pedigree,—"Chu-Chu," forgetful of plank-roads and cobblestones, wild with excitement, twinkling her small white feet beneath me? George laughs out of a cloud of dust, "Give her her head; don't you see she likes it?" and "Chu-Chu" seems to like it, and, whether bitten by native tarantula into native barbarism or emulous of the roan, "blood" asserts itself, and in a moment the peaceful servitude of years is beaten out in the music of her clattering hoofs. The creek widens to a deep gully. We dive into it and up on the opposite side, carrying a moving cloud of impalpable powder with us. Cattle are scattered over the plain, grazing quietly, or banded together in vast restless herds. George makes a wide, indefinite sweep with the "riata," as if to include them all in his *vaquero's* loop, and says, "Ours."

"About how many, George?"

"Don't know."

"How many?"

"Well, p'r'aps three thousand head," says George, reflecting. "We don't know; takes five men to look 'em up and keep run."

"What are they worth?"

"About thirty dollars a head."

I make a rapid calculation, and look my astonishment at the laughing George. Perhaps a recollection of the domestic economy of the Tryan household is expressed in that look for George averts his eye and says, apologetically,—

"I've tried to get the old man to sell and build, but you know he says it ain't no use to settle down, just yet. We must keep movin'. In fact, he built the shanty for that purpose, lest titles should fall through, and we'd have to get up and move stakes farther down."

Suddenly his quick eye detects some unusual sight in a herd we are passing, and with an exclamation he puts his roan into the centre of the mass. I follow, or rather "Chu-Chu" darts after the roan, and in a few moments we are in the midst of apparently inextricable horns and hoofs. "Toro!" shouts George, with vaquero enthusiasm, and the band opens the way for the swinging "riata." I can feel their steaming breaths, and their spume is cast on "Chu-Chu's" quivering flank.

Wild, devilish-looking beasts are they; not such shapes as Jove might have chosen to woo a goddess, nor such as peacefully ranges the downs of Devon, but lean and hungry Cassius-like bovines, economically got up to meet the exigencies of a six months' rainless climate, and accustomed to wrestle with the distracting wind and the blinding dust.

"That's not our brand," says George, "they're strange stock," and he points to what my scientific eye recognizes as the astrological sign of Venus deeply seared in the brown flanks of the bull he is chasing. But the herd are closing round us with low mutterings, and George has again recourse to the authoritative "Toro," and with swinging "riata" divides the "bossy bucklers" on either side. When we are free, and breathing somewhat more easily, I venture to ask George if they ever attack any one.

"Never horsemen,—sometimes footmen. Not through rage, you know, but curiosity. They think a man and his horse are one, and if they meet a chap afoot, they run him down and trample him under hoof, in the pursuit of knowledge. But," adds George, "here's the lower bench of the foot-hills, and here's Altascar's corral, and that white building you see yonder is the *casa*."

A whitewashed wall enclosed a court containing another adobe building, baked with the solar beams of many summers. Leaving our horses in the charge of a few peons in the courtyard, who were basking lazily in the sun. we entered a low doorway, where a deep shadow and an agreeable coolness fell upon us, as sudden and grateful as a plunge in cold water, from its contrast with the external glare and heat. In the centre of a low-ceiled apartment sat an old man with a black silk handkerchief tied about his head, the few grey hairs that escaped from its folds relieving his gamboge-coloured face. The odour of cigarritos was as incense added to the cathedral gloom of the building.

As Señor Altascar rose with well-bred gravity to receive us, George advanced with such a heightened colour, and such a blending of tenderness and respect in his manner, that I was touched to the heart by so much devotion in the careless youth. In fact, my eyes were still dazzled by the effect of the outer sunshine, and at first I did not see the white teeth and black eyes of Pepita, who slipped into the corridor as we entered.

It was no pleasant matter to disclose particulars of business which would deprive the old Señor of the greater part of that land we had just ridden over, and I did it with great embarrassment. But he listened calmly,—not a muscle of his dark face stirring,—and the smoke, curling placidly from his lips, showed his regular respiration. When I had finished, he offered quietly to accompany us to the line of demarcation. George had meanwhile disappeared, but a suspicious conversation, in broken Spanish and English, in the corridor, betrayed his vicinity. When he returned again, a little absent-minded, the old man, by far the coolest and most self-possessed of the party, extinguished his black silk cap beneath that stiff, uncomely *sombrero* which all native Californians affect. A *serapa* thrown over his shoulders, hinted that he was waiting. Horses are always ready saddled in Spanish ranchos, and in half an hour from the time of our arrival we were again "loping" in the staring sunlight.

But not as cheerfully as before. George and myself were weighed down by restraint, and Altascar was gravely quiet. To break the silence, and by way of a consolatory essay, I hinted to him that there might be further intervention or appeal, but the proffered oil and wine were returned with a careless shrug of the shoulders and a sententious *"Que bueno?*—Your courts are always just."

The Indian mound of the previous night's discovery was a bearing monument of the new line, and there we halted. We were surprised to find the old man, Tryan, waiting us. For the first time during our interview, the old Spaniard seemed moved, and the blood rose in his yellow cheek. I was anxious to close the scene, and pointed out the corner boundaries as clearly as my recollection served.

"The deputies will be here to-morrow to run the lines from this initial point, and there will be no further trouble, I believe, gentlemen."

Señor Altascar had dismounted, and was gathering a few tufts of dried grass in his hands. George and I exchanged glances. He presently arose from his stooping posture, and advancing to within a few paces of Joseph Tryan, said, in a voice broken with passion,—

"And I, Fernando Jesus Maria Altascar, put you in possession of my land in the fashion of my country."

He threw a sod to each of the cardinal points.

"I don't know your courts, your judges, or your *corregidores.* Take the *llano!*—and take this with it. May the drought seize your cattle till their tongues hang down as long as those of your lying lawyers! May it be the curse and torment of your old age, as you and yours have made it of mine!"

We stepped between the principal actors in this scene, which only the passion of Altascar made tragical, but Tryan, with a humility but ill concealing his triumph, interrupted,—

"Let him curse on. He'll find 'em coming home to him sooner than the cattle he has lost through his sloth and pride. The Lord is on the side of the just, as well as agin all slanderers and revilers."

Altascar but half guessed the meaning of the Missourian, yet sufficiently to drive from his mind all but the extravagant power of his native invective.

"Stealer of the Sacrament: Open not!—open not, I say, your lying, Judas lips to me! Ah! half-breed, with the soul of a cayote!—Car-r-r-ramba!"

With his passion reverberating among the consonants like distant thunder, he laid his hand upon the mane of his horse as though it had been the grey locks of his adversary, swung himself into the saddle, and galloped away.

George turned to me,—

"Will you go back with us to-night?"

I thought of the cheerless walls, the silent figures by the fire, and the roaring wind, and hesitated.

"Well, then, good-bye."

"Good-bye, George."

Another wring of the hands, and we parted. I had not ridden far when I turned and looked back. The wind had risen early that afternoon, and was already sweeping across the plain. A cloud of dust travelled before it, and a picturesque figure occasionally emerging therefrom was my last indistinct impression of George Tryan.

PART II—IN THE FLOOD

THREE months after the survey of the Espiritu Santo Rancho, I was again in the valley of the Sacramento. But a general and terrible visitation had erased the memory of that event as completely as I supposed it had obliterated the boundary monuments I had planted. The great flood of 1861-62 was at its height, when, obeying some indefinite yearning, I took my carpet-bag and embarked for the inundated valley.

There was nothing to be seen from the bright cabin windows of the *Golden City* but night deepening over the water. The only sound was the pattering rain, and that had grown monotonous for the past two weeks, and did not disturb the national gravity of my countrymen as they silently sat around the cabin stove. Some on errands of relief to friends and relatives wore anxious faces, and conversed soberly on the one absorbing topic. Others, like myself, attracted by curiosity, listened eagerly to newer details. But with that human disposition to seize upon any circumstance that might give chance event the exaggerated importance of instinct, I was half conscious of something more than curiosity as an impelling motive.

The dripping of rain, the low gurgle of water, and a leaden sky greeted us the next morning as we lay beside the half-submerged levee of Sacramento. Here, however, the novelty of boats to convey us to the hotels was an appeal that was irresistible. I resigned myself to a dripping rubber-cased mariner called "Joe," and, wrapping myself in a shining cloak of the like material, about as suggestive of warmth as court-plaster might have been, took my seat in the stern-sheets of his boat. It was no slight inward struggle to part from the steamer, that to most of the passengers was the only visible connecting link between us and the dry and habitable earth, but we pulled away and entered the city, stemming a rapid current as we shot the levee.

We glided up the long level of K Street,—once a cheerful, busy thoroughfare, now distressing in its silent desolation. The turbid water which seemed to meet the horizon edge before us flowed at right angles in sluggish rivers through the streets. Nature had revenged herself on the local taste by disarraying the regular rectangles, by huddling houses on street corners, where they presented abrupt gables to the current, or by capsizing them in compact ruin. Crafts of all kinds were gliding in and out of low-arched doorways. The water was over the top of the fences surrounding well kept gardens, in the first stories of hotels and private dwellings, trailing its slime on velvet carpets as well as roughly boarded floors. And a silence quite as suggestive as the visible desolation was in the voiceless streets that no longer echoed to carriage-wheel or footfall. The low ripple of water, the occasional splash of oars, or the warning cry of boatmen were the few signs of life and habitation.

With such scenes before my eyes and such sounds in my ears, as I lie lazily in the boat, is mingled the song of my gondolier who sings to the music of his oars. It is not quite as romantic as his brother of the Lido might improvise, but my Yankee "Giuseppe" has the advantage of earnestness and energy, and gives a graphic description of the terrors of the past week and of noble deeds of self-sacrifice and devotion, occasionally pointing out a balcony from which some California Bianca or Laura had been snatched, half clothed and famished. Giuseppe is otherwise peculiar, and refuses the proffered fare, for—am I not a citizen of San Francisco, which was first to respond to the suffering cry of Sacramento? and is not he, Giuseppe, a member of the Howard Society? No! Giuseppe is poor, but cannot take my money. Still, if I must spend it, there is the Howard Society, and the women and children without food and clothes at the Agricultural Hall.

I thank the generous gondolier, and we go to the Hall,—a dismal, bleak place, ghastly with the memories of last year's opulence and plenty, and here Giuseppe's fare is swelled by the stranger's mite. But here Giuseppe tells me of the "Relief Boat" which leaves for the flooded district in the interior, and here, profiting by the lesson he has taught me, I make the resolve to turn my curiosity to the account of others, and am accepted of those who go forth to succour and help the afflicted. Giuseppe takes charge of my carpet-bag, and does not part from me until I stand on the slippery deck of "Relief Boat No. 3."

An hour later I am in the pilot-house, looking down upon what was once the channel of a peaceful river. But its banks are only defined by tossing tufts of willow washed by the long swell that breaks over a vast inland sea. Stretches of "tule" land fertilized by its once regular channel and dotted by flourishing ranchos are now cleanly erased. The cultivated profile of the old landscape had faded. Dotted lines in symmetrical perspective mark orchards that are buried and chilled in the turbid flood. The roofs of a few farm houses are visible, and here and there the smoke curling from chimneys of half-submerged tenements show an undaunted life within. Cattle and sheep are gathered on

Indian mounds waiting the fate of their companions whose carcasses drift by us, or swing in eddies with the wrecks of barns and out-houses. Waggons are stranded everywhere where the tide could carry them. As I wipe the moistened glass, I see nothing but water, pattering on the deck from the lowering clouds, dashing against the window, dripping from the willows, hissing by the wheels, everywhere washing, coiling, sapping, hurrying in rapids, or swelling at last into deeper and vaster lakes, awful in their suggestive quiet and concealment.

As day fades into night the monotony of this strange prospect grows oppressive. I seek the engine-room, and in the company of some of the few half-drowned sufferers we have already picked up from temporary rafts, I forget the general aspect of desolation in their individual misery. Later we meet the San Francisco packet, and transfer a number of our passengers. From them we learn how inward bound vessels report to having struck the well-defined channel of the Sacramento, fifty miles beyond the bar. There is a voluntary contribution taken among the generous travellers for the use of our afflicted, and we part company with a hearty "God-speed" on either side. But our signal-lights are not far distant before a familiar sound comes back to us,—an indomitable Yankee cheer,—which scatters the gloom.

Our course is altered, and we are steaming over the obliterated banks far in the interior. Once or twice black objects loom up near us,—the wrecks of houses floating by. There is a slight rift in the sky towards the north, and a few bearing stars to guide us over the waste. As we penetrate into shallower water, it is deemed advisable to divide our party into smaller boats, and diverge over the submerged prairie. I borrow a pea-coat of one of the crew, and in that practical disguise am doubtfully permitted to pass into one of the boats. We give way northerly. It is quite dark yet, although the rift of cloud has widened.

It must have been about three o'clock, and we were lying upon our oars in an eddy formed by a clump of cottonwood, and the light of the steamer is a solitary, bright star in the distance, when the silence is broken by the "bow oar,"—

"Light ahead."

All eyes are turned in that direction. In a few seconds a twinkling light appears, shines steadily, and again disappears, as if by the shifting position of some black object apparently drifting close upon us.

"Stern, all; a steamer!"

"Hold hard there! Steamer be d—d!" is the reply of the coxswain. "It's a house, and a big one too."

It is a big one, looming in the starlight like a huge fragment of the darkness. The light comes from a single candle, which shines through a window as the great shape swings by. Some recollection is drifting back to me with it, as I listen with beating heart.

"There's some one in it, by Heavens! Give way, boys,—lay her alongside. Handsomely, now! The door's fastened; try the window; no! here's another!"

In another moment we are trampling in the water, which washes the floor to the depth of several inches. It is a large room, at the farther end of which an old man is sitting wrapped in a blanket, holding a candle in one hand, and apparently absorbed in the book he holds with the other. I spring toward him with an exclamation,—

"Joseph Tryan!"

He does not move. We gather closer to him, and I lay my hand gently on his shoulder, and say,—

"Look up, old man, look up! Your wife and children, where are they? The boys,—George! Are they here? are they safe?"

He raises his head slowly, and turns his eyes to mine, and we involuntarily recoil before his look. It is a calm and quiet glance, free from fear, anger, or pain; but it somehow sends the blood curdling through our veins. He bowed his head over his book again, taking no further notice of us. The men look at me compassionately, and hold their peace. I make one more effort:—

"Joseph Tryan, don't you know me? the surveyor who

surveyed your ranch,—the Espíritu Santo? Look up, old man!"

He shuddered, and wrapped himself closer in his blanket. Presently he repeated to himself, "The surveyor who surveyed your ranch,—Espíritu Santo," over and over again, as though it were a lesson he was trying to fix in his memory.

I was turning sadly to the boatmen, when he suddenly caught me fearfully by the hand and said,—

"Hush!"

We were silent.

"Listen!" He puts his arm around my neck and whispers in my ear, "I'm a *moving off!*"

"Moving off?"

"Hush! Don't speak so loud. Moving off. Ah! wot's that? Don't you hear?—there! listen!"

We listen and hear the water gurgle and click beneath the floor.

"It's them wot he sent!—Old Altascar sent. They've been here all night. I heard 'em first in the creek, when they came to tell the old man to move farther off. They came nearer and nearer. They whispered under the door, and I saw their eyes on the step,—their cruel, hard eyes. Ah! why don't they quit?"

I tell the men to search the room and see if they can find any further traces of the family, while Tryan resumes his old attitude. It is so much like the figure I remember on the breezy night that a superstitious feeling is fast overcoming me. When they have returned, I tell them briefly what I know of him, and the old man murmurs again,—

"Why don't they quit, then? They have the stock,—all gone—gone, gone for the hides and hoofs," and he groans bitterly.

"There are other boats below us. The shanty cannot have drifted far, and perhaps the family are safe by this time," says the coxswain, hopefully.

We lift the old man up, for he is quite helpless, and carry him to the boat. He is still grasping the Bible in his right hand, though its strengthening grace is blank to his vacant eye, and he cowers in the stern as we pull slowly to the steamer, while a pale gleam in the sky shows the coming day.

I was weary with excitement, and when we reached the steamer, and I had seen Joseph Tryan comfortably bestowed, I wrapped myself in a blanket near the boiler and presently fell asleep. But even then the figure of the old man often started before me, and a sense of uneasiness about George made a strong undercurrent to drifting dreams. I was awakened at about eight o'clock in the morning by the engineer, who told me one of the old man's sons had been picked up and was now on board.

"Is it George Tryan?" I ask quickly.

"Don't know; but he's a sweet one, whoever he is," adds the engineer, with a smile at some luscious remembrance. "You'll find him for'ard."

I hurry to the bow of the boat, and find, not George, but the irrepressible Wise, sitting on a coil of rope, a little dirtier and rather more dilapidated than I can remember having seen him.

He is examining, with apparent admiration, some rough, dry clothes that have been put out for his disposal. I cannot help thinking that circumstances have somewhat exalted his usual cheerfulness. He puts me at my ease by at once addressing me:—

"These are high old times, ain't they? I say, what do you reckon's become o' them thar bound'ry moniments you stuck? Ah!"

The pause which succeeds this outburst is the effect of a spasm of admiration at a pair of high boots, which, by great exertion, he has at last pulled on his feet.

"So you've picked up the old man in the shanty, clean crazy? He must have been soft to have stuck there instead o' leavin' with the old woman. Didn't know me from Adam; took me for George!"

At this affecting instance of paternal forgetfulness, Wise was evidently divided between amusement and chagrin. I took advantage of the contending emotions to ask about George.

"Don't know whar he is! If he'd tended stock instead of running about the prairie, packin' off wimmin and children, he might have saved suthin. He lost every hoof and hide, I'll bet a cookey. Say you," to a passing boatman, "when are you goin' to give us some grub? I'm hungry 'nough to skin and eat a hoss. Reckon I'll turn butcher when things is dried up, and save hides, horns, and taller."

I could not but admire this indomitable energy, which under softer climatic influences might have borne such goodly fruit.

"Have you any idea what you'll do, Wise?" I ask.

"Thar ain't much to do now," says the practical young man. "I'll have to lay over a spell, I reckon, till things comes straight. The land ain't worth much now, and won't be, I dessay, for some time. Wonder whar the ole man'll drive stakes next."

"I meant as to your father and George, Wise."

"O, the ole man and I'll go on to 'Miles's,' whar Tom packed the old woman and babies last week. George'll turn up somewhar atween this and Altascar's, ef he ain't thar now."

I ask how the Altascars have suffered.

"Well, I reckon he ain't lost much in stock. I shouldn't wonder if George helped him drive 'em up the foot-hills. And his 'casa's' built too high. O, thar ain't any water thar, you bet. Ah," says Wise, with reflective admiration, "those greasers ain't the darned fools people think 'em. I'll bet thar ain't one swamped out in all 'er Californy." But the appearance of "grub" cut this rhapsody short.

"I shall keep on a little farther," I say, "and try to find George."

Wise stared a moment at this eccentricity until a new light dawned upon him.

"I don't think you'll save much. What's the percentage,—workin' on shares, eh!"

I answer that I am only curious, which I feel lessens his

opinion of me, and with a sadder feeling than his assurance
of George's safety might warrant, I walked away.

From others whom we picked up from time to time we
heard of George's self-sacrificing devotion, with the praises
of the many he had helped and rescued. But I did not feel
disposed to return until I had seen him, and soon prepared
myself to take a boat to the lower "valda" of the foot-hills,
and visit Altascar. I soon perfected my arrangements, bade
farewell to Wise, and took a last look at the old man, who
was sitting by the furnace-fires quite passive and composed.
Then our boat-head swung round, pulled by sturdy and
willing hands.

It was again raining, and a disagreeable wind had risen.
Our course lay nearly west, and we soon knew by the strong
current that we were in the creek of the Espíritu Santo.
From time to time the wrecks of barns were seen, and we
passed many half-submerged willows hung with farming
implements.

We emerge at last into a broad silent sea. It is the "llano
de Espíritu Santo." As the wind whistles by me, piling the
shallower fresh water into mimic waves, I go back, in fancy,
to the long ride of October over that boundless plain, and
recall the sharp outlines of the distant hills which are now
lost in the lowering clouds. The men are rowing silently,
and I find my mind, released from its tension, growing benumbed and depressed as then. The water, too, is getting
more shallow as we leave the banks of the creek, and with
my hand dipped listlessly over the thwarts, I detect the
tops of chimisal, which shows the tide to have somewhat
fallen. There is a black mound, bearing to the north of the
line of alder, making an adverse current, which, as we sweep
to the right to avoid, I recognize. We pull close alongside
and I call to the men to stop.

There was a stake driven near its summit with the initials,
"L. E. S. I." Tied half-way down was a curiously worked
"riata." It was George's. It had been cut with some sharp
instrument, and the loose gravelly soil of the mound was

deeply dented with horse's hoofs. The stake was covered with horse-hairs. It was a record, but no clew.

The wind had grown more violent, as we still fought our way forward, resting and rowing by turns, and oftener "poling" the shallower surface, but the old "valda," or bench, is still distant. My recollection of the old survey enables me to guess the relative position of the meanderings of the creek, and an occasional simple professional experiment to determine the distance gives my crew the fullest faith in my ability. Night overtakes us in our impeded progress. Our condition looks more dangerous than it really is, but I urge the men, many of whom are still new in this mode of navigation, to greater exertion by assurance of perfect safety and speedy relief ahead. We go on in this way until about eight o'clock, and ground by the willows. We have a muddy walk for a few hundred yards before we strike a dry trail, and simultaneously the white walls of Altascar's appear like a snow-bank before us. Lights are moving in the courtyard; but otherwise the old tomb-like repose characterizes the building.

One of the peons recognized me as I entered the court, and Altascar met me on the corridor.

I was too weak to do more than beg his hospitality for the men who had dragged wearily with me. He looked at my hand, which still unconsciously held the broken "riata." I began, wearily, to tell him about George and my fears, but with a gentler courtesy than was even his wont, he gravely laid his hand on my shoulder.

"*Poco a poco* Señor,—not now. You are tired, you have hunger, you have cold. Necessary it is you should have peace."

He took us into a small room and poured out some French cognac, which he gave to the men that had accompanied me. They drank and threw themselves before the fire in the larger room. The repose of the building was intensified that night, and I even fancied that the footsteps on the corridor were lighter and softer. The old Spaniard's habitual gravity was deeper; we might have been shut out from the world as well as the whistling storm, behind those ancient walls with their time-worn inheritor.

Before I could repeat my inquiry he retired. In a few minutes two smoking dishes of "chupa" with coffee were placed before us, and my men ate ravenously. I drank the coffee, but my excitement and weariness kept down the instincts of hunger.

I was sitting sadly by the fire when he re-entered.

"You have eat?"

I said, "Yes," to please him.

"*Bueno*, eat when you can,—food and appetite are not always."

He said this with that Sancho-like simplicity with which most of his countrymen utter a proverb, as though it were an experience rather than a legend, and, taking the "riata" from the floor, held it almost tenderly before him.

"It was made by me, Señor."

"I kept it as a clew to him, Don Altascar," I said. "If I could find him——"

"He is here."

"Here! and"—but I could not say "well!" I understood the gravity of the old man's face, the hushed footfalls, the tomb-like repose of the building in an electric flash of consciousness; I held the clew to the broken riata at last. Altascar took my hand, and we crossed the corridor to a sombre apartment. A few tall candles were burning in sconces before the window.

In an alcove there was a deep bed with its counterpane, pillows, and sheets heavily edged with lace, in all that splendid luxury which the humblest of these strange people lavish upon this single item of their household. I stepped beside it and saw George lying, as I had seen him once before, peacefully at rest. But a greater sacrifice than that he had known was here, and his generous heart was stilled for ever.

"He was honest and brave," said the old man, and turned away.

There was another figure in the room; a heavy shawl

drawn over her graceful outline, and her long black hair hiding the hands that buried her downcast face. I did not seem to notice her, and, retiring presently, left the loving and loved together.

When we were again beside the crackling fire, in the shifting shadows of the great chamber, Altascar told me how he had that morning met the horse of George Tryan swimming on the prairie; how that, farther on, he found him lying, quite cold and dead, with no marks or bruises on his person; that he had probably become exhausted in fording the creek, and that he had as probably reached the mound only to die for the want of that help he had so freely given to others; that, as a last act, he had freed his horse. These incidents were corroborated by many who collected in the great chamber that evening,—women and children,—most of them succoured through the devoted energies of him who lay cold and lifeless above.

He was buried in the Indian mound,—the single spot of strange perennial greenness, which the poor aborigines had raised above the dusty plain. A little slab of sandstone, with the initials "G. T.," is his monument, and one of the bearings of the initial corner of the new survey of the "Espíritu Santo Rancho."

MR. THOMPSON'S PRODIGAL

WE all knew that Mr. Thompson was looking for his son, and a pretty bad one at that. That he was coming to California for this sole object was no secret to his fellow-passengers; and the physical peculiarities, as well as the moral weaknesses, of the missing prodigal, were made equally plain to us through the frank volubility of the parent.

"You was speaking of a young man which was hung at Red Dog for sluice-robbing," said Mr. Thompson to a steerage-passenger, one day; "be you aware of the colour of his eyes?"

"Black," responded the passenger.

"Ah," said Mr. Thompson, referring to some menta.
memoranda, "Char-les' eyes was blue."

He then walked away. Perhaps it was from this unsympathetic mode of inquiry; perhaps it was from that Western
predilection to take a humorous view of any principle or
sentiment persistently brought before them, that Mr.
Thompson's quest was the subject of some satire among the
passengers. A gratuitous advertisement of the missing
Charles, addressed to "Jailers and Guardians," circulated
privately among them; everybody remembered to have met
Charles under distressing circumstances. Yet it is but due
to my countrymen to state that when it was known that
Thompson had embarked some wealth in this visionary
project, but little of this satire found its way to his ears,
and nothing was uttered in his hearing that might bring a
pang to a father's heart, or imperil a possible pecuniary advantage of the satirist. Indeed, Mr. Bracey Tibbets' jocular
proposition to form a joint-stock company to "prospect" for
the missing youth, received at one time quite serious entertainment.

Perhaps to superficial criticism Mr. Thompson's nature
was not picturesque nor lovable. His history, as imparted
at dinner one day by himself, was practical even in its sin-
gularity. After a hard and wilful youth and maturity—in
which he had buried a broken-spirited wife, and driven his
son to sea—he suddenly experienced religion.

"I got it in New Orleans in '59," said Mr. Thompson, with
the general suggestion of referring to an epidemic. "Enter
ye the narrer gate. Parse me the beans."

Perhaps this practical equality upheld him in his apparently hopeless search. He had no clew to the whereabouts
of his runaway son—indeed, scarcely a proof of his present
existence. From his indifferent recollection of the boy of
twelve, he now expected to identify the man of twenty-five.

It would seem that he was successful. How he succeeded
was one of the few things he did not tell. There are, I believe, two versions of the story. One, that Mr. Thompson,

visiting a hospital, discovered his son by reason of a peculiar hymn, chanted by the sufferer, in a delirious dream of his boyhood. This version, giving as it did wide range to the finer feelings of the heart, was quite popular; and as told by the Rev. Mr. Gushington, on his return from his California tour, never failed to satisfy an audience. The other was less simple, and as I shall adopt it here, deserves more elaboration.

It was after Mr. Thompson had given up searching for his son among the living, and had taken to the examination of cemeteries, and a careful inspection of the "cold *hic jacets* of the dead." At this time he was a frequent visitor of "Lone Mountain"—a dreary hill-top, bleak enough in its original isolation, and bleaker for the white-faced marbles by which San Francisco anchored her departed citizens, and kept them down in a shifting sand that refused to cover them, and against a fierce and persistent wind that strove to blow them utterly away. Against this wind the old man opposed a will quite as persistent—a grizzled, hard face, and a tall, crape-bound hat drawn tightly over his eyes—and so spent days in reading the mortuary inscriptions audibly to himself. The frequency of scriptural quotation pleased him, and he was fond of corroborating them by a pocket Bible.

"That's from Psalms," he said, one day, to an adjacent grave-digger.

The man made no reply.

Not at all rebuffed, Mr. Thompson at once slid down into the open grave, with a more practical inquiry: "Did you ever, in your profession, come across Char-les Thompson?"

"Thompson be d—d," said the grave-digger, with great directness.

"Which, if he hadn't religion, I think he is," responded the old man, as he clambered out of the grave.

It was, perhaps, on this occasion that Mr. Thompson stayed later than usual. As he turned his face towards the city, lights were beginning to twinkle ahead, and a fierce wind, made visible by fog, drove him forward, or, lying in wait, charged him angrily from the corners of deserted suburban streets. It was on one of these corners that something else, quite as indistinct and malevolent, leaped upon him with an oath, a presented pistol, and a demand for money. But it was met by a will of iron and a grip of steel. The assailant and assailed rolled together on the ground. But the next moment the old man was erect; one hand grasping the captured pistol, the other clutching at arm's length the throat of a figure, surly, youthful, and savage.

"Young man," said Mr. Thompson, setting his thin lips together, "what might be your name?"

"Thompson!"

The old man's hand slid from the throat to the arm of his prisoner, without relaxing its firmness.

"Char-les Thompson, come with me," he said, presently, and marched his captive to the hotel. What took place there has not transpired, but it was known the next morning that Mr. Thompson had found his son.

It is proper to add to the above improbable story, that there was nothing in the young man's appearance or manners to justify it. Grave, reticent, and handsome, devoted to his newly found parent, he assumed the emoluments and responsibilities of his new condition with a certain serious ease that more nearly approached that which San Francisco society lacked, and—rejected. Some chose to despise this quality as a tendency to "psalm-singing;" others saw in it the inherited qualities of the parent, and were ready to prophesy for the son the same hard old age. But all agreed that it was not inconsistent with the habits of money-getting, for which father and son were respected.

And yet the old man did not seem to be happy. Perhaps it was that the consummation of his wishes left him without a practical mission; perhaps—and it is the more probable— he had little love for the son he had regained. The obedience he exacted was freely given, the reform he had set his heart upon was complete; and yet, somehow, it did not seem to please him. In reclaiming his son, he had fulfilled all the requirements that his religious duty required of him, and yet the act seemed to lack sanctification. In this perplexity he read again the parable of the Prodigal Son —which he had long adopted for his guidance—and found that he had omitted the final feast of reconciliation. This seemed to offer the proper quality of ceremoniousness in the sacrament between himself and his son; and so, a year after the appearance of Charles, he set about giving him a party.

"Invite everybody, Char-les," he said, dryly; "everybody who knows that I brought you out of the wine-husks of iniquity, and the company of harlots; and bid them eat, drink, and be merry."

Perhaps the old man had another reason, not yet clearly analyzed. The fine house he had built on the sand-hills sometimes seemed lonely and bare. He often found himself trying to reconstruct, from the grave features of Charles, the little boy which he but dimly remembered in the past, and of which lately he had been thinking a great deal. He believed this to be a sign of impending old age and childishness; but coming, one day, in his formal drawing-room, upon a child of one of the servants, who had strayed therein, he would have taken him in his arms, but the child fled from before his grizzled face. So that it seemed eminently proper to invite a number of people to his house, and, from the array of San Francisco maidenhood, to select a daughter-in-law. And then there would be a child—a boy, whom he could "rare up" from the beginning, and—love— as he did not love Charles.

We were all at the party. The Smiths, Joneses, Browns, and Robinsons also came, in that fine flow of animal spirits, unchecked by any respect for the entertainer, which most of us are apt to find so fascinating. The proceedings would have been somewhat riotous, but for the social position of the actors. In fact, Mr. Bracey Tibbets, having naturally a fine appreciation of a humorous situation, but further impelled by the bright eyes of the Jones girls, conducted himself so remarkably as to attract the serious regard of Mr. Charles Thompson, who approached him, saying quietly: "You look ill, Mr. Tibbets; let me conduct you to your carriage. Resist, you hound, and I'll throw you through that window. This way, please; the room is close and distressing." It is hardly necessary to say that but a part of this speech was audible to the company, and that the rest was not divulged by Mr. Tibbits, who afterwards regretted the sudden illness which kept him from witnessing a certain amusing incident, which the fastest Miss Jones characterized as the "richest part of the blow-out," and which I hasten to record:

It was at supper. It was evident that Mr. Thompson had overlooked much lawlessness in the conduct of the younger people, in his abstract contemplation of some impending event. When the cloth was removed, he rose to his feet, and grimly tapped upon the table. A titter, that broke out among the Jones girls, became epidemic on one side of the board. Charles Thompson, from the foot of the table, looked up in tender perplexity. "He's going to sing a Doxology"—"He's going to pray"—"Silence for a speech," ran round the room.

"It's one year to-day, Christian brothers and sisters," said Mr. Thompson, with grim deliberation, "one year to-day since my son came home from eating of wine-husks and spending of his substance on harlots." (The tittering suddenly ceased.) "Look at him now. Char-les Thompson, stand up." (Charles Thompson stood up.) "One year ago to-day—and look at him now."

He was certainly a handsome prodigal, standing there in his cheerful evening-dress—a repentant prodigal, with sad, obedient eyes turned upon the harsh and unsympathetic glance of his father. The youngest Miss Smith, from the pure depths of her foolish little heart, moved unconsciously toward him.

"It's fifteen years ago since he left my house," said Mr. Thompson, "a rovier and a prodigal. I was myself a man of sin, O Christian friends—a man of wrath and bitterness"—("Amen," from the eldest Miss Smith)—"but, praise be to God, I've fled the wrath to come. It's five years ago since I got the peace that passeth understanding. Have you got it, friends?" (A general sub-chorus of "No, no," from the girls, and "Pass the word for it," from Midshipman Coxe, of the U. S. sloop *Wethersfield*.) "Knock, and it shall be opened to you.

"And when I found the error of my ways, and the preciousness of grace," continued Mr. Thompson, "I came to give it to my son. By sea and land I sought him far, and fainted not. I did not wait for him to come to me—which the same I might have done, and justified myself by the Book of books, but I sought him out among his husks, and—" (the rest of the sentence was lost in the rustling withdrawal of the ladies). "Works, Christian friends, is my motto. By their works shall ye know them, and there is mine."

The particular and accepted work to which Mr. Thompson was alluding had turned quite pale, and was looking fixedly toward an open door leading to the verandah, lately filled by gaping servants, and now the scene of some vague tumult. As the noise continued, a man, shabbily dressed, and evidently in liquor, broke through the opposing guardians, and staggered into the room. The transition from the fog and darkness without to the glare and heat within, evidently dazzled and stupefied him. He removed his battered hat, and passed it once or twice before his eyes, as he steadied himself, but unsuccessfully, by the back of a chair. Suddenly, his wandering glance fell upon the pale face of Charles Thompson; and with a gleam of childlike recognition, and a weak, falsetto laugh, he darted forward, caught at the table, upset the glasses, and literally fell upon the prodigal's breast.

"Sha'ly! yo' d—d ol' scoun'rel, hoo rar ye!"

"Hush!—sit down!—hush!" said Charles Thompson, hurriedly endeavouring to extricate himself from the embrace of his unexpected guest.

"Look at'm!" continued the stranger, unheeding the admonition, but suddenly holding the unfortunate Charles at arms' length, in loving and undisguised admiration of his festive appearance. "Look at'm! Ain't he nasty? Sha'ls, I'm prow of yer!"

"Leave the house!" said Mr. Thompson, rising, with a dangerous look in his cold, gray eye. Char-les, how dare you?"

"Simmer down, ole man! Sha'ls, who's th' ol' bloat? Eh?"

"Hush, man; here, take this!" With nervous hands, Charles Thompson filled a glass with liquor. "Drink it and go—until to-morrow—any time, but—leave us!—go now." But even then, ere the miserable wretch could drink, the old man, pale with passion, was upon him. Half carrying him in his powerful arms, half dragging him through the circling crowd of frightened guests, he had reached the door, swung open by the waiting servants, when Charles Thompson started from a seeming stupor, crying—

"Stop!"

The old man stopped. Through the open door the fog and wind drove chilly. "What does this mean?" he asked, turning a baleful face on Charles.

"Nothing—but stop—for God's sake. Wait till to-morrow, but not to-night. Do not—I implore you—do this thing."

There was something in the tone of the young man's voice—something, perhaps, in the contact of the struggling wretch he held in his powerful arms; but a dim, indefinite fear took possession of the old man's heart. "Who?" he whispered, hoarsely, "is this man?"

Charles did not answer.

"Stand back, there, all of you," thundered Mr. Thompson, to the crowding guests around him. "Char-les—come here! I command you—I—I—I—beg you—tell me *who* is this man?"

Only two persons heard the answer that came faintly from the lips of Charles Thompson:

"YOUR SON."

When the day broke over the bleak sandhills, the guests

had departed from Mr. Thompson's banquet-halls. The lights still burned dimly and coldly in the deserted rooms—deserted by all but three figures, that huddled together in the chill drawing-room, as if for warmth. One lay in drunken slumber on a couch; at his feet sat he who had been known as Charles Thompson; and beside them, haggard and shrunken to half his size, bowed the figure of Mr. Thompson, his gray eye fixed, his elbows upon his knees, and his hands clasped over his ears, as if to shut out the sad, entreating voice that seemed to fill the room.

"God knows I did not set about to wilfully deceive. The name I gave that night was the first that came into my thought—the name of one whom I thought dead—the dissolute companion of my shame. And when you questioned further, I used the knowledge that I gained from him to touch your heart to set me free—only, I swear, for that! But when you told me who you were, and I first saw the opening of another life before me—then—then. O, sir, if I was hungry, homeless, and reckless when I would have robbed you of your gold, I was heart-sick, helpless, and desperate when I would have robbed you of your love."

The old man stirred not. From his luxurious couch the newly found prodigal snored peacefully.

"I had no father I could claim. I never knew a home but this. I was tempted. I have been happy—very happy."

He rose and stood before the old man.

"Do not fear that I shall come between your son and his inheritance. To-day I leave this place, never to return. The world is large, sir, and, thanks to your kindness, I now see the way by which an honest livelihood is gained. Good-bye. You will not take my hand? Well, well. Good-bye."

He turned to go. But when he had reached the door he suddenly came back, and, raising with both hands the grizzled head, he kissed it once and twice.

"Char-les."

There was no reply.

"Char-les!"

The old man rose with a frightened air, and tottered
feebly to the door. It was open. There came to him the
awakened tumult of a great city, in which the prodigal's
footsteps were lost for ever.

MELONS

As I do not suppose the most gentle of readers will believe
that anybody's sponsors in baptism ever wilfully assumed
the responsibility of such a name, I may as well state that
I have reason to infer that Melons was simply the nick-
name of a small boy I once knew. If he had any other, I
never knew it.

Various theories were often projected by me to account
for this strange cognomen. His head, which was covered
with a transparent down, like that which clothes very small
chickens, plainly permitting the scalp to show through, to
an imaginative mind might have suggested that succulent
vegetable. That his parents, recognising some poetical significance in the fruits of the season, might have given this
name to an August child, was an Oriental explanation. That
from his infancy he was fond of indulging in melons, seemed
on the whole the most likely, particularly as Fancy was not
bred in McGinnis's Court. He dawned upon me as Melons.
His proximity was indicated by shrill, youthful voices, as
"Ah, Melons!"—or playfully, "Hi, Melons!"—or authori-
tatively, "You, Melons!"

McGinnis's Court was a democratic expression of some
obstinate and radical property-holder. Occupying a limited
space between two fashionable thoroughfares, it refused to
conform to circumstances, but sturdily paraded its unkempt
glories, and frequently asserted itself in ungrammatical
language. My window—a rear room on the ground floor—
in this way derived blended light and shadow from the
Court. So low was the window-sill, that had I been the
least predisposed to somnambulism, it would have broken

out under such favourable auspices, and I should have haunted McGinnis's Court. My speculations as to the origin of the Court were not altogether gratuitous, for by means of this window I once saw the Past, as through a glass darkly. It was a Celtic shadow that early one morning obstructed my ancient lights. It seemed to belong to an individual with a pea-coat, a stubby pipe, and bristling beard. He was gazing intently at the Court, resting on a heavy cane, somewhat in the way that heroes dramatically visit the scenes of their boyhood. As there was little of architectural beauty in the Court, I came to the conclusion that it was McGinnis looking after his property. The fact that he carefully kicked a broken bottle out of the road, somewhat strengthened me in the opinion. But he presently walked away, and the Court knew him no more. He probably collected his rents by proxy—if he collected them at all.

Beyond Melons, of whom all this is purely introductory, there was little to interest the most sanguine and hopeful nature. In common with all such localities, a great deal of washing was done, in comparison with the visible results.— There was always something whisking on the line, and always something whisking through the Court, that looked as if it ought to be there. A fish geranium—of all plants kept for the recreation of mankind, certainly the greatest illusion—straggled under the window. Through its dusty leaves I caught the first glance of Melons.

His age was about seven. He looked older, from the venerable whiteness of his head, and it was impossible to conjecture his size, as he always wore clothes apparently belonging to some shapely youth of nineteen. A pair of pantaloons, that, when sustained by a single suspender, completely equipped him—formed his every-day suit. How, with this lavish superfluity of clothing, he managed to perform the surprising gymnastic feats it has been my privilege to witness, I have never been able to tell. His "turning the crab," and other minor dislocations, were always attended with success. It was not an unusual sight at any hour of the day to find Melons suspended on a line, or to

see his venerable head appearing above the roofs of the out-
houses. Melons knew the exact height of every fence in the
vicinity, its facilities for scaling, and the possibility of seiz-
ure on the other side. His more peaceful and quieter amuse-
ments consisted in dragging a disused boiler by a large
string, with hideous outcries, to imaginary fires.

Melons was not gregarious in his habits. A few youths
of his own age sometimes called upon him, but they eventually became abusive, and their visits were more strictly
predatory incursions for old bottles and junk, which formed
the staple of McGinnis's Court. Overcome by loneliness
one day, Melons inveigled a blind harper into the Court.
For two hours did that wretched man prosecute his unhallowed calling, unrecompensed, and going round and
round the Court, apparently under the impression that it
was some other place, while Melons surveyed him from an
adjoining fence with calm satisfaction. It was this absence
of conscientious motives that brought Melons into dis-
repute with his aristocratic neighbours. Orders were issued
that no child of wealthy and pious patronage should play
with him. This mandate, as a matter of course, invested
Melons with a fascinating interest to them. Admiring
glances were cast at Melons from nursery windows. Baby
fingers beckoned to him. Invitations to tea (on wood and
pewter) were lisped to him from aristocratic back-yards. It
was evident he was looked upon as a pure and noble being,
untrammelled by the conventionalities of parentage, and
physically as well as mentally exalted above them. One
afternoon an unusual commotion prevailed in the vicinity of
McGinnis's Court. Looking from my window, I saw Melons
perched on the roof of a stable, pulling up a rope by which
one "Tommy," an infant scion of an adjacent and wealthy
house, was suspended in mid-air. In vain the female relatives of Tommy, congregated in the back-yard, expostulated
with Melons; in vain the unhappy father shook his fist at
him. Secure in his position, Melons redoubled his exertions
and at last landed Tommy on the roof. Then it was that

the humiliating fact was disclosed that Tommy had been acting in collusion with Melons. He grinned delightedly back at his parents, as if "by merit raised to that bad eminence." Long before the ladder arrived that was to succour him, he became the sworn ally of Melons, and I regret to say, incited by the same audacious boy, "chaffed" his own flesh and blood below him. He was eventually taken, though—of course—Melons escaped. But Tommy was restricted to the window after that, and the companionship was limited to "Hi, Melons!" and "You Tommy!" and Melons, to all practical purposes, lost him for ever. I looked afterward to see some signs of sorrow on Melons' part, but in vain; he buried his grief, if he had any, somewhere in his one voluminous garment.

At about this time my opportunities of knowing Melons became more extended. I was engaged in filling a void in the Literature of the Pacific Coast. As this void was a pretty large one, and as I was informed that the Pacific Coast languished under it, I set apart two hours each day to this work of filling in. It was necessary that I should adopt a methodical system, so I retired from the world and locked myself in my room at a certain hour each day, after coming from my office. I then carefully drew out my portfolio and read what I had written the day before. This would suggest some alteration, and I would carefully re-write it. During this operation I would turn to consult a book of reference, which invariably proved extremely interesting and attractive. It would generally suggest another and better method of "filling in." Turning this method over reflectively in my mind, I would finally commence the new method, which I eventually abandoned for the original plan. At this time I would become convinced that my exhausted faculties demanded a cigar. The operation of lighting a cigar usually suggested that a little quiet reflection and meditation would be of service to me, and I always allowed myself to be guided by prudential instincts. Eventually, seated by my window, as before stated, Melons asserted

himself. Though our conversation rarely went further than
"Hello, Mister!" and "Ah, Melons!" a vagabond instinct we
felt in common, implied a communion deeper than words.
In this spiritual commingling the time passed, often beguiled
by gymnastics on the fence or line (always with an eye to
my window) until dinner was announced, and I found a
more practical void required my attention. An unlooked-
for incident drew us in closer relation.

A sea-faring friend just from a tropical voyage had presented me with a bunch of bananas. They were not quite
ripe, and I hung them before my window to mature in the
sun of McGinnis's Court, whose forcing qualities were remarkable. In the mysteriously mingled odours of ship and
shore which they diffused throughout my room, there was
a lingering reminiscence of low latitudes. But even that
joy was fleeting and evanescent: they never reached maturity.

Coming home one day as I turned the corner of that
fashionable thoroughfare before alluded to, I met a small
boy eating a banana. There was nothing remarkable in
that, but as I neared McGinnis's Court I presently met
another small boy, also eating a banana. A third small boy
engaged in a like occupation obtruded a painful coincidence
upon my mind. I leave the psychological reader to determine the exact co-relation between this circumstance and
the sickening sense of loss that overcame me on witnessing
it. I reached my room—and found the bunch of bananas
were gone.

There was but one who knew of their existence, but one
who frequented my window, but one capable of the gymnastic effort to procure them, and that was—I blush to say it—
Melons. Melons the depredator—Melons, despoiled by
larger boys of his ill-gotten booty, or reckless and indis-
creetly liberal; Melons—now a fugitive on some neighbouring house-top. I lit a cigar, and drawing my chair to the
window, sought surcease of sorrow in the contemplation of
the fish geranium. In a few moments something white

passed my window at about the level of the edge. There was no mistaking that hoary head, which now represented to me only aged iniquity. It was Melons, that venerable, juvenile hypocrite.

He affected not to observe me, and would have withdrawn quietly, but that horrible fascination which causes the murderer to revisit the scene of his crime, impelled him toward my window. I smoked calmly and gazed at him without speaking. He walked several times up and down the Court with a half rigid, half belligerent expression of eye and shoulder, intended to represent the carelessness of innocence.

Once or twice he stopped, and putting his arms their whole length into his capacious trowsers, gazed with some interest at the additional width they thus acquired. Then he whistled. The singular conflicting conditions of John Brown's body and soul were at that time beginning to attract the attention of youth, and Melons' performance of that melody was always remarkable. At last he met my eye. He winced slightly, but recovered himself, and going to the fence, stood for a few moments on his hands, with his bare feet quivering in the air. Then he turned toward me and threw out a conversational preliminary.

"They is a cirkis,"—said Melons gravely, hanging with his back to the fence and his arms twisted round the palings —"a cirkis over yonder!"—indicating the locality with his foot—"with hosses, and hossback riders. They is a man wot rides six hosses to onct—six hosses to onct—and nary saddle"—and he paused in expectation.

Even this equestrian novelty did not affect me. I still kept a fixed gaze on Melons' eye, and he began to tremble and visibly shrink in his capacious garment. Some other desperate means—conversion with Melons was always a desperate means—must be resorted to. He recommenced more artfully:

"Do you know Carrots?"

I had a faint remembrance of a boy of that euphonious

name, with scarlet hair, who was a playmate and persecutor of Melons. But I said nothing.

"Carrots is a bad boy. Killed a policeman onct. Wears a dirk knife in his boots, and saw him to-day looking in your windy."

I felt that this must end here. I rose sternly and addressed Melons.

"Melons, this is all irrelevant and impertinent to the case. *You* took those bananas. Your proposition regarding Carrots, even if I were inclined to accept it as credible information, does not alter the material issue. You took those bananas. The offence under the statutes of California is felony. How far Carrots may have been accessory to the fact either before or after, is not my intention at present to discuss. The act is complete. Your present conduct shows the *animo furandi* to have been equally clear."

By the time I had finished this exordium, Melons had disappeared, as I fully expected.

He never re-appeared. The remorse that I have experienced for the part I had taken in what I fear may have resulted in his utter and complete extermination, alas! he may not know, except through these pages. For I have never seen him since. Whether he ran away and went to sea to re-appear at some future day as the most ancient of mariners, or whether he buried himself completely in his trousers, I never shall know. I have read the papers anxiously for accounts of him.

I have gone to the Police Office in the vain attempt of identifying him as a lost child. But I never saw or heard of him since. Strange fears have sometimes crossed my mind that his venerable appearance may have been actually the result of senility, and that he may have been gathered peacefully to his fathers in a green old age. I have even had doubts of his existence, and have sometimes thought that he was providentially and mysteriously offered to fill the void I have before alluded to. In that hope I have written these pages.

THE ROMANCE OF MADRONO HOLLOW

THE latch on the garden gate of the Folinsbee Ranch clicked twice. The gate itself was so much in shadow that lovely night, that "old man Folinsbee," sitting on his porch, could distinguish nothing but a tall white hat and beside it a few fluttering ribbons, under the pines that marked the entrance. Whether because of this fact, or that he considered a sufficient time had elapsed since the clicking of the latch for more positive disclosure, I do not know; but after a few moments' hesitation he quietly laid aside his pipe and walked slowly down the winding path toward the gate. At the Ceanothus hedge he stopped and listened.

There was not much to hear. The hat was saying to the ribbons that it was a fine night, and remarking generally upon the clear outline of the Sierras against the blue-black sky. The ribbons, it so appeared, had admired this all the way home, and asked the hat if it had ever seen anything half so lovely as the moonlight on the summit? The hat never had; it recalled some lovely nights in the South in Alabama ("in the South in Ahlabahm" was the way the old man heard it), but then there were other things that made this night seem so pleasant. The ribbons could not possibly conceive what the hat could be thinking about. At this point there was a pause, of which Mr. Folinsbee availed himself to walk very grimly and craunchingly down the gravel walk toward the gate. Then the hat was lifted, and disappeared in the shadow, and Mr. Folinsbee confronted only the half-foolish, half-mischievous, but wholly pretty face of his daughter.

It was afterwards known to Madroño Hollow that sharp words passed between "Miss Jo" and the old man, and that the latter coupled the names of one Culpepper Starbottle and his uncle, Colonel Starbottle, with certain uncomplimentary epithets, and that Miss Jo retaliated sharply. "Her father's blood before her father's face boiled up and proved her truly of his race," quoted the blacksmith, who leaned toward the noble verse of Byron. "She saw the old man's bluff and raised him," was the directer comment of the college-bred Masters.

Meanwhile the subject of these animadversions proceeded slowly along the road to a point where the Folinsbee mansion came in view,—a long, narrow, white building, unpretentious, yet superior to its neighbours, and bearing some evidences of taste and refinement in the vines that clambered over its porch, in its French windows, and the white muslin curtains that kept out the fierce California sun by day, and were now touched with silver in the gracious moonlight, Culpepper leaned against the low fence, and gazed long and earnestly at the building. Then the moonlight vanished ghost-like from one of the windows, a material glow took its place, and a girlish figure, holding a candle, drew the white curtains together. To Culpepper it was a vestal virgin standing before a hallowed shrine; to the prosaic observer, I fear it was only a fair-haired young woman, whose wicked black eyes still shone with unfilial warmth. Howbeit, when the figure had disappeared he stepped out briskly into the moonlight of the high road. Here he took off his distinguishing hat to wipe his forehead, and the moon shone full upon his face.

It was not an unprepossessing one, albeit a trifle too thin and lank and bilious to be altogether pleasant. The cheekbones were prominent, and the black eyes sunken in their orbits. Straight black hair fell slantwise off a high but narrow forehead, and swept part of a hollow cheek. A long black mustache followed the perpendicular curves of his mouth. It was on the whole a serious, even Quixotic face, but at times it was relieved by a rare smile of such tender and even pathetic sweetness, that Miss Jo is reported to have said that, if it would only last through the ceremony, she would have married its possessor on the spot. "I once told him so," added that shameless young woman; "but the man instantly fell into a settled melancholy, and hasn't smiled since."

A half-mile below the Folinsbee Ranch the white road dipped and was crossed by a trail that ran through

Madroño Hollow. Perhaps because it was a near cut-off to
the settlement, perhaps from some less practical reason,
Culpepper took this trail, and in a few moments stood
among the rarely beautiful trees that gave their name to the
valley. Even in that uncertain light the weird beauty of
these harlequin masqueraders was apparent; their red
trunks—a blush in the moonlight, a deep blood-stain in the
shadow—stood out against the silvery green foliage. It
was as if Nature in some gracious moment had here caught
and crystallized the gypsy memories of the transplanted
Spaniard, to cheer him in his lonely exile.

As Culpepper entered the grove he heard loud voices.
As he turned toward a clump of trees, a figure so bizarre
and characteristic that it might have been a resident
Daphne,—a figure over-dressed in crimson silk and lace,
with bare brown arms and shoulders, and a wreath of
honeysuckle,—stepped out of the shadow. It was followed
by a man. Culpepper started. To come to the point
briefly, he recognized in the man the features of his respected uncle, Colonel Starbottle; in the female, a lady
who may be briefly described as one possessing absolutely
no claim to an introduction to the polite reader. To hurry
over equally unpleasant details, both were evidently under
the influence of liquor.

From the excited conversation that ensued, Culpepper
gathered that some insult had been put upon the lady at a
public ball which she had attended that evening; that the
Colonel, her escort, had failed to resent it with the sanguinary completeness that she desired. I regret that, even in a
liberal age, I may not record the exact and even picturesque
language in which this was conveyed to her hearers.
Enough that at the close of a fiery peroration, with feminine
inconsistency she flew at the gallant Colonel, and would
have visited her delayed vengeance upon his luckless head,
but for the prompt interference of Culpepper. Thwarted
in this, she threw herself upon the ground, and then into
unpicturesque hysterics. There was a fine moral lesson, not
only in this grotesque performance of her sex which cannot

afford to be grotesque, but in the ludicrous concern with which it inspired the two men. Culpepper, to whom woman was more or less angelic, was pained and sympathetic; the Colonel, to whom she was more or less improper, was exceedingly terrified and embarrassed. Howbeit the storm was soon over, and after Mistress Dolores had returned a little dagger to its sheath (her garter), she quietly took herself out of Madroño Hollow, and happily out of these pages for ever. The two men, left to themselves, conversed in low tones. Dawn stole upon them before they separated: the Colonel quite sobered and in full possession of his usual jaunty self-assertion; Culpepper with a baleful glow in his hollow cheek, and in his dark eyes a rising fire.

The next morning the general ear of Madroño Hollow was filled with rumours of the Colonel's mishap. It was asserted that he had been invited to withdraw his female companion from the floor of the Assembly Ball at the Independence Hotel, and that failing to do this both were expelled. It is to be regretted that in 1854 public opinion was divided in regard to the propriety of this step, and that there was some discussion as to the comparative virtue of the ladies who were not expelled, but it was generally conceded that the real *casus belli* was political. "Is this a dashed Puritan meeting?" had asked the Colonel, savagely. "It's no Pike County shindig," had responded the floor manager, cheerfully. "You're a Yank!" had screamed the Colonel, profanely qualifying the noun. "Get! you border ruffian," was the reply. Such at least was the substance of the report. As, at that sincere epoch, expressions like the above were usually followed by prompt action, a fracas was confidently looked for.

Nothing, however, occurred. Colonel Starbottle made his appearance next day upon the streets with somewhat of his usual pomposity, a little restrained by the presence of his nephew, who accompanied him, and who, as a universal favourite, also exercised some restraint upon the curious and impertinent. But Culpepper's face wore a look of anxiety quite at variance with his usual grave repose. "The Don don't seem to take the old man's set-back kindly," observed the sympathizing blacksmith. "P'r'aps he was sweet on Dolores himself," suggested the sceptical expressman.

It was a bright morning, a week after this occurrence, that Miss Jo Folinsbee stepped from her garden into the road. This time the latch did not click as she cautiously closed the gate behind her. After a moment's irresolution, which would have been awkward but that it was charmingly employed, after the manner of her sex, in adjusting a bow under a dimpled but rather prominent chin, and in pulling down the fingers of a neatly fitting glove, she tripped towards the settlement. Small wonder that a passing teamster drove his six mules into the wayside ditch and imperilled his load, to keep the dust from her spotless garments; small wonder that the "Lightning Express" withheld its speed and flash to let her pass, and that the expressman, who had never been known to exchange more than rapid monosyllables with his fellow-man, gazed after her with breathless admiration. For she was certainly attractive. In a country where the ornamental sex followed the example of youthful Nature, and were prone to overdress and glaring efflorescence, Miss Jo's simple and tasteful raiment added much to the physical charm of, if it did not actually suggest a sentiment, to her presence. It said that Euchredeck Billy, working in the gulch at the crossing, never saw Miss Folinsbee pass but that he always remarked apologetically to his partner, that "he believed he *must* write a letter home." Even Bill Masters, who saw her in Paris presented to the favourable criticism of that most fastidious man the late Emperor, said that she was stunning, but a big discount on what she was at Madroño Hollow.

It was still early morning, but the sun, with California extravagance, had already begun to beat hotly on the little chip hat and blue ribbons, and Miss Jo was obliged to seek the shade of a by-path. Here she received the timid advances of a vagabond yellow dog graciously, until, emboldened by his success, he insisted upon accompanying her, and, becoming slobberingly demonstrative, threatened her spotless skirt with his dusty paws, when she drove him from her with some slight acerbity, and a stone which haply fell within fifty feet of its destined mark. Having thus proved her ability to defend herself, with characteristic inconsistency she took a small panic, and, gathering her white skirts in one hand, and holding the brim of her hat over her eyes with the other, she ran swiftly at least a hundred yards before she stopped. Then she began picking some ferns, and a few wild-flowers still spared to the withered fields, and then a sudden distrust of her small ankles seized her, and she inspected them narrowly for those burrs and bugs and snakes which are supposed to lie in wait for helpless womanhood. Then she plucked some golden heads of wild oats, and with a sudden inspiration placed them in her black hair, and then came quite unconsciously upon the trail leading to Madroño Hollow.

Here she hesitated. Before her ran the little trail, vanishing at last into the bosky depths below. The sun was very hot. She must be very far from home. Why should she not rest awhile under the shade of a madroño?

She answered these questions by going there at once. After thoroughly exploring the grove, and satisfying herself that it contained no other living human creature, she sat down under one of the largest trees, with a satisfactory little sigh. Miss Jo loved the madroño. It was a cleanly tree; no dust ever lay upon its varnished leaves; its immaculate shade never was known to harbour grub or insect.

She looked up at the rosy arms interlocked and arched above her head. She looked down at the delicate ferns and cryptogams at her feet. Something glittered at the root of the tree. She picked it up; it was a bracelet. She examined it carefully for cipher or inscription; there was none. She could not resist a natural desire to clasp it on her arm, and to survey it from that advantageous viewpoint. This absorbed her attention for some moments; and when she looked up again she beheld at a little distance Culpepper Starbottle.

He was standing where he had halted, with instinctive delicacy, on first discovering her. Indeed, he had even deliberated whether he ought not to go away without disturbing her. But some fascination held him to the spot. Wonderful power of humanity! Far beyond jutted an outlying spur of the Sierra, vast, compact, and silent. Scarcely a hundred yards away a league-long chasm dropped its sheer walls of granite a thousand feet. On every side rose up the serried ranks of pine trees, in whose close-set files centuries of storm and change had wrought no breach. Yet all this seemed to Culpepper to have been planned by an all-wise Providence as the natural background to the figure of a pretty girl in a yellow dress.

Although Miss Jo had confidently expected to meet Culpepper somewhere in her ramble, now that he came upon her suddenly, she felt disappointed and embarrassed. His manner, too, was more than usually grave and serious, and more than ever seemed to jar upon that audacious levity which was this giddy girl's power and security in a society where all feeling was dangerous. As he approached her she rose to her feet, but almost before she knew it he had taken her hand and drawn her to a seat beside him. This was not what Miss Jo had expected, but nothing is so difficult to predicate as the exact preliminaries of a declaration of love.

What did Culpepper say? Nothing, I fear, that will add anything to the wisdom of the reader; nothing, I fear, that Miss Jo had not heard substantially from other lips before. But there was a certain conviction, fire-speed, and fury in the manner that was deliciously novel to the young lady. It was certainly something to be courted in the nineteenth century with all the passion and extravagance of the sixteenth; it was something to hear, amid the slang of a frontier society, the language of knight-errantry poured into her ear by this lantern-jawed, dark-browed descendant of the Cavaliers.

I do not know that there was anything more in it. The facts, however, go to show that at a certain point Miss Jo dropped her glove, and that in recovering it Culpepper possessed himself, first of her hand and then her lips. When they stood up to go Culpepper had his arm around her waist, and her black hair, with its sheaf of golden oats, rested against the breast-pocket of his coat. But even then I do not think her fancy was entirely captive. She took a certain satisfaction in this demonstration of Culpepper's splendid height, and mentally compared it with a former flame, one Lieutenant McMirk, an active, but under-sized Hector, who subsequently fell a victim to the incautiously composed and monotonous beverages of a frontier garrison. Nor was she so much pre-occupied, but that her quick eyes, even while absorbing Culpepper's glances, were yet able to detect, at a distance, the figure of a man approaching. In an instant she slipped out of Culpepper's arm, and whipping her hands behind her, said, "There's that horrid man!"

Culpepper looked up, and beheld his respected uncle panting and blowing over the hill. His brow contracted as he turned to Miss Jo: "You don't like my uncle?"

"I hate him!" Miss Jo was recovering her ready tongue.

Culpepper blushed. He would have liked to enter upon some details of the Colonel's pedigree and exploits, but there was not time. He only smiled sadly. The smile melted Miss Jo. She held out her hand quickly, and said, with even more than her usual effrontery, "Don't let that man get you into any trouble. Take care of yourself, dear, and don't let anything happen to you."

Miss Jo intended this speech to be pathetic; the tenure of life among her lovers had hitherto been very uncertain. Culpepper turned toward her, but she had already vanished in the thicket.

The Colonel came up panting. "I've looked all over town for you, and be dashed to you, sir. Who was that with you?"

"A lady." (Culpepper never lied, but he was discreet.)

"D—m 'em all! Look yar, Culp, I've spotted the man who gave the order to put me off the floor" ("flo" was what the Colonel said) "the other night!"

"Who was it?" asked Culpepper, listlessly.

"Jack Folinsbee."

"Who?"

"Why, the son of that dashed nigger-worshipping, psalm-singing Puritan Yankee. What's the matter, now! Look yar, Culp, you ain't goin' back on your blood, ar' ye? You ain't goin' back on your word? Ye ain't going down at the feet of this trash, like a whipped hound!"

Culpepper was silent. He was very white. Presently he looked up and said quietly, "No."

Culpepper Starbottle had challenged Jack Folinsbee, and the challenge was accepted. The cause alleged was the expelling of Culpepper's uncle from the floor of the Assembly Ball by the order of Folinsbee. This much Madroño Hollow knew and could swear to; but there were other strange rumours afloat, of which the blacksmith was an able expounder. "You see, gentlemen," he said to the crowd gathering round his anvil, "I ain't got no theory of this affair, I only give a few facts as have come to my knowledge. Culpepper and Jack meets quite accidentally like in Bob's saloon. Jack goes up to Culpepper and says, 'A word with you.' Culpepper bows and steps aside in this way, Jack standing about *here*." (The blacksmith demonstrates the position of the parties with two old horseshoes on the anvil.) "Jack pulls a bracelet from his pocket and says, 'Do you know that bracelet?' Culpepper says, 'I do not,' quite cool-like and easy. Jack says, 'You gave it to my sister.' Culpepper says, still cool as you please, 'I did not.' Jack says, 'You lie, G—d d—mn you,' and draws his derringer. Culpepper jumps forward about here" (reference is made to the diagram) "and Jack fires. Nobody hit. It's a mighty cur'o's thing, gentlemen," continued the blacksmith, dropping suddenly into the abstract, and leaning meditatively on his anvil,—"it's a mighty cur'o's thing that nobody gets hit so often. You and me empties our revolvers sociably at each other over a little game, and the room full, and nobody gets hit! That's what gets me."

"'Never mind, Thompson," chimed in Bill Masters,

"there's another and better world where we shall know all
that and—become better shots. Go on with your story."

"Well, some grabs Culpepper and some grabs Jack, and
so separates them. Then Jack tells 'em as how he had seen
his sister wear a bracelet which he knew was one that had
been given to Dolores by Colonel Starbottle. That Miss Jo
wouldn't say where she got it, but owned up to having seen
Culpepper that day. Then the most cur'o's thing of it yet,
what does Culpepper do but rise up and takes all back that
he said, and allows that he *did* give her the bracelet. Now,
my opinion, gentlemen, is that he lied; it ain't like that
man to give a gal that he respects anything off of that piece
Dolores. But it's all the same now, and there's but one
thing to be done."

The way this one thing was done belongs to the record of
Madroño Hollow. The morning was bright and clear; the
air was slightly chill, but that was from the mist which
arose along the banks of the river. As early as six o'clock
the designated ground—a little opening in the madroño
grove—was occupied by Culpepper Starbottle, Colonel Starbottle, his second, and the surgeon. The Colonel was exalted and excited, albeit in a rather imposing, dignified way,
and pointed out to the surgeon the excellence of the ground,
which at that hour was wholly shaded from the sun, whose
steady stare is more or less discomposing to your duellist.
The surgeon threw himself on the grass and smoked his
cigar. Culpepper quiet and thoughtful, leaned against a
tree and gazed up the river. There was a strange suggestion of a picnic about the group, which was heightened
when the Colonel drew a bottle from his coat-tails, and, taking a preliminary draught, offered it to the others. "Cock-
tails, sir," he explained with dignified precision. "A gentleman, sir, should never go out without 'em. Keeps off the
morning chill. I remember going out in '53 with Hank
Boompirater. Good ged, sir, the man had to put on his
overcoat, and was shot in it. Fact."

But the noise of wheels drowned the Colonel's reminis-
cences, and a rapidly driven buggy, containing Jack Folins-

bee, Calhoun Bungstarter, his second, and Bill Masters drew
up on the ground. Jack Folinsbee leaped out gaily. "I
had the jolliest work to get away without the governor's
hearing," he began, addressing the group before him with the
greatest volubility. Calhoun Bungstarter touched his arm,
and the young man blushed. It was his first duel.

"If you are ready, gentlemen," said Mr. Bungstarter,
"we had better proceed to business. I believe it is understood that no apology will be offered or accepted. We may
as well settle preliminaries at once, or I fear we shall be
interrupted. There is a rumour in town that the Vigilance
Committee are seeking our friends the Starbottles, and I
believe, as their fellow-countryman, I have the honour to be
included in their warrant."

At this probability of interruption, that gravity which
had hitherto been wanting fell upon the group. The preliminaries were soon arranged and the principals placed in
position. Then there was a silence.

To a spectator from the hill, impressed with the picnic
suggestion, what might have been the popping of two
champagne corks broke the stillness.

Culpepper had fired in the air. Colonel Starbottle uttered a low curse. Jack Folinsbee sulkily demanded another
shot.

Again the parties stood opposed to each other. Again
the word was given, and what seemed to be the simul-
taneous report of both pistols rose upon the air. But after
an interval of a few seconds all were surprised to see Culpepper slowly raise his unexploded weapon and fire it harm-
lessly above his head. Then throwing the pistol upon the
ground, he walked to a tree and leaned silently against it.

Jack Folinsbee flew into a paroxysm of fury. Colonel
Starbottle raved and swore. Mr. Bungstarter was properly
shocked at their conduct. "Really, gentlemen, if Mr. Culpepper Starbottle declines another shot, I do not see how
we can proceed."

But the Colonel's blood was up, and Jack Folinsbee was
equally implacable. A hurried consultation ensued, which

proprietor of the "Half-Way House" as "lemming sody" still oppressed me. Even the facetiæ of the gallant express-man who knew everybody's Christian name along the route, who rained letters, newspapers and bundles from the top of the stage, whose legs frequently appeared in frightful proximity to the wheels, who got on and off while we were going at full speed, whose gallantry, energy, and superior knowledge of travel crushed all us other passengers to en-vious silence, and who just then was talking with several persons and manifestly doing something else at the same time—even this had failed to interest me. So I stood gloomily, clutching my shawl and carpet bag, and watched the stage roll away, taking a parting look at the gallant expressman as he hung on the top rail with one leg, and lit his cigar from the pipe of a running footman. I then turned toward the Wingdam Temperance Hotel.

It may have been the weather, or it may have been the pie, but I was not impressed favourably with the house. Perhaps it was the name extending the whole length of the building, with a letter under each window, making the people who looked out dreadfully conspicuous. Perhaps it was that "Temperance" always suggested to my mind rusks and weak tea. It was uninviting. It might have been called the "Total Abstinence" Hotel, from the lack of any-thing to intoxicate or enthrall the senses. It was designed with an eye to artistic dreariness. It was so much too large for the settlement, that it appeared to be a very slight improvement on out-doors. It was unpleasantly new. There was the forest flavour of dampness about it, and a slight spicing of pine. Nature outraged, but not entirely subdued, sometimes broke out afresh in little round, sticky, resinous tears on the doors and windows. It seemed to me that boarding there must seem like a perpetual picnic. As I entered the door, a number of the regular boarders rushed out of a long room, and set about trying to get the taste of something out of their mouths, by the application of to-bacco in various forms. A few immediately ranged them-selves around the fire-place, with their legs over each other's chairs, and in that position silently resigned themselves to indigestion. Remembering the pie, I waived the invitation of the landlord to supper, but suffered myself to be conducted into the sitting-room. "Mine host" was a magnificent looking, heavily bearded specimen of the animal man. He reminded me of somebody or something connected with the drama. I was sitting beside the fire, mutely wondering what it could be, and trying to follow the particular chord of memory thus touched, into the intricate past, when a little delicate-looking woman appeared at the door, and leaning heavily against the casing, said in an exhausted tone, "Husband!" As the landlord turned toward her, that particular remembrance flashed before me, in a single line of blank verse. It was this: "Two souls with but one single thought, two hearts that beat as one."

It was Ingomar and Parthenia his wife. I imagined a different denouement from the play. Ingomar had taken Parthenia back to the mountains, and kept a hotel for the benefit of the Alemanni, who resorted there in large numbers. Poor Parthenia was pretty well fagged out, and did all the work without "help." She had two "young barbarians," a boy and a girl. She was faded—but still good looking.

I sat and talked with Ingomar, who seemed perfectly at home and told me several stories of the Alemanni, all bearing a strong flavour of the wilderness, and being perfectly in keeping with the house. How he, Ingomar, had killed a certain dreadful "bar," whose skin was just up "yar," over his bed. How he, Ingomar, had killed several "bucks" whose skins had been prettily fringed and embroidered by Parthenia, and even now clothed him. How he, Ingomar, had killed several "Injins," and was once nearly scalped himself. All this with that ingenious candour which is perfectly justifiable in a barbarian, but which a Greek might feel inclined to look upon as "blowing." Thinking of the wearied Parthenia, I began to consider for the first time that perhaps she had better married the old Greek. Then she would at least have always looked neat. Then she would not have worn a woollen dress flavoured with all the dinners of the past year. Then she would not have been obliged to wait on the table with her hair half down. Then the two children would not have hung about her skirts with dirty fingers, palpably dragging her down day by day. I suppose it was the pie which put such heartless and improper ideas in my head, and so I rose up and told Ingomar I believed I'd go to bed. Preceded by that redoubtable barbarian and a flaring tallow candle, I followed him upstairs to my room. It was the only single room he had, he told me; he had built it for the convenience of married parties who might stop here, but that event not happening yet, he had left it half furnished. It had cloth on one side, and large cracks on the other. The wind, which always swept over Wingdam at night time, puffed through the apartment from different apertures. The window was too small for the hole in the side of the house where it hung, and rattled noisily. Everything looked cheerless and dispiriting. Before Ingomar left me, he brought that "bar-skin," and throwing it over the solemn bier which stood in one corner, told me he reckoned that would keep me warm, and then bade me good night. I undressed myself, the light blowing out in the middle of that ceremony, crawled under the "bar-skin," and tried to compose myself to sleep.

But I was staringly wide awake. I heard the wind sweep down the mountain side, and toss the branches of the melancholy pine, and then enter the house, and try all the doors along the passage. Sometimes strong currents of air blew my hair all over the pillow, as with strange whispering breaths. The green timber along the walls seemed to be sprouting, and sent a dampness even through the "bar-skin." I felt like Robinson Crusoe in his tree, with the ladder pulled up—or like the rocked baby of the nursery song. After lying awake half-an-hour, I regretted having stopped at "Wingdam;" at the end of the third quarter, I wished I had not gone to bed, and when a restless hour passed, I got up and dressed myself. There had been a fire down in the big room. Perhaps it was still burning. I opened the door and groped my way along a passage, vocal with the snores of the Alemanni and the whistling of the night wind; I partly fell down-stairs, and at last entering the big room, saw the fire still burning. I drew a chair toward it, poked it with my foot, and was astonished to see, by the up-springing flash, that Parthenia was sitting there also, holding a faded-looking baby.

I asked her why she was sitting up?

She did not go to bed on Wednesday night, before the mail arrived, and then she awoke her husband, and there were passengers to 'tend to.

"Did she not get tired, sometimes?"

"A little, but Abner"—the Barbarian's Christian name— "had promised to get her more help next spring, if business was good."

"How many boarders had she?"

"She believed about forty came to regular meals, and there was transient custom, which was as much as she and her husband could 'tend to. But *he* did a great deal of work."

"What work?"

"Oh! bringing in the wood, and looking after the traders' things."

"How long had she been married?"

"About nine years. She had lost a little girl and boy. Three children living. *He* was from Illinois; she from Boston. Had an education (Boston Female High School— Geometry, Algebra, a little Latin and Greek). Mother and father died. Came to Illinois alone to teach school. Saw *him*—yes—a love match ('Two souls,' etc., etc.) Married and emigrated to Kansas. Thence across the Plains to California. Always on the outskirts of civilization. *He* liked it.

"She might sometimes have wished to go home. Would like to, on account of her children. Would like to give them an education. Had taught them a little herself, but couldn't do much on account of other work. Hoped that the boy would be like his father—strong and hearty. Was fearful the girl would be more like her. Had often thought she was not fit for a pioneer's wife."

"Why?"

"Oh, she was not strong enough, and had seen some of his friends' wives in Kansas who could do more work. But he never complained—he was so kind"—("Two souls," etc.)

Sitting there with her head leaning pensively on one hand, holding the poor, wearied and limp looking baby wearily on the other arm—dirty, drabbled and forlorn, with the fire-light playing upon her features no longer fresh or young, but still refined and delicate, and even in her grotesque slovenliness still bearing a faint reminiscence of birth and breeding, it was not to be wondered that I did not fall into excessive raptures over the barbarian's kindness. Embold-ened by my sympathy, she told me how she had given up, little by little, what she imagined to be the weakness of her early education, until she found that she acquired but little strength in her new experience. How, translated to a back-woods society, she was hated by the women, and called proud and "fine," and how her dear husband lost popularity on that account with his fellows. How, led partly by his roving instincts, and partly from other circumstances, he started with her to California. An account of that tedious journey. How it was a dreary, dreary waste in her memory, only a blank plain marked by a little cairn of stones—a child's grave. How she had noticed that little Willie failed. How she had called Abner's attention to it, but, man-like, he knew nothing about children, and pooh-poohed it, and was worried by the stock. How it happened that after they had passed Sweetwater, she was walking beside the waggon one night, and looking at the western sky, and she heard a little voice say "mother." How she looked into the waggon and saw that little Willie was sleeping comfortably, and did not wish to wake him. How that in a few moments more she heard the same voice saying, "mother." How she came back to the waggon and leaned down over him, and felt his breath upon her face, and again covered him up tenderly, and once more resumed her weary journey beside him, praying to God for his recovery. How, with her face turned to the sky, she heard the same voice saying, "mother," and directly a great, bright star shot away from its brethren and expired. And how she knew what had happened, and ran to the waggon again only to pillow a little pinched and cold white face upon her weary bosom. The thin, red hands went up to her eyes here, and for a few moments she sat still. The wind tore round the house and made a frantic rush at the front door, and from his couch of skins in the inner room, Ingomar, the barbarian, snored peacefully.

"Of course she always found a protector from insult and outrage in the great courage and strength of her husband?"

"Oh yes; when Ingomar was with her she feared nothing. But she was nervous, and had been frightened once!"

"How?"

"They had just arrived in California. They kept house then, and had to sell liquor to traders. Ingomar was hospitable, and drank with everybody, for the sake of popularity and business, and Ingomar got to like liquor, and was easily affected by it. And how one night there was a boisterous crowd in the bar-room; she went in and tried to get him away, but only succeeded in awakening the coarse gallantry of the half-crazed revellers. And how, when she had at last got him in the room with her frightened children, he sank down on the bed in a stupor, which made her think the liquor was drugged. And how she sat beside him all night, and near morning heard a step in the passage, and looking toward the door, saw the latch slowly moving up and down, as if somebody were trying it. And how she shook her husband, and tried to waken him, but without effect. And how at last the door yielded slowly at the top (it was bolted below), as if by a gradual pressure without; and how a hand protruded through the opening. And how, as quick as lightning, she nailed that hand to the wall with her scissors (her only weapon), but the point broke, and somebody got away with a fearful oath. How she never told her husband of it, for fear he would kill that somebody;

but how on one day a stranger called here, and as she was handing him his coffee, she saw a queer triangular scar on the back of his hand."

She was still talking, and the wind was still blowing, and Ingomar was still snoring from his couch of skins, when there was a shout high up the straggling street, and a clattering of hoofs, and rattling of wheels. The mail had arrived. Parthenia ran with the faded baby to awaken Ingomar, and almost simultaneously the gallant expressman stood again before me, addressing me by my Christian name, and inviting me to drink out of a mysterious black bottle. The horses were speedily watered, and the business of the gallant expressmen concluded, and bidding Parthenia good-bye, I got on the stage, and immediately fell asleep, and dreamt of calling on Parthenia and Ingomar, and being treated with pie to an unlimited extent, until I woke up the next morning in Sacramento. I have some doubts as to whether all this was not a dyspeptic dream, but I never witness the drama, and hear that noble sentiment concerning "Two souls," etc., without thinking of Wingdam and poor Parthenia.

BROWN OF CALAVERAS

A SUBDUED tone of conversation, and the absence of cigar-smoke, and boot-heels, at the windows of the Wingdam stage-coach, made it evident that one of the inside passengers was a woman. A disposition on the part of loungers, at the stations, to congregate before the window, and some concern in regard to the appearance of coats, hats, and collars, further indicated that she was lovely. All of which Mr. Jack Hamlin, on the box-seat, noted with the smile of cynical philosophy. Not that he depreciated the sex, but that he recognized therein a deceitful element, the pursuit of which sometimes drew mankind away from the equally uncertain blandishments of poker—of which it may be remarked that Mr. Hamlin was a professional exponent.

So that, when he placed his narrow boot on the wheel and leaped down, he did not even glance at the window from which a green veil was fluttering, but lounged up and down with that listless and grave indifference of his class, which was, perhaps, the next thing to good breeding. His closely buttoned figure, and self-contained air, were in marked contrast to the other passengers, and their feverish restlessness, and boisterous emotion; and even Bill Masters, a graduate of Harvard, with his slovenly dress, his overflowing vitality, his intense appreciation of lawlessness and barbarism, and his mouth filled with crackers and cheese, I fear, cut but an unromantic figure beside this lonely calculator of chances, with his pale Greek face, and Homeric gravity.

The driver called "all aboard," and Mr. Hamlin returned to the coach. His foot was upon the wheel, and his face raised to the level of the open window, when, at the same moment, what appeared to him to be the finest eyes in the world, suddenly met his. He quietly dropped down again, addressed a few words to one of the inside passengers, effected an exchange of seats, and as quietly took his place inside. Mr. Hamlin never allowed his philosophy to interfere with decisive and prompt action.

I fear that this irruption of Jack cast some restraint upon the other passengers—particularly those who were making themselves most agreeable to the lady. One of them leaned forward, and apparently conveyed to her information regarding Mr. Hamlin's profession, in a single epithet. Whether Mr. Hamlin heard it, or whether he recognized in the informant a distinguished jurist, from whom, but a few evenings before, he had won several thousand dollars, I cannot say. His colourless face betrayed no sign; his black eyes, quietly observant, glanced indifferently past the legal gentleman, and rested on the much more pleasing features of his neighbour. An Indian stoicism—said to be an inheritance from his maternal ancestor—stood him in good service, until the rolling wheels rattled upon the river-gravel at Scott's Ferry, and the stage drew up at the International Hotel, for dinner. The legal gentleman and a Member of Congress leaped out, and stood ready to assist the descending goddess, while Colonel Starbottle, of Siskiyou, took charge of her parasol and shawl. In this multiplicity of attention, there was a momentary confusion and delay. Jack Hamlin quietly opened the *opposite* door of the coach, took the lady's hand—with that decision and positiveness which a hesitating and undecided sex know how to admire—and in an instant had dexterously and gracefully swung her to the ground, and again lifted her to the platform. An audible chuckle on the box, I fear, came from that other cynic, "Yuba Bill," the driver. "Look keerfully arter that baggage, Kernel," said the expressman, with affected concern, as he looked after Colonel Starbottle, gloomily bringing up the rear of the triumphant procession to the waiting-room.

Mr. Hamlin did not stay for dinner. His horse was already saddled, and awaiting him. He dashed over the ford, up the gravelly hill, and out into the dusty perspective of the Wingdam Road, like one leaving an unpleasant fancy behind him. The inmates of dusty cabins by the road-side shaded their eyes with their hands, and looked after him, recognizing the man by his horse, and speculating what "was up with Comanche Jack." Yet much of this interest centred in the horse, in a community where the time made by "French Pete's" mare, in his run from the Sheriff of Calaveras, eclipsed all concern in the ultimate fate of that worthy.

The sweating flanks of his gray at length recalled him to himself. He checked his speed, and, turning into a by-road —sometimes used as a cut-off—trotted leisurely along, the reins hanging listlessly from his fingers. As he rode on, the character of the landscape changed, and became more pastoral. Openings in groves of pine and sycamore disclosed some rude attempts at cultivation—a flowering vine trailed over the porch of one cabin, and a woman rocked her cradled babe under the roses of another. A little farther on, Mr. Hamlin came upon some bare-legged children wading in the willowy creek, and so wrought upon them with a badinage peculiar to himself that they were emboldened to climb up his horse's legs and over his saddle, until he was fain to develop an exaggerated ferocity of demeanour, and to escape leaving behind some kisses and coin. And then, advancing deeper into the woods, where all signs of habitation failed, he began to sing—uplifting a tenor so singularly sweet, and shaded by a pathos so subduing and tender, that I wot the robins and linnets stopped to listen. Mr. Hamlin's voice was not cultivated; the subject of his song was some sentimental lunacy, borrowed from the negro minstrels, but there was some occult quality of tone and expression that thrilled through all a spirit inexpressibly touching. Indeed, it was a wonderful sight to see this sentimental blackleg, with a pack of cards in his pocket and a revolver at his back, sending his voice before him through the dim woods with a plaint about his "Nelly's Grave," in a way that overflowed the eyes of the listener. A sparrow-hawk, fresh from his sixth victim, possibly recognizing in Mr. Hamlin a kindred spirit, stared at him in surprise, and was fain to confess the superiority of man. With a superior predatory capacity, *he* couldn't sing.

But Mr. Hamlin presently found himself again on the high-road, and at his former pace. Ditches and banks of gravel, denuded hill-sides, stumps, and decayed trunks of trees took the place of woodland and ravine, and indicated his approach to civilization. Then a church-steeple came in sight, and he knew that he had reached home. In a few moments he was clattering down the single narrow street, that lost itself in a chaotic ruin of races, ditches, and tailings at the foot of the hill, and dismounted before the gilded windows of the "Magnolia" saloon. Passing through the long bar-room, he pushed open a green-baize door, entered a dark passage, opened another door with a pass-key, and found himself in a dimly lighted room, whose furniture, though elegant and costly for the locality, showed signs of abuse. The inlaid centre-table was overlaid with stained disks that were not contemplated in the original design.

The embroidered arm-chairs were discoloured, and the green velvet lounge on which Mr. Hamlin threw himself, was soiled at the foot with the red soil of Wingdam.

Mr. Hamlin did not sing in his cage. He lay still, looking at a highly-coloured painting above him, representing a young creature of opulent charms. It occurred to him then, for the first time, that he had never seen exactly that kind of a woman, and that, if he should, he would not, probably, fall in love with her. Perhaps he was thinking of another style of beauty. But just then some one knocked at the door. Without rising, he pulled a cord that apparently shot back a bolt; for the door swung open, and a man entered.

The new-comer was broad-shouldered and robust—a vigour not borne out in the face, which, though handsome, was singularly weak, and disfigured by dissipation. He appeared to be also under the influence of liquor, for he started on seeing Mr. Hamlin, and said, "I thought Kate was here;" stammered, and seemed confused and embarrassed.

Mr. Hamlin smiled the smile which he had before worn on the Wingdam coach, and sat up, quite refreshed, and ready for business.

"You didn't come up on the stage," continued the new-comer, "did you?"

"No," replied Hamlin; "I left it at Scott's Ferry. It isn't due for half an hour yet. But how's luck, Brown?"

"D—— bad," said Brown, his face suddenly assuming an expression of weak despair: "I'm cleaned out again. Jack," he continued, in a whining tone, that formed a pitiable contrast to his bulky figure, "can't you help me with a hundred till to-morrow's clean-up? You see I've got to send money home to the old woman, and—you've won twenty times that amount from me."

The conclusion was, perhaps, not entirely logical, but Jack overlooked it, and handed the sum to his visitor. "The old-woman business is about played out, Brown," he added, by way of commentary; "why don't you say you want to buck agin' faro? You know you ain't married!"

"Fact, sir," said Brown, with a sudden gravity, as if the mere contact of the gold with the palm of his hand had imparted some dignity to his frame. "I've got a wife—a d—— good one, too, if I do say it—in the States. It's three years since I've seen her, and a year since I've writ to her. When things is about straight, and we get down to the lead, I'm going to send for her."

"And Kate?" queried Mr. Hamlin, with his previous smile.

Mr. Brown, of Calaveras, essayed an archness of glance, to cover his confusion, which his weak face and whisky-muddled intellect but poorly carried out, and said:

"D—— it, Jack, a man must have a little liberty, you know. But come, what do you say to a little game? Give us a show to double this hundred."

Jack Hamlin looked curiously at his fatuous friend. Perhaps he knew that the man was predestined to lose the money, and preferred that it should flow back into his own coffers, rather than any other. He nodded his head, and drew his chair towards the table. At the same moment, there came a rap upon the door.

"It's Kate," said Mr. Brown.

Mr. Hamlin shot back the bolt, and the door opened. But for the first time in his life he staggered to his feet, utterly unnerved and abashed, and for the first time in his life, the hot blood crimsoned his colourless cheeks to his forehead. For before him stood the lady he had lifted from the Wingdam coach, whom Brown—dropping his cards with an hysterical laugh—greeted as

"My old woman, by thunder!"

They say that Mrs. Brown burst into tears, and reproaches of her husband. I saw her, in 1857, at Marysville, and disbelieved the story. And the *Wingdam Chronicle*, of the next week, under the head of "Touching Reunion," said:

"One of those beautiful and touching incidents, peculiar to California life, occurred, last week, in our city. The wife of one of Wingdam's eminent pioneers, tired of the effete civilization of the East, and its inhospitable climate, resolved to join her noble husband, upon these golden shores. Without informing him of her intention, she undertook the long journey, and arrived last week. The joy of the husband may be easier imagined than described. The meeting is said to have been indescribably affecting. We trust her example may be followed."

Whether owing to Mrs. Brown's influence, or to some more successful speculations, Mr. Brown's financial fortune, from that day, steadily improved. He bought out his partners in the "Nip and Tuck" lead, with money said to have been won at poker, a week or two after his wife's arrival, but which rumour, adopting Mrs. Brown's theory that Brown had foresworn the gaming-table, alleged to have been furnished by Mr. Jack Hamlin. He built and furnished the "Wingdam House," which pretty Mrs. Brown's great popularity kept overflowing with guests. He was elected to the Assembly, and gave largess to churches. A street in Wingdam was named in his honour.

Yet, it was noted that in proportion as he waxed wealthy and fortunate, he grew pale, thin, and anxious. As his wife's popularity increased, he became fretful and impatient. The most uxorious of husbands—he was absurdly jealous. If he did not interfere with his wife's social liberty, it was because—it was maliciously whispered—that his first and only attempt was met by an outburst from Mrs. Brown that terrified him into silence. Much of this kind of gossip came from those of her own sex whom she had supplanted in the chivalrous attentions of Wingdam: which, like most popular chivalry, was devoted to an admiration of power, whether of masculine force or feminine beauty. It should be remembered, too, in her extenuation, that, since her arrival, she had been the unconscious priestess of a mythological worship, perhaps not more ennobling to her womanhood than that which distinguished an older Greek democracy. I think that Brown was dimly conscious of this. But his only confidant was Jack Hamlin, whose infelix reputation naturally precluded any open intimacy with the family, and whose visits were infrequent.

It was midsummer, and a moonlight night; and Mrs. Brown, very rosy, large-eyed, and pretty, sat upon the piazza, enjoying the fresh incense of the mountain breeze, and it is to be feared, another incense, which was not so fresh, nor quite as innocent. Beside her sat Colonel Starbottle and Judge Boompointer, and a later addition to her court, in the shape of a foreign tourist. She was in good spirits.

"What do you see down the road?" inquired the gallant Colonel, who had been conscious for the last few minutes, that Mrs. Brown's attention was diverted.

"Dust," said Mrs. Brown, with a sigh. "Only Sister Anne's 'flock of sheep.'"

The Colonel, whose literary recollections did not extend farther back than last week's paper, took a more practical view. "It ain't sheep," he continued; "it's a horseman. Judge, ain't that Jack Hamlin's gray?"

But the Judge didn't know; and, as Mrs. Brown suggested, the air was growing too cold for further investigations, they retired to the parlour.

Mr. Brown was in the stable, where he generally retired after dinner. Perhaps it was to show his contempt for his wife's companions; perhaps, like other weak natures, he found pleasure in the exercise of absolute power over inferior animals. He had a certain gratification in the training of a chestnut mare, whom he could beat or caress as pleased him, which he couldn't do with Mrs. Brown. It was here that he recognized a certain gray horse which had just come in, and, looking a little farther on, found his rider. Brown's greeting was cordial and hearty; Mr. Hamlin's somewhat restrained. But at Brown's urgent request, he followed him up the back-stairs, to a narrow corridor, and thence to a small room looking out upon the stable-yard. It was plainly furnished with a bed, a table, a few chairs, and a rack for guns and whips.

"This here's my home, Jack," said Brown with a sigh, as he threw himself upon the bed, and motioned his companion to a chair. "Her room's t'other end of the hall. It's mor'n six months since we've lived together, or met, except at meals. It's mighty rough papers on the head of the house —ain't it?" he said with a forced laugh. "But I'm glad to see ye, Jack, d—— glad," and he reached from the bed, and again shook the unresponsive hand of Jack Hamlin.

"I brought ye up here, for I didn't want to talk in the stable; though, for the matter of that, it's all round town. Don't strike a light. We can talk here in the moonshine. Put up your feet on that winder, and sit here beside me. Thar's whisky in that jug."

Mr. Hamlin did not avail himself of the information. Brown, of Calaveras, turned his face to the wall, and continued:

"If I didn't love the woman, Jack, I wouldn't mind. But it's loving her, and seeing her, day after day, goin' on at this rate, and no one to put down the brake: that's what gets me! But I'm glad to see ye, Jack, d—— glad."

In the darkness, he groped about until he had found and wrung his companion's hand again. He would have detained it, but Jack slipt it into the buttoned breast of his coat, and asked, listlessly, "How long has this been going on?"

"Ever since she came here; ever since the day she walked into the Magnolia. I was a fool then; Jack, I'm a fool now:

but I didn't know how much I loved her till then. And she hasn't been the same woman sence.

"But that ain't all, Jack; and it's what I wanted to see you about, and I'm glad you've come. It ain't that she doesn't love me any more; it ain't that she fools with every chap that comes along, for, perhaps, I staked her love and lost it, as I did everything else at the Magnolia; and, perhaps, foolin' is natural to some women, and there ain't no great harm done, 'cept to the fools. But, Jack, I think—I think she loves somebody else. Don't move, Jack; don't move; if your pistol hurts ye, take it off.

"It's been more'n six months now that she's seemed unhappy and lonesome, and kinder nervous and scared like. And, sometimes, I've ketched her lookin' at me sort of timid and pitying. And she writes to somebody. And, for the last week, she's been gathering her own things—trinkets, and furbelows, and jew'lry—and, Jack, I think, she's goin' off. I could stand all but that. To have her steal away like a thief——" He put his face downwards to the pillow, and, for a few moments, there was no sound but the ticking of a clock on the mantel. Mr. Hamlin lit a cigar, and moved to the open window. The moon no longer shone in the room, and the bed and its occupant were in shadow. "What shall I do, Jack?" said the voice from the darkness.

The answer came promptly and clearly from the window-side: "Spot the man, and kill him on sight."

"But, Jack."

"He's took the risk!"

"But will that bring *her* back?"

Jack did not reply, but moved from the window towards the door.

"Don't go yet, Jack; light the candle, and sit by the table. It's a comfort to see ye, if nothin' else."

Jack hesitated, and then complied. He drew a pack of cards from his pocket and shuffled them, glancing at the bed. But Brown's face was turned to the wall. When **Mr.**

Hamlin had shuffled the cards, he cut them, and dealt one card on the opposite side of the table and towards the bed, and another on his side of the table, for himself. The first was a deuce; his own card, a king. He then shuffled and cut again. This time "dummy" had a queen, and himself a four-spot. Jack brightened up for the third deal. It brought his adversary a deuce, and himself a king again. "Two out of three," said Jack, audibly.

"What's that, Jack?" said Brown.

"Nothing."

Then Jack tried his hand with dice; but he always threw sixes, and his imaginary opponent aces. The force of habit is sometimes confusing.

Meanwhile, some magnetic influence in Mr. Hamlin's presence, or the anodyne of liquor, or both, brought surcease of sorrow, and Brown slept. Mr. Hamlin moved his chair to the window, and looked out on the town of Wingdam, now sleeping peacefully—its harsh outlines softened and subdued, its glaring colours mellowed and sobered in the moonlight that flowed over all. In the hush he could hear the gurgling of water in the ditches, and the sighing of the pines beyond the hill. Then he looked up at the firmament, and, as he did so, a star shot across the twinkling field. Presently another, and then another. The phenomenon suggested to Mr. Hamlin a fresh augury. If, in another fifteen minutes, another star should fall—He sat there, watch in hand, for twice that time, but the phenomenon was not repeated.

The clock struck two, and Brown still slept. Mr. Hamlin approached the table, and took from his pocket a letter, which he read by the flickering candle-light. It contained only a single line, written in pencil, in a woman's hand:

"Be at the corral, with the buggy, at three."

The sleeper moved uneasily, and then awoke. "Are you there, Jack?"

"Yes."

"Don't go yet. I dreamed, just now, Jack—dreamed of old times. I thought that Sue and me was being married agin, and that the parson, Jack, was—who do you think!—you!"

The gambler laughed, and seated himself on the bed—the paper still in his hand.

"It's a good sign, ain't it?" queried Brown.

"I reckon. Say old man hadn't you better get up."

The "old man," thus affectionately appealed to, rose, with the assistance of Hamlin's outstretched hand.

"Smoke?"

Brown mechanically took the proffered cigar.

"Light?"

Jack had twisted the letter into a spiral, lit it, and held it for his companion. He continued to hold it until it was consumed, and dropped the fragment—a fiery star—from the open window. He watched it as it fell, and then returned to his friend.

"Old man," he said, placing his hands upon Brown's shoulders, "in ten minutes I'll be on the road, and gone like that spark. We won't see each other again; but, before I go, take a fool's advice: sell out all you've got, take your wife with you, and quit the country. It ain't no place for you, nor her. Tell her she must go; make her go, if she won't. Don't whine because you can't be a saint, and she ain't an angel. Be a man—and treat her like a woman. Don't be a d—— fool. Good-bye."

He tore himself from Brown's grasp, and leaped down the stairs like a deer. At the stable-door he collared the half-sleeping hostler and backed him against the wall. "Saddle my horse in two minutes or I'll——" The ellipsis was frightfully suggestive.

"The missus said you was to have the buggy," stammered the man.

"D—n the buggy!"

The horse was saddled as fast as the nervous hands of the astounded hostler could manipulate buckle and strap.

"Is any thing up, Mr. Hamlin?" said the man, who, like all his class, admired the *élan* of his fiery patron, and was really concerned in his welfare.

"Stand aside!"

The man fell back. With an oath, a bound, and clatter, Jack was into the road. In another moment, to the man's half-awakened eyes, he was but a moving cloud of dust in the distance, toward which a star just loosed from its brethren was trailing a stream of fire.

But, early that morning, the dwellers by the Wingdam turnpike, miles away, heard a voice, pure as a sky-lark's, singing afield. They who were asleep, turned over on their rude couches to dream of youth, and love, and olden days. Hard-faced men and anxious gold-seekers, already at work, ceased their labours and leaned upon their picks, to listen to a romantic vagabond ambling away against the rosy sunrise.

———

JOHN JENKINS;

OR, THE SMOKER REFORMED

BY T. S. A-TH-R

CHAPTER I

"ONE cigar a day!" said Judge Boompointer. "One cigar a day!" repeated John Jenkins, as with trepidation he dropped his half-consumed cigar under his work-bench.

"One cigar a day is three cents a day," remarked Judge Boompointer, gravely, "and do you know, sir, what one cigar a day, or three cents a day, amounts to in the course of four years?"

John Jenkins, in his boyhood, had attended the village school, and possessed considerable arithmetical ability. Taking up a shingle which lay upon his work-bench, and producing a piece of chalk, with a feeling of conscious pride he made an exhaustive calculation:

"Exactly forty-three dollars and eighty cents," he replied, wiping the perspiration from his heated brow, while his face flushed with honest enthusiasm.

"Well, sir, if you saved three cents a day, instead of wasting it, you would now be the possessor of a new suit of clothes, an illustrated Family Bible, a pew in the church, a complete set of Patent Office Reports, a hymn-book, and a paid subscription to *Arthur's Home Magazine*, which could be purchased for exactly forty-three dollars and eighty cents —and," added the Judge, with increasing sternness, "if you calculate leap-year, which you seem to have strangely omitted—you have three cents more, sir; *three cents more!* What would that buy you, sir?"

"A cigar," suggested John Jenkins; but colouring again deeply he hid his face.

"No, sir," said the Judge, with a sweet smile of benevolence stealing over his stern features; "properly invested, it would buy you that which passeth all price. Dropped into the missionary box, who can tell what heathen, now idly and joyously wantoning in nakedness and sin, might be brought to a sense of his miserable condition, and made, through that three cents, to feel the torments of the wicked?"

With these words the Judge retired, leaving John Jenkins buried in profound thought. "Three cents a day," he muttered. "In forty years I might be worth four hundred and thirty-eight dollars and ten cents—and then I might marry Mary. Ah, Mary?" The young carpenter sighed, and drawing a twenty-five cent daguerreotype from his vest pocket, gazed long and fervidly upon the features of a young girl in book muslin and a coral necklace. Then, with a resolute expression, he carefully locked the door of his workshop and departed.

Alas! his good resolutions were too late. We trifle with the tide of fortune which too often nips us in the bud and casts the dark shadow of misfortune over the bright lexicon of youth. That night the half-consumed fragment of John Jenkin's cigar set fire to his workshop and burned it up, together with all his tools and materials. There was no insurance.

Chapter II

THE DOWNWARD PATH

"Then you still persist in marrying John Jenkins?" queried Judge Boompointer, as he playfully, with paternal familiarity, lifted the golden curls of the village belle, Mary Jones.

"I do," replied the fair young girl, in a low voice, that resembled rock candy in its saccharine firmness; "I do. He has promised to reform. Since he lost all his property by fire——"

"The result of his pernicious habit, though he illogically persists in charging it to me," interrupted the Judge.

"Since then," continued the young girl, "he has endeavoured to break himself of the habit. He tells me that he has substituted the stalks of the Indian ratan, the outer part of a leguminous plant called the smoking-bean, and the fragmentary and unconsumed remainder of cigars which occur at rare and uncertain intervals along the road, which, as he informs me, though deficient in quality and strength, are comparatively inexpensive." And, blushing, at her own eloquence, the young girl hid her curls on the Judge's arm.

"Poor thing," muttered Judge Boompointer. "Dare I tell her all? Yet I must."

"I shall cling to him," continued the young girl, rising with her theme, "as the young vine clings to some hoary ruin. Nay, nay, chide me not, Judge Boompointer. I will marry John Jenkins!"

The Judge was evidently affected. Seating himself at the table, he wrote a few lines hurriedly upon a piece of paper, which he folded and placed in the fingers of the destined bride of John Jenkins.

"Mary Jones," said the Judge, with impressive earnest-ness, "take this trifle as a wedding gift from one who re-spects your fidelity and truthfulness. At the altar let it be a reminder of me." And covering his face hastily with a handkerchief, the stern and iron-willed man left the room. As the door closed, Mary unfolded the paper. It was an order on the corner grocery for three yards of flannel, a paper of needles, four pounds of soap, one pound of starch, and two boxes of matches!

"Noble and thoughtful man!" was all Mary Jones could exclaim, as she hid her face in her hands and burst into a flood of tears.

*   *   *   *   *   *   *

The bells of Cloverdale are ringing merrily. It is a wedding. "How beautiful they look!" is the exclamation that passes from lip to lip, as Mary Jones, leaning timidly on the arm of John Jenkins, enters the church. But the bride is agitated, and the bridegroom betrays a feverish nervousness. As they stand in the vestibule, John Jenkins fumbles earnestly in his vest pocket. Can it be the ring he is anxious about? No. He draws a small brown substance from his pocket, and biting off a piece, hastily replaces the fragment and gazes furtively around. Sure no one saw him? Alas! the eyes of two of that wedding party saw the fatal act. Judge Boompointer shook his head sternly. Mary Jones sighed and breathed a silent prayer. Her husband chewed!

Chapter III and Last

"What! more bread?" said John Jenkins, gruffly. "You're always asking for money for bread. D—nation! Do you want to ruin me by your extravagance?" and as he uttered these words he drew from his pocket a bottle of whisky, a pipe, and a paper of tobacco. Emptying the first at a draught, he threw the empty bottle at the head of his eldest boy, a youth of twelve summers. The missile struck the child full in the temple, and stretched him a lifeless corpse. Mrs. Jenkins, whom the reader will hardly recognise as the once gay and beautiful Mary Jones, raised the dead body of her son in her arms, and, carefully placing the unfortunate youth beside the pump in the back yard, returned with saddened step to the house. At another time, and in brighter days, she might have wept at the occurrence. She was past tears now.

"Father, your conduct is reprehensible!" said little Harrison Jenkins, the youngest boy. "Where do you expect to go when you die?"

"Ah!" said John Jenkins, fiercely; "this comes of giving children a liberal education; this is the result of Sabbath schools. Down, viper!"

A tumbler thrown from the same parental fist laid out the youthful Harrison cold. The four other children had, in the meantime, gathered round the table with anxious expectancy. With a chuckle, the now changed and brutal John Jenkins produced four pipes, and, filling them with tobacco, handed one to each of his offspring and bade them smoke. "It's better than bread!" laughed the wretch hoarsely.

Mary Jenkins, though of a patient nature, felt it her duty now to speak. "I have borne much, John Jenkins," she said. "But I prefer that the children should not smoke. It is an unclean habit, and soils their clothes. I ask this as a special favour!"

John Jenkins hesitated—the pangs of remorse began to seize him.

"Promise me this, John!" urged Mary upon her knees.

"I promise!" reluctantly answered John.

"And you will put the money in a savings bank?"

"I will," repeated her husband; "and *I'll* give up smoking, too."

" 'Tis well, John Jenkins!" said Judge Boompointer, appearing suddenly from behind the door, where he had been concealed during this interview. "Nobly said, my man. Cheer up! I will see that the children are decently buried." The husband and wife fell into each other's arms. And Judge Boompointer, gazing upon the affecting spectacle, burst into tears.

From that day John Jenkins was an altered man.

THE POET OF SIERRA FLAT

As the enterprising editor of the "Sierra Flat Record" stood at his case setting type for his next week's paper, he could not help hearing the woodpeckers who were busy on the roof above his head. It occurred to him that possibly the birds had not yet learned to recognize in the rude structure any improvement on nature, and this idea pleased him so much that he incorporated it in the editorial article which he was then doubly composing. For the editor was also printer of the "Record;" and although that remarkable journal was reputed to exert a power felt through all Calaveras and a greater part of Tuolumne County, strict economy was one of the conditions of its beneficent existence.

Thus pre-occupied, he was startled by the sudden irruption of a small roll of manuscript, which was thrown through the open door and fell at his feet. He walked quickly to the threshold and looked down the tangled trail which led to the high road. But there was nothing to suggest the presence of his mysterious contributor. A hare limped slowly away, a green-and-gold lizard paused upon a pine stump, the woodpeckers ceased their work. So complete had been his sylvan seclusion, that he found it difficult to connect any human agency with the act; rather the hare seemed to have an inexpressibly guilty look, the woodpeckers to maintain a significant silence, and the lizard to be conscience-stricken into stone.

An examination of the manuscript, however, corrected this injustice to defenceless nature. It was evidently of human origin,—being verse, and of exceeding bad quality. The editor laid it aside. As he did so he thought he saw a face at the window. Sallying out in some indignation, he penetrated the surrounding thicket in every direction, but his search was as fruitless as before. The poet, if it were he, was gone.

A few days after this the editorial seclusion was invaded by voices of alternate expostulation and entreaty. Stepping to the door, the editor was amazed at beholding Mr. Morgan McCorkle, a well-known citizen of Angelo, and a subscriber to the "Record," in the act of urging, partly by force and partly by argument, an awkward young man toward the building. When he had finally effected his object, and, as it were, safely landed his prize in a chair, Mr. McCorkle took off his hat, carefully wiped the narrow isthmus of forehead which divided his black brows from his stubby hair, and, with an explanatory wave of his hand toward his reluctant companion, said, "A borned poet, and the cussedest fool you ever seed!"

Accepting the editor's smile as a recognition of the introduction, Mr. McCorkle panted and went on: "Didn't want to come! 'Mister Editor don't want to see me, Morg,' sez he. 'Milt,' sez I, 'he do; a borned poet like you and a

gifted genius like he oughter come together sociable!' And
I fetched him. Ah, will yer?" The born poet had, after
exhibiting signs of great distress, started to run. But Mr.
McCorkle was down upon him instantly, seizing him by his
long linen coat and settled him back in his chair. " 'Tain't
no use stampeding. Yer ye are and yer ye stays. For yer
a borned poet,—ef ye are as shy as a jackass rabbit. Look
at 'im now!"

He certainly was not an attractive picture. There was
hardly a notable feature in his weak face, except his eyes,
which were moist and shy, and not unlike the animal to
which Mr. McCorkle had compared him. It was the face
that the editor had seen at the window.

"Knowed him for fower year, since he war a boy," continued Mr. McCorkle in a loud whisper. "Allers the same,
bless you! Can jerk a rhyme as easy as turnin' jack. Never
had any eddication; lived out in Missooray all his life. But
he's chock full o' poetry. On'y this mornin' sez I to him,
—he camps along o' me,—'Milt!' sez I, 'are breakfast
ready?' and he up and answers back quite peart and
chipper, 'The breakfast it is ready, and the birds is singing
free, and it's risin' in the dawnin' light is happiness to me!'
When a man," said Mr. McCorkle, dropping his voice with
deep solemnity, "gets off things like them, without any call
to do it, and handlin' flapjacks over a cook-stove at the
same time,—that man's a borned poet."

There was an awkward pause. Mr. McCorkle beamed
patronizingly on his *protégé*. The born poet looked as if he
were meditating another flight,—not a metaphorical one.
The editor asked if he could do any thing for them.

"In course you can," responded Mr. McCorkle, "that's
jest it. Milt, where's that poetry?"

The editor's countenance fell as the poet produced from
his pocket a roll of manuscript. He, however, took it mechanically and glanced over it. It was evidently a duplicate
of the former mysterious contribution.

The editor then spoke briefly but earnestly. I regret that I cannot recall his exact words, but it appeared that never before, in the history of the "Record," had the pressure been so great upon its columns. Matters of paramount importance, deeply affecting the material progress of Sierra, questions touching the absolute integrity of Calaveras and Tuolumne as social communities, were even now waiting expression. Weeks, nay, months, must elapse before that pressure would be removed, and the "Record" could grapple with any but the sternest of topics. Again the editor had noticed with pain the absolute decline of poetry in the foothills of the Sierras. Even the works of Byron and Moore attracted no attention in Dutch Flat, and a prejudice seemed to exist against Tennyson in Grass Valley. But the editor was not without hope for the future. In the course of four or five years, when the country was settled—

"What would be the cost to print this yer?" interrupted Mr. McCorkle quietly.

"About fifty dollars as an advertisement," responded the editor with cheerful alacrity.

Mr. McCorkle placed the sum in the editor's hand. "Yer see thet's what I sez to Milt, 'Milt,' sez I, 'pay as you go, for you are a borned poet. Hevin' no call to write, but doin' it free and spontaneous like, in course you pays. Thet's why Mister Editor never printed your poetry.'"

"What name shall I put to it?" asked the editor.

"Milton."

It was the first word that the born poet had spoken during the interview, and his voice was so very sweet and musical that the editor looked at him curiously, and wondered if he had a sister.

"Milton; is that all?"

"Thet's his furst name," explained Mr. McCorkle.

The editor here suggested that as there had been another poet of that name—

"Milt might be took for him! Thet's bed," reflected Mr.

McCorkle with simple gravity. "Well, put down his hull name,—Milton Chubbuck."

The editor made a note of the fact. "I'll set it up now," he said. This was also a hint that the interview was ended. The poet and the patron, arm in arm, drew towards the door. "In next week's paper," said the editor smilingly, in answer to the child-like look of inquiry in the eyes of the poet, and in another moment they were gone.

The editor was as good as his word. He straightway betook himself to his case, and, unrolling the manuscript, began his task. The woodpeckers on the roof recommenced theirs, and in a few moments the former sylvan seclusion was restored. There was no sound in the barren, barn-like room but the birds above, and below the click of the composing-rule as the editor marshalled the types into lines in his stick, and arrayed them in solid column on the galley. Whatever might have been his opinion of the copy before him, there was no indication of it in his face, which wore the stolid indifference of his craft. Perhaps this was unfortunate, for as the day wore on and the level rays of the sun began to pierce the adjacent thicket, they sought out and discovered an anxious ambushed figure drawn up beside the editor's window,—a figure that had sat there motionless for hours. Within, the editor worked on as steadily and impassively as Fate. And without, the born poet of Sierra Flat sat and watched him, as waiting its decree.

The effect of the poem on Sierra Flat was remarkable and unprecedented. The absolute vileness of its doggerel, the gratuitous imbecility of its thought, and above all the crowning audacity of the fact that it was the work of a citizen and published in the county paper, brought it instantly into popularity. For many months Calaveras had languished for a sensation; since the last vigilance committee nothing had transpired to dispel the listless *ennui* begotten of stagnant business and growing civilization. In more prosperous moments the office of the "Record" would have been simply glutted and the editor deported; at present the paper was in such demand that the edition was speedily exhausted. In brief, the poem of Mr. Milton Chubbuck came like a special providence to Sierra Flat. It was read by camp fires, in lonely cabins, in flaring bar-rooms, and noisy saloons, and declaimed from the boxes of stage-coaches. It was sung in Poker Flat, with the addition of a local chorus, and danced as an unhallowed rhythmic dance by the Pyrrhic phalanx of One Horse Gulch, known as "The Festive Stags of Calaveras." Some unhappy ambiguities of expression gave rise to many new readings, notes, and commentaries, which, I regret to state, were more often marked by ingenuity than delicacy of thought or expression.

Never before did poet acquire such sudden local reputation. From the seclusion of McCorkle's cabin and the obscurity of culinary labours, he was hailed forth into the glowing sunshine of Fame. The name of Chubbuck was written in letters of chalk on unpainted walls, and carved with a pick on the sides of tunnels. A drink known variously as "The Chubbuck Tranquillizer," or "The Chubbuck Exalter," was dispensed at the bars. For some weeks, a rude design for a Chubbuck statue, made up of illustrations from circus and melodeon posters, representing the genius of Calaveras in brief skirts on a flying steed in the act of crowning the poet Chubbuck, was visible at Keeler's Ferry. The poet himself was overborne with invitations to drink, and extravagant congratulations. The meeting between Colonel Starbottle of Siskyion and Chubbuck, as previously arranged by our "Boston," late of Roaring Camp, is said to have been indescribably affecting. The Colonel embraced him unsteadily. "I could not return to my constituents at Siskyion, sir, if this hand which has grasped that of the gifted Prentice and the lamented Poe, should not have been honoured by the touch of the god-like Chubbuck. Gentlemen, American literature is looking up. Thank you, I will take sugar in mine." It was "Boston" who indited letters of congratulations from H. W. Longfellow, Tennyson, and Browning to Mr. Chubbuck, deposited them in the Sierra Flat post-office, and obligingly consented to dictate the replies.

The simple faith and unaffected delight with which these manifestations were received by the poet and his patron might have touched the hearts of these grim masters of irony, but for the sudden and equal development in both of the variety of weak natures. Mr. McCorkle basked in the popularity of his *protégé*, and became alternately supercilious or patronizing toward the dwellers of Sierra Flat; while the poet, with hair carefully oiled and curled, and bedecked with cheap jewellery and flaunting neck-handkerchief, paraded himself before the single hotel. As may be imagined, this new disclosure of weakness afforded intense satisfaction to Sierra Flat, gave another lease of popularity to the poet, and suggested another idea to the facetious "Boston."

At that time a young lady, popularly and professionally known as the "California Pet," was performing to enthusiastic audiences in the interior. Her specialty lay in the personation of youthful masculine character; as a *gamin* of the street she was irresistible, as a negro-dancer she carried the honest miner's heart by storm. A saucy, pretty brunette, she had preserved a wonderful moral reputation even under the Jove-like advances of showers of gold that greeted her appearance on the stage at Sierra Flat. A prominent and delighted member of that audience was Milton Chubbuck. He attended every night. Every day he lingered at the door of the Union Hotel for a glimpse of the "California Pet." It was not long before he received a note from her, —in "Boston's" most popular and approved female hand,— acknowledging his admiration. It was not long before "Boston" was called upon to indite a suitable reply. At last, in furtherance of his facetious design, it became necessary for "Boston" to call upon the young actress herself and secure her personal participation. To her he unfolded a plan, the successful carrying out of which he felt would secure his fame to posterity as a practical humourist. The "California Pet's" black eyes sparkled approvingly and mischievously. She only stipulated that she should see the man first,—a concession to her feminine weakness which years of dancing Juba and wearing trousers and boots had not wholly eradicated from her wilful breast. By all means, it should be done. And the interview was arranged for the next week.

It must not be supposed that during this interval of popularity Mr. Chubbuck had been unmindful of his poetic qualities. A certain portion of each day he was absent from town,—"a communin' with natur'," as Mr. McCorkle expressed it, and actually wandering in the mountain trails, or lying on his back under the trees, or gathering fragrant herbs and the bright-coloured berries of the Marzanita. These and his company he generally brought to the editor's office, late in the afternoon, often to that enterprising journalist's infinite weariness. Quiet and uncommunicative, he would sit there patiently watching him at his work until the hour for closing the office arrived, when he would as quietly depart. There was something so humble and unobtrusive in these visits, that the editor could not find it in his heart to deny them, and accepting them, like the woodpeckers, as a part of his sylvan surroundings, often forgot even his presence. Once or twice moved by some beauty of expression in the moist, shy eyes, he felt like seriously admonishing his visitor of his idle folly; but his glance falling upon the oiled hair and the gorgeous necktie, he invariably thought better of it. The case was evidently hopeless.

The interview between Mr. Chubbuck and the "California Pet" took place in a private room of the Union Hotel; propriety being respected by the presence of that archhumourist "Boston." To this gentleman we are indebted for the only true account of the meeting. However reticent Mr. Chubbuck might have been in the presence of his own sex, towards the fairer portion of humanity he was, like most poets, exceedingly voluble. Accustomed as the "California Pet" had been to excessive compliment, she was fairly embarrassed by the extravagant praises of her visitor. Her personation of boy characters, her dancing of the "Champion Jig," were particularly dwelt upon with fervid but unmistakable admiration. At last, recovering her audacity and emboldened by the presence of "Boston," the "California Pet" electrified her hearers by demanding, half-jestingly, half-viciously, if it were as a boy or a girl that she was the subject of his flattering admiration.

"That knocked him out o' time," said the delighted "Boston," in his subsequent account of the interview. "But do you believe the d—d fool actually asked her to take him with her?—wanted to engage in the company."

The plan, as briefly unfolded by "Boston," was to prevail upon Mr. Chubbuck to make his appearance in costume (already designed and prepared by the inventor) before a Sierra Flat audience, and recite an original poem at the Hall immediately on the conclusion of the "California Pet's" performance. At a given signal the audience were to rise and deliver a volley of unsavory articles (previously provided by the originator of the scheme); then a select few were to rush on the stage, seize the poet, and, after marching him in triumphal procession through town, were to deposit him beyond its uttermost limits, with strict injunctions never to enter it again. To the first part of the plan the poet was committed, for the latter portion it was easy enough to find participants.

The eventful night came, and with it an audience that packed the long narrow room with one dense mass of human beings. The "California Pet" never had been so joyous, so reckless, so fascinating and audacious before. But the applause was tame and weak compared to the ironical out⸴

burst that greeted the second rising of the curtain and the entrance of the born poet of Sierra Flat. Then, there was a hush of expectancy, and the poet stepped to the foot-lights and stood with his manuscript in his hand.

His face was deadly pale. Either there was some suggestion of his fate in the faces of his audience, or some mysterious instinct told him of his danger. He attempted to speak, but faltered, tottered, and staggered to the wings.

Fearful of losing his prey, "Boston" gave the signal and leaped upon the stage. But at the same moment a light figure darted from behind the scenes, and delivering a kick that sent the discomfited humourist back among the musicians, cut a pigeon-wing, executed a double-shuffle, and then advancing to the foot-lights with that inimitable look, that audacious swagger and utter *abandon* which had so thrilled and fascinated them a moment before, uttered the characteristic speech: "Wot are you goin' to hit a man fur, when he's down, s-a-a-y?"

The look, the drawl, the action, the readiness, and above all the downright courage of the little woman, had its effect. A roar of sympathetic applause followed the act. "Cut and run while you can," she whispered hurriedly over her one shoulder, without altering the other's attitude of pert and saucy defiance toward the audience. But even as she spoke the poet tottered and sank fainting upon the stage. Then she threw a despairing whisper behind the scenes, "Ring down the curtain."

There was a slight movement of opposition in the audience, but among them rose the burly shoulders of Yuba Bill, the tall, erect figure of Henry York, of Sandy Bar, and the colourless, determined face of John Oakhurst. The curtain came down.

Behind it knelt the "California Pet" beside the prostrate poet. "Bring me some water. Run for a doctor. Stop! CLEAR OUT, ALL OF YOU!"

She had unloosed the gaudy cravat and opened the shirt-collar of the insensible figure before her. Then she burst into an hysterical laugh.

"Manuela!"

Her tiring woman, a Mexican half-breed, came toward her.

"Help me with him to my dressing-room, quick; then stand outside and wait. If any one questions you, tell them he's gone. Do you hear? HE'S gone."

The old woman did as she was bade. In a few moments the audience had departed. Before morning so also had the "California Pet," Manuela; and—the poet of Sierra Flat.

But, alas! with them also had departed the fair fame of the "California Pet." Only a few, and these it is to be feared of not the best moral character themselves, still had faith in the stainless honour of their favourite actress. "It was a mighty foolish thing to do, but it'll all come out right yet." On the other hand, a majority gave her full credit and approbation for her undoubted pluck and gallantry, but deplored that she should have thrown it away upon a worthless object. To elect for a lover the despised and ridiculed vagrant of Sierra Flat, who had not even the manliness to stand up in his own defence, was not only evidence of inherent moral depravity, but was an insult to community. Colonel Starbottle saw in it only another instance of the extreme frailty of the sex; he had known similar cases; and remembered distinctly, sir, how a well-known Philadelphia heiress, one of the finest women that ever rode in her kerridge, that, gad, sir! had thrown over a Southern member of Congress to consort with a d—d nigger. The Colonel had also noticed a singular look in the dog's eye which he did not entirely fancy. He would not say anything against the lady, sir, but he had noticed— And here haply the Colonel became so mysterious and darkly confidential as to be unintelligible and inaudible to the bystanders.

A few days after the disappearance of Mr. Chubbuck, a

singular report reached Sierra Flat, and it was noticed that "Boston," who since the failure of his elaborate joke had been even more depressed in spirits than is habitual with great humourists, suddenly found that his presence was required in San Francisco. But as yet nothing but the vaguest surmises were afloat, and nothing definite was known.

It was a pleasant afternoon when the editor of the "Sierra Flat Record" looked up from his case and beheld the figure of Mr. Morgan McCorkle standing in the doorway. There was a distressed look on the face of that worthy gentleman that at once enlisted the editor's sympathizing attention. He held an open letter in his hand, as he advanced toward the middle of the room.

"As a man as has allers borne a fair reputation," began Mr. McCorkle slowly, "I should like, if so be as I could, Mister Editor, to make a correction in the columns of your valooable paper."

Mr. Editor begged him to proceed.

"Ye may not disremember that about a month ago I fetched here what so be as we'll call a young man whose name might be as it were Milton—Milton Chubbuck."

Mr. Editor remembered perfectly.

"Thet same party I'd knowed better nor fower year, two on 'em campin' out together. Not that I'd known him all the time, fur he whar shy and strange at spells, and had odd ways that I took war nat'ral to a borned poet. Ye may remember that I said he was a borned poet?"

The editor distinctly did.

"I picked this same party up in St. Jo., takin' a fancy to his face, and kinder calklating he'd runn'd away from home, —for I'm a married man, Mr. Editor, and hev children of my own,—and thinkin' belike he was a borned poet."

"Well," said the editor.

"And as I said before, I should like now to make a correction in the columns of your valooable paper."

"What correction?" asked the editor.

"I said, ef you remember my words, as how he was a borned poet."

"Yes."

"From statements in this yer letter it seems as how I war wrong."

"Well?"

"He war a woman."

THE PRINCESS BOB AND HER FRIENDS

SHE was a Klamath Indian. Her title was, I think, a compromise between her claim as daughter of a chief, and gratitude to her earliest white protector, whose name, after the Indian fashion, she had adopted.

"Bob" Walker had taken her from the breast of her dead mother at a time when the sincere volunteer soldiery of the California frontier were impressed with the belief that extermination was the manifest destiny of the Indian race.

He had with difficulty restrained the noble zeal of his compatriots long enough to convince them that the exemption of one Indian baby would not invalidate this theory.

And he took her to his home—a pastoral clearing on the banks of the Salmon River—where she was cared for after a frontier fashion.

Before she was nine years old, she had exhausted the scant kindliness of the thin, overworked Mrs. Walker.

As a play-fellow of the young Walkers she was unreliable; as a nurse for the baby she was inefficient.

She lost the former in the trackless depths of a redwood forest; she basely abandoned the latter in an extemporized cradle, hanging like a chrysalis to a convenient bough.

She lied and she stole,—two unpardonable sins in a frontier community, where truth was a necessity and provisions were the only property.

Worse than this, the outskirts of the clearing were some-times haunted by blanketed tatterdemalions with whom she had mysterious confidences.

Mr. Walker more than once regretted his indiscreet humanity, but she presently relieved him of responsibility, and possibly of blood-guiltiness, by disappearing entirely.

When she re-appeared, it was at the adjacent village of Logport, in the capacity of housemaid to a trader's wife, who, joining some little culture to considerable conscientiousness, attempted to instruct her charge.

But the Princess proved an unsatisfactory pupil to even so liberal a teacher.

She accepted the alphabet with great good-humour, but always as a pleasing and recurring novelty, in which all interest expired at the completion of each lesson.

She found a thousand uses for her books and writing materials other than those known to civilized children.

She made a curious necklace of bits of slate-pencil, she constructed a miniature canoe from the pasteboard covers of her primer, she bent her pens into fish-hooks, and tattooed the faces of her younger companions with blue ink.

Religious instruction she received as good-humouredly, and learned to pronounce the name of the Deity with a cheerful familiarity that shocked her preceptress.

Nor could her reverence be reached through analogy; she knew nothing of the Great Spirit, and professed entire ignorance of the Happy Hunting-Grounds.

Yet she attended divine service regularly, and as regularly asked for a hymn-book; and it was only through the discovery that she had collected twenty-five of these volumes, and had hidden them behind the woodpile, that her connection with the First Baptist Church of Logport ceased.

She would occasionally abandon these civilized and Christian privileges, and disappear from her home, returning after several days of absence with an odour of bark and fish, and a peace-offering to her mistress, in the shape of venison or game.

To add to her troubles, she was now fourteen, and, according to the laws of her race, a woman.

I do not think the most romantic fancy would have called her pretty.

Her complexion defied most of those ambiguous similes through which poets unconsciously apologize for any deviation from the Caucasian standard.

It was not wine nor amber-coloured; if anything it was smoky.

Her face was tattooed with red and white lines on one cheek, as if a fine-toothed comb had been drawn from cheek bone to jaw, and, but for the good-humour that beamed from her small berry-like eyes and shone in her white teeth, would have been repulsive.

She was short and stout.

In her scant drapery and unrestrained freedom she was hardly statuesque, and her more unstudied attitudes were marred by a simian habit of softly scratching her left ankle with the toes of her right foot, in moments of contemplation.

I think I have already shown enough to indicate the incongruity of her existence with even the low standard of civilization that obtained at Logport in the year 1860.

It needed but one more fact to prove the far-sighted political sagacity and prophetic ethics of those sincere advocates of extermination, to whose virtues I have done but scant justice in the beginning of this article.

This fact was presently furnished by the Princess.

After one of her periodical disappearances,—this time unusually prolonged,—she astonished Logport by returning with a half-breed baby of a week old in her arms.

That night a meeting of the hard-featured serious matrons of Logport was held at Mrs. Brown's.

The immediate banishment of the Princess was demanded.

Soft-hearted Mrs. Brown endeavoured vainly to get a mitigation or suspension of the sentence.

But, as on a former occasion, the Princess took matters into her own hands.

A few mornings afterwards, a wicker cradle containing an Indian baby was found hanging on the handle of the door of the First Baptist Church.

It was the Parthian arrow of the flying Princess.

From that day Logport knew her no more.

It had been a bright clear day on the upland, so clear that the ramparts of Fort Jackson and the flagstaff were plainly visible twelve miles away from the long curving peninsula that stretched a bared white arm around the peaceful waters of Logport Bay.

It had been a clear day upon the sea-shore, albeit the air was filled with the flying spume and shifting sand of a straggling beach, whose low dunes were dragged down by the long surges of the Pacific, and thrown up again by the tumultuous trade winds.

But the sun had gone down in a bank of fleecy fog that was beginning to roll in upon the beach.

Gradually the headland at the entrance of the harbour and the light-house disappeared, then the willow fringe that marked the line of Salmon River vanished, and the ocean was gone.

A few sails still gleamed on the waters of the bay, but the advancing fog wiped them out one by one, crept across the steel-blue expanse, swallowed up the white mills and single spire of Logport, and joining with reinforcements from the marshes, moved solemnly upon the hills.

Ten minutes more and the landscape was utterly blotted out; simultaneously the wind died away, and a death-like silence stole over sea and shore.

The faint clang, high over-head, of unseen brent, the nearer call of invisible plover, the lap and wash of undistinguishable waters, and the monotonous roll of the vanished ocean, were the only sounds.

As night deepened, the far-off booming of the fog-bell on the headland at intervals stirred the thick air.

Hard by the shore of the bay, and half hidden by a drifting sand-hill, stood a low nondescript structure, to whose composition sea and shore had equally contributed.

It was built partly of logs and partly of drift-wood and tarred canvas.

Joined to one end of the main building—the ordinary log-cabin of the settler—was the half-round pilot-house of some wrecked steamer, while the other gable terminated in half of a broken whale-boat.

Nailed against the boat were the dried skins of wild animals, and scattered about lay the flotsam and jetsam of many years' gathering, bamboo crates, casks, hatches, blocks, oars, boxes, part of a whale's vertebræ, and the blades of sword-fish.

Drawn up on the beach of a little cove before the house lay a canoe.

As the night thickened and the fog grew more dense, these details grew imperceptible, and only the windows of the pilot-house, lit up by a roaring fire within the hut, gleamed redly through the mist.

By this fire, beneath a ship's lamp that swung from the roof, two figures were seated, a man and a woman.

The man, broad-shouldered and heavily bearded, stretched his listless powerful length beyond a broken bamboo chair, with his eyes fixed on the fire.

The woman crouched cross-legged upon the broad earthen hearth, with her eyes blinkingly fixed on her companion.

They were small, black, round, berry-like eyes, and as the firelight shone upon her smoky face, with its one striped cheek of gorgeous brilliancy, it was plainly the Princess Bob and no other.

Not a word was spoken.

They had been sitting thus for more than an hour, and there was about their attitude a suggestion that silence was habitual.

Once or twice the man rose and walked up and down the narrow room, or gazed absently from the windows of the pilot-house, but never by look or sign betrayed the slightest consciousness of his companion.

At such times the Princess from her nest by the fire followed him with eyes of canine expectancy and wistfulness.

But he would as inevitably return to his contemplation of the fire, and the Princess to her blinking watchfulness of his face.

They had sat there silent and undisturbed for many an evening in fair weather and foul.

They had spent many a day in sunshine and storm, gathering the unclaimed spoil of sea and shore.

They had kept these mute relations, varied only by the incidents of the hunt or meagre household duties, for three years, ever since the man, wandering moodily over the lonely sands, had fallen upon the half-starved woman lying in the little hollow where she had crawled to die.

It had seemed as if they would never be disturbed, until now, when the Princess started, and, with the instinct of her race, bent her ear to the ground.

The wind had risen and was rattling the tarred canvas. But in another moment there plainly came from without the hut the sound of voices.

Then followed a rap at the door; then another rap; and then, before they could rise to their feet, the door was flung briskly open.

"I beg your pardon," said a pleasant but somewhat decided contralto voice, "but I don't think you heard me knock. Ah, I see you did not. May I come in?"

There was no reply.

Had the battered figure-head of the Goddess of Liberty, which lay deeply embedded in the sand on the beach, sud-

denly appeared at the door demanding admittance, the occupants of the cabin could not have been more speechlessly
and hopelessly astonished than at the form which stood in
the open doorway.

It was that of a slim, shapely, elegantly dressed young
woman.

A scarlet-lined silken hood was half-thrown back from
the shining mass of the black hair that covered her small
head; from her pretty shoulders dropped a fur cloak, only
restrained by a cord and tassel in her small gloved hand.
Around her full throat was a double necklace of large white
beads, that by some cunning feminine trick relieved with its
infantile suggestion the strong decision of her lower face.

"Did you say yes? Ah, thank you. We may come in,
Barker."

Here a shadow in a blue army overcoat followed her into
the cabin, touched its cap respectfully, and then stood silent
and erect against the wall.

"Don't disturb yourself in the least, I beg. What a dis-
tressingly unpleasant night! Is this your usual climate?"

Half graciously, half absently over-looking the still embarrassed silence of the group, she went on,—

"We started from the fort over three hours ago,—three
hours ago, wasn't it, Barker?" (the erect Barker touched
his cap,)—"to go to Captain Emmon's quarters on Indian
Island,—I think you call it Indian Island, don't you?" (she
was appealing to the awe-stricken Princess)—"and we got
into the fog and lost our way; that is, Barker lost his way,"
(Barker touched his cap deprecatingly,) "and goodness
knows where we didn't wander to until we mistook your
light for the lighthouse and pulled up here. No, no, pray
keep your seat, do! Really I must insist."

Nothing could exceed the languid grace of the latter part
of this speech,—nothing except the easy unconsciousness
with which she glided by the offered chair of her stammering, embarrassed host, and stood beside the open hearth.

"Barker will tell you," she continued, warming her feet by the fire, "that I am Miss Portfire, daughter of Major Portfire, commanding the post. Ah, excuse me, child!" (she had accidentally trodden upon the bare yellow toes of the Princess.) "Really, I did not know you were there. I am very near-sighted."

In confirmation of her statement, she put to her eyes a dainty double eye-glass that dangled from her neck.

"It's a shocking thing to be near-sighted, isn't it?"

If the shamefaced uneasy man to whom this remark was addressed could have found words to utter the thoughts that even in his confusion struggled uppermost in his mind, he would, looking at the bold, dark eyes that questioned him, have denied the fact. But he only stammered, "Yes."

The next moment, however, Miss Portfire had apparently forgotten him, and was examining the Princess through her glass.

"And what is your name, child?"

The Princess, beautified by the eyes and eye-glass, showed all her white teeth at once, and softly scratched her leg.

"Bob."

"Bob? What a singular name!"

Miss Portfire's host hastened to explain the origin of the Princess's title.

"Then *you* are Bob." (Eye-glass.)

"No, my name is Grey,—John Grey." And he actually achieved a bow where awkwardness was rather the air of imperfectly recalling a forgotten habit.

"Grey?—ah, let me see. Yes, certainly. You are Mr. Grey the recluse, the hermit, the philosopher, and all that sort of thing. Why, certainly; Dr. Jones, our surgeon, has told me all about you. Dear me, how interesting a rencontre! Lived all alone here for seven—was it seven years?—yes, I remember now. Existed quite *au natural*, one might say. How odd! Not that I know anything about that sort of thing, you know. I've lived always among people, and am really quite a stranger, I assure you. But honestly, Mr.—I beg your pardon—Mr. Grey, how do you like it?"

She had quietly taken his chair and thrown her cloak and hood over its back, and was now thoughtfully removing her gloves.

Whatever were the arguments—and they were doubtless many and profound,—whatever the experience,—and it was doubtless hard and satisfying enough,—by which this unfortunate man had justified his life for the last seven years, somehow they suddenly became trivial and terribly ridiculous before this simple but practical question.

"Well, you shall tell me all about it after you have given me something to eat. We will have time enough; Barker cannot find his way back in this fog to-night. Now don't put yourselves to any trouble on my account. Barker will assist."

Barker came forward.

Glad to escape the scrutiny of his guest, the hermit gave a few rapid directions to the Princess in her native tongue, and disappeared in the shed.

Left a moment alone, Miss Portfire took a quick, half-audible, feminine inventory of the cabin.

"Books, guns, skins, *one* chair, *one* bed, no pictures, and no looking-glass!"

She took a book from the swinging shelf and resumed her seat by the fire as the Princess re-entered with fresh fuel.

But while kneeling on the hearth the Princess chanced to look up and met Miss Portfire's dark eyes over the edge of her book.

"Bob!"

The Princess showed her teeth.

"Listen. Would you like to have fine clothes, rings, and beads like these, to have your hair nicely combed and put up so? Would you?"

The Princess nodded violently.

"Would you like to live with me and have them? An-swer quickly. Don't look round for *him*. Speak for your-self. Would you? Hush; never mind now."

The hermit re-entered, and the Princess, blinking, re-treated into the shadow of the whale-boat shed, from which she did not emerge even when the homely repast of cold venison, ship-biscuit, and tea was served.

Miss Portfire noticed her absence.

"You really must not let me interfere with your usual simple ways. Do you know this is exceedingly interesting to me, so pastoral and patriarchal, and all that sort of thing. I must insist upon the Princess coming back; really, I must."

But the Princess was not to be found in the shed, and Miss Portfire, who the next minute seemed to have forgotten all about her, took her place in the single chair before an extemporized table.

Barker stood behind her, and the hermit leaned against the fireplace.

Miss Portfire's appetite did not come up to her protesta-tions.

For the first time in seven years it occurred to the hermit that his ordinary victual might be improved. He stam-mered out something to that effect.

"I have eaten better, and worse," said Miss Portfire, quietly.

"But I thought you—that is, you said—"

"I spent a year in the hospitals, when father was on the Potomac," returned Miss Portfire composedly. After a pause she continued: "You remember after the second Bull Run— But, dear me! I beg your pardon; of course, you know nothing about the war and all that sort of thing, and don't care."

She put up her eyeglass and quietly surveyed his broad muscular figure against the chimney.

"Or, perhaps, your prejudices— But then, as a hermit

you know you have no politics, of course. Please don't let me bore you."

To have been strictly consistent, the hermit should have exhibited no interest in this topic.

Perhaps it was owing to some quality in the narrator, but he was constrained to beg her to continue in such phrases as his unfamiliar lips could command.

So that little by little Miss Portfire yielded up incident and personal observation of the contest then raging; with the same half-abstracted, half-unconcerned air that seemed habitual to her, she told the stories of privation, of suffering, of endurance, and of sacrifice. With the same assumption of timid deference that concealed her great self-control, she talked of principles and rights.

Apparently without enthusiasm and without effort, of which his morbid nature would have been suspicious, she sang the great American Iliad in a way that stirred the depths of her solitary auditor to its massive foundations.

Then she stopped and asked quietly,—

"Where is Bob?"

The hermit started. He would look for her. But Bob, for some reason, was not forthcoming. Search was made within and without the hut, but in vain.

For the first time that evening, Miss Portfire showed some anxiety.

"Go," she said to Barker, "and find her. She *must* be found; stay, give me your overcoat, I'll go myself."

She threw the overcoat over her shoulders and stepped out into the night.

In the thick veil of fog that seemed suddenly to inwrap her, she stood for a moment irresolute, and then walked toward the beach, guided by the low wash of waters on the sand.

She had not taken many steps before she stumbled over some dark crouching object.

Reaching down her hand she felt the coarse wiry mane of the Princess.

"Bob!"

There was no reply.

"Bob. I've been looking for you, come."

"Go 'way."

"Nonsense, Bob. I want you to stay with me to-night, come."

"Injin squaw no good for waugee woman. Go 'way."

"Listen, Bob. You are daughter of a chief: so am I. Your father had many warriors: so has mine. It is good that you stay with me. Come."

The Princess chuckled, and suffered herself to be lifted up.

A few moments later and they re-entered the hut, hand in hand.

With the first red streaks of dawn the next day the erect Barker touched his cap at the door of the hut.

Beside him stood the hermit, also just risen from his blanketed nest in the sand.

Forth from the hut, fresh as the morning air, stepped Miss Portfire, leading the Princess by the hand.

Hand in hand also they walked to the shore, and when the Princess had been safely bestowed in the stern sheets, Miss Portfire turned and held out her own to her late host.

"I shall take the best of care of her of course. You will come and see her often. I should ask you to come and see me, but you are a hermit, you know, and all that sort of thing. But if it's the correct anchorite thing, and can be done, my father will be glad to requite you for this night's hospitality. But don't do anything on my account that interferes with your simple habits. Good-bye."

She handed him a card, which he took mechanically.

"Good-bye."

The sail was hoisted, and the boat shoved off. As the

fresh morning breeze caught the white canvas it seemed to bow a parting salutation.

There was a rosy flush of promise on the water, and as the light craft darted forward toward the ascending sun, it seemed for a moment uplifted in its glory.

Miss Portfire kept her word.

If thoughtful care and intelligent kindness could regenerate the Princess, her future was secure.

And it really seemed as if she were for the first time inclined to heed the lessons of civilization and profit by her new condition.

An agreeable change was first noticed in her appearance.

Her lawless hair was caught in a net, and no longer strayed over her low forehead. Her unstable bust was stayed and upheld by French corsets; her plantigrade shuffle was limited by heeled boots. Her dresses were neat and clean, and she wore a double necklace of glass beads.

With this physical improvement there also seemed some moral awakening.

She no longer stole nor lied.

With the possession of personal property came a respect for that of others.

With increased dependence on the word of those about her came a thoughtful consideration of her own.

Intellectually she was still feeble, although she grappled sturdily with the simple lessons which Miss Portfire set before her.

But her zeal and simple vanity outran her discretion, and she would often sit for hours with an open book before her, which she could not read.

She was a favourite with the officers at the fort, from the Major, who shared his daughter's prejudices and often yielded to her powerful self-will, to the subalterns, who liked her none the less that their natural enemies, the frontier volunteers, had declared war against her helpless sisterhood.

The only restraint put upon her was the limitation of her liberty to the enclosure of the fort and parade; and only once did she break this parole, and was stopped by the sentry as she stepped into a boat at the landing.

The recluse did not avail himself of Miss Portfire's invitation.

But after the departure of the Princess he spent less of his time in the hut, and was more frequently seen in the distant marshes of Eel River and on the upland hills.

A feverish restlessness, quite opposed to his usual phlegm, led him into singular freaks strangely inconsistent with his usual habits and reputation.

The purser of the occasional steamer which stopped at Logport with the mails reported to have been boarded, just inside the bar, by a strange-bearded man, who asked for a newspaper containing the last war telegrams.

He tore his red shirt into narrow strips, and spent two days with his needle over the pieces and the tattered remnant of his only white garment; and a few days afterward the fishermen on the bay were surprised to see what, on nearer approach, proved to be a rude imitation of the national flag floating from a spar above the hut.

One evening, as the fog began to drift over the sand-hills, the recluse sat alone in his hut.

The fire was dying unheeded on the hearth, for he had been sitting there for a long time completely absorbed in the blurred pages of an old newspaper.

Presently he arose, and, refolding it—an operation of great care and delicacy in its tattered condition—placed it under the blankets of his bed.

He resumed his seat by the fire, but soon began drumming with his fingers on the arm of his chair.

Eventually this assumed the time and accent of some air.

Then he began to whistle softly and hesitatingly as if trying to recall a forgotten tune.

Finally this took shape in a rude resemblance, not unlike that which his flag bore to the national standard, to Yankee Doodle.

Suddenly he stopped.

There was an unmistakable rapping at the door.

The blood which had at first rushed to his face now forsook it and settled slowly around his heart.

He tried to rise, but could not.

Then the door was flung open, and a figure with a scarlet-lined hood and fur mantle stood on the threshold.

With a mighty effort he took one stride to the door.

The next moment he saw the wide mouth and white teeth of the Princess, and was greeted by a kiss that felt like a baptism.

To tear the hood and mantle from her figure in the sudden fury that seized him, and to fiercely demand the reason of this masquerade, was his only return to her greeting.

"Why are you here? Did you steal these garments?" he again demanded in her guttural language, as he shook her roughly by the arm.

The Princess hung her head.

"Did you?" he screamed, as he reached wildly for his rifle.

"I did."

His hold relaxed, and he staggered back against the wall.

The Princess began to whimper.

Between her sobs, she was trying to explain that the Major and his daughter were going away, and that they wanted to send her to the Reservation; but he cut her short.

"Take off those things!"

The Princess tremblingly obeyed.

He rolled them up, placed them in the canoe she had just left, and then leaped into the frail craft.

She would have followed, but with a great oath he threw her from him, and with one stroke of his paddle swept out into the fog, and was gone.

"Jessamy," said the Major, a few days after, as he sat at

dinner with his daughter, "I think I can tell you something to match the mysterious disappearance and return of your wardrobe. Your crazy friend, the recluse, has enlisted this morning in the Fourth Artillery. He's a splendid-looking animal, and there's the right stuff for a soldier in him, if I'm not mistaken. He's in earnest, too, for he enlists in the regiment ordered back to Washington. Bless me, child, another goblet broken; you'll ruin the mess in glass-ware, at this rate!"

"Have you heard anything more of the Princess, papa?"

"Nothing, but perhaps it's as well that she has gone. These cursed settlers are at their old complaints again about what they call 'Indian depredations,' and I have just received orders from head-quarters to keep the settlement clear of all vagabond aborigines. I am afraid, my dear, that a strict construction of the term would include your *protégée*."

The time for the departure of the Fourth Artillery had come.

The night before was thick and foggy.

At one o'clock, a shot on the ramparts called out the guard, and roused the sleeping garrison.

The new sentry, Private Grey, had challenged a dusky figure creeping on the glacis, and, receiving no answer had fired.

The guard sent out presently returned, bearing a lifeless figure in their arms.

The new sentry's zeal, joined with an ex-frontiersman's aim, was fatal.

They laid the helpless, ragged form before the guard-house door, and then saw for the first time that it was the Princess.

Presently she opened her eyes.

They fell upon the agonized face of her innocent slayer, but haply without intelligence or reproach.

"Georgy!" she whispered.

"Bob!"

"All's same now. Me get plenty well soon. Me make no more fuss. Me go to Reservation."

Then she stopped, a tremor ran through her limbs, and she lay still. She had gone to the Reservation.

Not that devised by the wisdom of man, but that one set apart from the foundations of the world for the wisest as well as the meanest of His creatures.

HOW SANTA CLAUS CAME TO SIMPSON'S BAR

It had been raining in the valley of the Sacramento. The North Fork had overflowed its banks and Rattlesnake Creek was impassable.

The few boulders that had marked the Summer ford at Simpson's Crossing were obliterated by a vast sheet of water stretching to the foothills. The up stage was stopped at Granger's; the last mail had been abandoned in the *tules*, the rider swimming for his life.

"An area," remarked the *Sierra Avalanche* with pensive local pride, "as large as the State of Massachusetts is now under water."

Nor was the weather any better in the foothills.

The mud lay deep on the mountain road; waggons that neither physical force nor moral objurgation could move from the evil ways into which they had fallen, incumbered the track, and the way to Simpson's Bar was indicated by broken-down teams and hard-swearing.

And farther on, cut-off and inaccessible, rained upon and bedraggled, smitten by high winds and threatened by high water, Simpson's Bar, on the eve of Christmas-day, 1862, clung like a swallow's nest to the rocky entablature and splintered capitals of Table Mountain, and shook in the blast.

As night shut down on the settlement, a few lights gleamed through the mist from the windows of cabins on either side of the highway now crossed and gullied by lawless streams and swept by marauding winds.

Happily most of the population were gathered at Thompson's store, clustered around a red-hot stove, at which they silently spat in some accepted sense of social communion that perhaps rendered conversation unnecessary.

Indeed, most methods of diversion had long since been exhausted on Simpson's Bar; high water had suspended the regular occupations on gulch and on river, and a consequent lack of money and whisky had taken the zest from most illegitimate recreation.

Even Mr. Hamlin was fain to leave the Bar with fifty dollars in his pocket—the only amount actually realized of the large sums won by him in the successful exercise of his arduous profession.

"Ef I was asked," he remarked somewhat later—"ef I was asked to pint out a purty little village where a retired sport as didn't care for money could exercise hisself frequent and lively, I'd say Simpson's Bar; but for a young man with a large family depending on his exertions, it don't pay."

As Mr. Hamlin's family consisted mainly of female adults, this remark is quoted rather to show the breadth of his humour than the exact extent of his responsibilities.

Howbeit, the unconscious objects of this satire sat that evening in the listless apathy begotten of idleness and lack of excitement.

Even the sudden splashing of hoofs before the door did not arouse them.

Dick Bullen alone paused in the act of scraping out his pipe, and lifted his head, but no other one of the group indicated any interest in, or recognition of, the man who entered.

It was a figure familiar enough to the company, and known in Simpson's Bar as "The Old Man."

A man of perhaps fifty years; grizzled and scant of hair, but still fresh and youthful of complexion. A face full of ready, but not very powerful sympathy, with a chameleon-like aptitude for taking on the shade and colour of contiguous moods and feelings.

He had evidently just left some hilarious companions, and did not at first notice the gravity of the group, but clapped the shoulder of the nearest man jocularly, and threw himself into a vacant chair.

"Jest heard the best thing out, boys! Ye know Smiley, over yar—Jim Smiley—funniest man in the Bar? Well, Jim was jest telling the richest yarn about——"

"Smiley's a —— fool," interrupted a gloomy voice.

"A particular —— skunk," added another, in sepulchral accents.

A silence followed these positive statements.

The Old Man glanced quickly around the group. Then his face slowly changed.

"That's so," he said, reflectively after a pause, "certainly a sort of a skunk and suthin of a fool. In course."

He was silent for a moment, as in painful contemplation of the unsavoriness and folly of the unpopular Smiley.

"Dismal weather, ain't it?" he added, now fully embarked on the current of prevailing sentiment. "Mighty rough papers on the boys, and no show for money this season. And to-morrow's Christmas."

There was a movement among the men at this announcement, but whether of satisfaction or disgust was not plain.

"Yes," continued the Old Man in the lugubrious tone he had within the last few moments unconsciously adopted— "yes, Christmas, and to-night's Christmas-eve. Ye see, boys, I kinder thought—that is, I sorter had an idee, jest passm like you know—that may be ye'd all like to come over to my house to-night and have a sort of tear round.

But I suppose, now, you wouldn't? Don't feel like it, may be?" he added, with anxious sympathy, peering into the faces of his companions.

"Well, I don't know," responded Tom Flynn, with some cheerfulness. "P'r'aps we may. But how about your wife, Old Man? What does she say to it?"

The Old Man hesitated.

His conjugal experience had not been a happy one, and the fact was known to Simpson's Bar.

His first wife, a delicate, pretty little woman, had suffered keenly and secretly from the jealous suspicions of her husband, until one day he invited the whole Bar to his house to expose her infidelity.

On arriving, the party found the shy, *petite* creature quietly engaged in her household duties, and retired abashed and discomfited.

But the sensitive woman did not easily recover from the shock of this extraordinary outrage.

It was with difficulty she regained her equanimity sufficiently to release her lover from the closet in which he was concealed, and escape with him.

She left a boy of three years to comfort her bereaved husband.

The Old Man's present wife had been his cook. She was large, loyal, and aggressive.

Before he could reply, Joe Dimmick suggested with great directness that it was the "Old Man's house," and that, invoking the Divine Power, if the case were his own, he would invite who he pleased, even if in so doing he imperilled his salvation. The Powers of Evil, he further remarked, should contend against him vainly.

All this delivered with a terseness and vigour lost in this necessary translation.

"In course. Certainly. Thet's it," said the Old Man with a sympathetic frown. "Thar's no trouble about thet. It's my own house, built every stick on it myself. Don't you be afeared o' her, boys. She may cut up a trifle rough —ez wimmin do—but she'll come round."

Secretly the Old Man trusted to the exaltation of liquo and the power of a courageous example to sustain him in such an emergency.

As yet, Dick Bullen, the oracle and leader of Simpson's Bar, had not spoken. He now took his pipe from between his lips.

"Old Man, how's that yer Johnny gettin' on? Seems to me he didn't look so peart the last time I seed him on the bluff heavin' rocks at Chinamen. Didn't seem to take much interest in it. Thar was a gang of 'em by yar yesterday— drownded out up the river—and I kinder thought o' Johnny, and how he'd miss 'em! May be now, we'd be in the way ef he was sick?"

The father, evidently touched not only by this pathetic picture of Johnny's deprivation, but by the considerate delicacy of the speaker, hastened to assure him that Johnny was better, and that a "little fun might 'liven him up."

Whereupon Dick arose, shook himself, and saying, "I'm ready. Lead the way, Old Man: here goes," himself led the way with a leap, a characteristic howl, and darted out into the night.

As he passed through the outer room he caught up a blazing brand from the hearth.

The action was repeated by the rest of the party, closely following and elbowing each other, and before the astonished proprietor of Thompson's grocery was aware of the intention of his guests, the room was deserted.

The night was pitchy dark. In the first gust of wind their temporary torches were extinguished, and only the red brands dancing and flitting in the gloom like drunken will-o'-the-wisps indicated their whereabouts.

Their way led up Pine Tree Cañon, at the head of which a broad, low bark-thatched cabin burrowed in the mountain side.

It was the home of the Old Man, and the entrance to the tunnel in which he worked, when he worked at all.

Here the crowd paused for a moment, out of delicate deference to their host, who came up panting in the rear.

"P'r'aps ye'd better hold on a second out yer, whilst I go in and see thet things is all right," said the Old Man, with an indifference he was far from feeling.

The suggestion was graciously accepted, the door opened and closed on the host, and the crowd, leaning their backs against the wall, and cowering under the eaves, waited and listened.

For a few moments there was no sound but the dripping of water from the eaves, and the stir and rustle of wrestling boughs above them.

Then the men became uneasy, and whispered suggestion and suspicion passed from the one to the other.

"Reckon she's caved in his head the first lick!"

"Decoyed him inter the tunnel, and barred him up, likely."

"Got him down, and sittin' on him."

"Prob'ly biling suthing to heave on us; stand clear the door, boys!"

For just then the latch clicked, the door slowly opened, and a voice said—

"Come in out o' the wet."

The voice was neither that of the Old Man nor of his wife. It was the voice of a small boy, its weak treble broken by that preternatural hoarseness which only vagabondage and the habit of premature self-assertion can give.

It was the face of a small boy that looked up at theirs— a face that might have been pretty and even refined, but that it was darkened by evil knowledge from within, and dirt and hard experience from without.

He had a blanket around his shoulders, and had evidently just risen from his bed.

"Come in," he repeated, "and don't make no noise. The Old Man's in there talking to mar," he continued, pointing to an adjacent room which seemed to be a kitchen, from which the Old Man's voice came in deprecating accents.

"Let me be," he added, querulously to Dick Bullen, who had caught him up, blanket and all, and was affecting to toss him into the fire; "let go o' me, you d—d fool, d'ye hear?"

Thus adjured, Dick Bullen lowered Johnny to the ground with a smothered laugh, while the men, entering quietly, ranged themselves around a long table of rough boards which occupied the centre of the room.

Johnny then gravely proceeded to a cupboard, and brought out several articles which he deposited on the table.

"Thar's whisky and crackers, and red herons and cheese." He took a bite of the latter on his way to the table. "And sugar." He scooped up a mouthful *en route* with a small and very dirty hand. "And terbacker. Thar's dried appils too on the shelf, but I don't admire 'em. Appils is swellin'. Thar," he concluded; "now wade in, and don't be afeared. I don't mind the old woman. She don't b'long to me. S'long."

He had stepped to the threshold of a small room, scarcely larger than a closet, partitioned off from the main apartment, and holding in its dim recess a small bed.

He stood there a moment looking at the company, his bare feet peeping from the blanket, and nodded.

"Hello, Johnny! You ain't goin' to turn in agin, are ye?" said Dick.

"Yes, I are," responded Johnny, decidedly.

"Why, wot's up, old fellow?"

"I'm sick."

"How sick?"

"I've got a fevier. And childblains. And roomatiz," returned Johnny, and vanished within. After a moment's pause, he added in the dark, apparently from under the bedclothes—"and biles!"

There was an embarrassing silence. The men looked at each other and at the fire.

Even with the appetizing banquet before them, it seemed as if they might again fall into the despondency of Thompson's grocery, when the voice of the Old Man, incautiously lifted, came deprecatingly from the kitchen.

"Certainly! Thet's so. In course they is. A gang o' lazy drunken loafers, and that ar Dick Bullen's the ornariest of all. Didn't hev no more sabe than to come round yar with sickness in the house and no provision. Thet's what I said: 'Bullen,' sez I, 'it's crazy drunk you are, or a fool,' sez I, 'to think o' such a thing.' 'Staples,' I sez, 'be you a man, Staples, and 'spect to raise h—ll under my roof and invalids lyin' round?' But they would come— they would. Thet's wot you must 'spect o' such trash as lays round the Bar."

A burst of laughter from the men followed this unfortunate exposure.

Whether it was overheard in the kitchen, or whether the Old Man's irate companion had just then exhausted all other modes of expressing her contemptuous indignation, I cannot say, but a back door was suddenly slammed with great violence.

A moment later and the Old Man reappeared, haply unconscious of the cause of the late hilarious outburst, and smiled blandly.

"The old woman thought she'd jest run over to Mrs. McFadden's for a sociable call," he explained, with jaunty indifference, as he took a seat at the board.

Oddly enough, it needed this untoward incident to relieve the embarrassment that was beginning to be felt by the party, and their natural audacity returned with their host. I do not propose to record the convivialities of that evening. The inquisitive reader will accept the statement that the conversation was characterized by the same intellectual exaltation, the same cautious reverence, the same fastidious delicacy, the same rhetorical precision, and the same logical and coherent discourse somewhat later in the evening, which distinguish similar gatherings of the masculine sex in more civilized localities, and under more favorable auspices.

No glasses were broken in the absence of any; no liquor was uselessly spilt on floor or table in the scarcity of that article.

It was nearly midnight when the festivities were interrupted.

"Hush," said Dick Bullen, holding up his hand.

It was the querulous voice of Johnny from his adjacent closet.

"O dad."

The Old Man arose hurriedly and disappeared in the closet. Presently he reappeared.

"His rheumatiz is coming on agin bad," he explained, "and he wants rubbin'."

He lifted the demijohn of whisky from the table and shook it. It was empty.

Dick Bullen put down his tin cup with an embarrassed laugh. So did the others.

The Old Man examined their contents, and said, hopefully,—

"I reckon that's enough; he don't need much. You hold on all o' you for a spell, and I'll be back;" and vanished in the closet with an old flannel shirt and the whisky.

The door closed but imperfectly, and the following dialogue was distinctly audible.

"Now, sonny, whar does she ache worst?"

"Sometimes over yar and sometimes under yer; but it's most powerful from yer to yer. Rub yer, dad."

A silence seemed to indicate a brisk rubbing. Then Johnny:

"Hevin' a good time out yer, dad?"

"Yes, sonny."

"To-morrer's Chrismiss, ain't it?"

"Yes, sonny. How does she feel now?"

"Better. Rub a little furder down. Wot's Chrismiss, anyway? Wot's it all about?"

"O, it's a day."

This exhaustive definition was apparently satisfactory, for there was a silent interval of rubbing. Presently Johnny again:

"Mar sez that everywhere else but yer everybody gives things to everybody Chrismiss, and then she just waded inter you. She sez thar's a man they call Sandy Claws, not a white man, you know, but a kind o' Chinemin, comes down the chimbley night afore Chrismiss and gives things to chillern—boys like me. Put's 'em in their butes! Thet's what she tried to play upon me. Easy now, pop, whar are you rubbin' to—thet's a mile from the place. She jest made that up, didn't she, jest to aggrewate me and you? Don't rub thar— Why, dad?"

In the great quiet that seemed to have fallen upon the house the sigh of the near pines and the drip of leaves without was very distinct.

Johnny's voice, too, was lowered as he went on,—

"Don't you take on now, fur I'm gettin' all right fast. Wot's the boys doin' out thar?"

The Old Man partly opened the door and peered through.

His guests were sitting there sociably enough, and there were a few silver coins in a lean buckskin purse on the table.

"Bettin' on suthin,—some little game or 'nother. They're all right," he replied to Johnny, and recommenced his rubbing.

"I'd like to take a hand and win some money," said Johnny, reflectively, after a pause.

The Old Man glibly repeated what was evidently a familiar formula, that if Johnny would wait until he struck it 'ich in the tunnel he'd have lots of money, &c., &c.

"Yes," said Johnny, "but you don't. And whether you

strike it or I win it, it's about the same. It's all luck. But it's mighty cur'o's about Chrismiss—ain't it? Why do they call it Chrismiss?"

Perhaps from some instinctive deference to the overhearing of his guests, or from some vague sense of incongruity, the Old Man's reply was so low as to be inaudible beyond the room.

"Yes," said Johnny, with some slight abatement of interest, "I've heard o' him before. Thar, that'll do, dad. I don't ache near so bad as I did. Now wrap me tight is this yer blanket. So. Now," he added in a muffled whisper, "sit down yer by me till I go asleep."

To assure himself of obedience, he disengaged one hand from the blanket, and grasping his father's sleeve, again composed himself to rest.

For some moments the Old Man waited patiently.

Then the unwonted stillness of the house excited his curiosity, and without moving from the bed, he cautiously opened the door with his disengaged hand, and looked into the main room.

To his infinite surprise it was dark and deserted.

But even then a smouldering log on the hearth broke, and by the upspringing blaze he saw the figure of Dick Bullen sitting by the dying embers.

"Hello!"

Dick started, rose, and came somewhat unsteadily towards him.

"Whar's the boys?" said the Old Man.

"Gone up the cañon on a little *pasear*. They're coming back for me in a minit. I'm waitin' round for 'em. What are you starin' at, Old Man," he added with a forced laugh; "do you think I'm drunk?"

The Old Man might have been pardoned the supposition, for Dick's eyes were humid and his face flushed.

He loitered and lounged back to the chimney, yawned, shook himself, buttoned up his coat and laughed.

"Liquor ain't so plenty as that, Old Man. Now don't you git up," he continued as the Old Man made a movement to release his sleeve from Johnny's hand. "Don't you mind manners. Sit jist whar you be; I'm goin' in a jiffy. Thar, that's them now."

There was a low tap at the door.

Dick Bullen opened it quickly, nodded "good night" to his host, and disappeared.

The Old Man would have followed him but for the hand that still unconsciously grasped his sleeve. He could have easily disengaged it; it was small, weak, and emaciated. But perhaps because it was small, weak, and emaciated, he changed his mind, and drawing his chair closer to the bed, rested his head upon it. In this defenceless attitude the potency of his earlier potations surprised him. The room flickered and faded before his eyes, reappeared, faded again, went out, and left him—asleep.

Meantime, Dick Bullen, closing the door, confronted his companions.

"Are you ready?" said Staples.

"Ready!" said Dick; "what's the time?"

"Past twelve," was the reply; "can you make it?—it's nigh on fifty miles, the round trip hither and yon."

"I reckon," returned Dick shortly. "Whar's the mare?"

"Bill and Jack's holdin' her at the crossin'."

"Let 'em hold on a minit longer," said Dick.

He turned and re-entered the house softly.

By the light of the guttering candle and dying fire he saw that the door of the little room was open.

He stepped toward it on tiptoe and looked in.

The Old Man had fallen back in his chair, snoring, his helpless feet thrust out in a line with his collapsed shoulders, and his hat pulled over his eyes.

Beside him, on a narrow wooden bedstead, lay Johnny, muffled tightly in a blanket that hid all save a strip of forehead and a few curls damp with perspiration.

Dick Bullen made a step forward, hesitated, and glanced over his shoulder into the deserted room.

Everything was quiet.

With a sudden resolution he parted his huge mustaches with both hands, and stooped over the sleeping boy.

But even as he did so a mischievous blast, lying in wait, swooped down the chimney, rekindling the hearth, and lit up the room with a shameless glow, from which Dick fled in bashful terror.

His companions were already waiting for him at the crossing.

Two of them were struggling in the darkness with some strange misshapen bulk, which, as Dick came nearer, took the semblance of a great yellow horse.

It was the mare.

She was not a pretty picture.

From her Roman nose to her rising haunches, from her arched spine, hidden by the stiff *machillas* of a Mexican saddle, to her thick, straight, bony legs, there was not a line of equine grace.

In her half-blind but wholly vicious white eyes, in her protruding under lip, in her monstrous colour, there was nothing but ugliness and vice.

"Now, then," said Staples, "stand cl'ar of her heels, boys, and up with you. Don't miss your first holt of her mane, and mind ye get your off stirrup quick. Ready!"

There was a leap, a scrambling struggle, a bound, a wild retreat of the crowd, a circle of flying hoofs, two springless leaps that jarred the earth, a rapid play and jingle of spurs, a plunge, and then the voice of Dick somewhere in the darkness.

"All right!"

"Don't take the lower road back onless you're hard pushed for time! Don't hold her in down hill! We'll be at the ford at five. G'lang! Hoopa! Mula! Go!"

A splash, a spark struck from the ledge in the road, a clatter in the rocky cut beyond, and Dick was gone.

    *   *   *   *   *   *

Sing, O Muse, the ride of Richard Bullen! Sing, O Muse, of chivalrous men! the sacred quest, the doughty deeds, the battery of low churls, the fearsome ride and grewsome perils of the flower of Simpson's Bar! Alack! she is dainty, this Muse! She will have none of this bucking brute and swaggering, ragged rider, and I must fain follow him, in prose, afoot!

It was one o'clock; and yet he had only gained Rattlesnake Hill. For in that time Jovita had rehearsed to him all her imperfections and practiced all her vices.

Thrice had she stumbled.

Twice had she thrown up her Roman nose in a straight line with the reins, and resisting bit and spur, struck out madly across country.

Twice had she reared, and rearing, fallen backward; and twice had the agile Dick, unharmed, regained his seat before she found her vicious legs again.

And a mile beyond them, at the foot of a long hill, was Rattlesnake Creek.

Dick knew that here was the crucial test of his ability to perform his enterprise, set his teeth grimly, put his knees well into her flanks, and changed his defensive tactics to brisk aggression.

Bullied and maddened, Jovita began the descent of the hill.

Here the artful Richard pretended to hold her in with ostentatious objurgation and well-feigned cries of alarm.

It is unnecessary to add that Jovita instantly ran away.

Nor need I state the time made in the descent; it is written in the chronicles of Simpson's Bar.

Enough that in another moment, as it seemed to Dick, she was splashing on the overflowed banks of Rattlesnake Creek.

As Dick expected, the momentum she had acquired carried her beyond the point of balking, and holding her well together for a mighty leap, they dashed into the middle of the swiftly-flowing current.

A few moments of kicking, wading, and swimming, and Dick drew a long breath on the opposite bank.

The road from Rattlesnake Creek to Red Mountain was tolerably level.

Either the plunge in Rattlesnake Creek had dampened her baleful fire, or the art which led to it had shown her the superior wickedness of her rider, for Jovita no longer wasted her surplus energy in wanton conceits.

Once she bucked, but it was from force of habit; once she shied, but it was from a new freshly-painted meeting-house at the crossing of the county-road.

Hollows, ditches, gravelly deposits, patches of freshly-springing grasses flew from beneath her rattling hoofs.

She began to smell unpleasantly, once or twice she coughed slightly, but there was no abatement of her strength or speed.

By two o'clock he had passed Red Mountain and begun the descent to the plain.

Ten minutes later the driver of the fast Pioneer coach was overtaken and passed by a "man on a Pinto hoss"— an event sufficiently notable for remark.

At half-past two Dick rose in his stirrups with a great shout.

Stars were glittering through the rifted clouds, and beyond him, out of the plain, rose two spires, a flag-staff, and a straggling line of black objects.

Dick jingled his spurs and swung his *riata*, Jovita bounded forward, and in another moment they swept into Tuttleville, and drew up before the wooden piazza of "The Hotel of All Nations."

What transpired that night at Tuttleville is not strictly a part of this record.

Briefly I may state, however, that after Jovita had been handed over to a sleepy hostler, whom she at once kicked into unpleasant consciousness, Dick sallied out with the barkeeper for a tour of the sleeping town.

Lights still gleamed from a few saloons and gambling-houses; but, avoiding these, they stopped before several closed shops, and by persistent tapping and judicious outcry roused the proprietors from their beds, and made them unbar the doors of their magazines and expose their wares.

Sometimes they were met by curses, but oftener by interest and some concern in their needs, and the interview was invariably concluded by a drink.

It was three o'clock before this pleasantry was given over, and with a small water-proof bag of india-rubber strapped on his shoulders, Dick returned to the hotel.

But here he was waylaid by Beauty—Beauty opulent in charms, affluent in dress, persuasive in speech, and Spanish in accent!

In vain she repeated the invitation in "Excelsior," happily scorned by all Alpine-climbing youth, and rejected by this child of the Sierras—a rejection softened in this instance by a laugh and his last gold coin.

And then he sprang to the saddle and dashed down the lonely street and out into the lonelier plain, where presently the lights, the black line of houses, the spires and the flag-staff sank into the earth behind him again and were lost in the distance.

The storm had cleared away, the air was brisk and cold, the outlines of adjacent landmarks were distinct, but it was half-past four before Dick reached the meeting-house and the crossing of the county road.

To avoid the rising grade he had taken a longer and more circuitous road, in whose viscid mud Jovita sank fetlock deep at every bound.

It was a poor preparation for a steady ascent of five miles more; but Jovita, gathering her legs under her, took it with her usual blind, unreasoning fury, and a half-hour later reached the long level that led to Rattlesnake Creek.

Another half-hour would bring him to the creek.

He threw the reins lightly upon the neck of the mare, chirruped to her and began to sing.

Suddenly Jovita shied with a bound that would have unseated a less practised rider.

Hanging to her rein was a figure that had leaped from the bank, and at the same time from the road before her arose a shadowy horse and rider.

"Throw up your hands," commanded this second apparition with an oath.

Dick felt the mare tremble, quiver, and apparently sink under him.

He knew what it meant, and was prepared.

"Stand aside, Jack Simpson, I know you, you d—d thief. Let me pass, or——"

He did not finish the sentence.

Jovita rose straight in the air with a terrific bound, throwing the figure from her bit with a single shake of her vicious head, and charged her deadly malevolence down on the impediment before her.

An oath, a pistol-shot, horse and highwayman rolled over in the road, and the next moment Jovita was a hundred yards away.

But the good right arm of her rider, shattered by a bullet, dropped helplessly at his side.

Without slackening his speed he shifted the reins to his left hand.

But a few moments later he was obliged to halt and tighten the saddle-girths that had slipped in the onset.

This in his crippled condition took some time.

He had no fear of pursuit, but looking up he saw that the eastern stars were already paling, and that the distant peaks had lost their ghostly whiteness, and now stood out blackly against a lighter sky.

Day was upon him.

Then completely absorbed in a single idea, he forgot the pain of his wound, and mounting again dashed on towards Rattlesnake Creek.

But now Jovita's breath came broken by gasps, Dick reeled in his saddle, and brighter and brighter grew the sky.

Ride, Richard; run, Jovita; linger, O day!

For the last few rods there was a roaring in his ears.

Was it exhaustion from loss of blood, or what?

He was dazed and giddy as he swept down the hill, and did not recognize his surroundings.

Had he taken the wrong road, or was this Rattlesnake Creek?

It was.

But the brawling creek he had swum a few hours before hid risen, more than doubled its volume, and now rolled a swift and resistless river between him and Rattlesnake Hill.

For the first time that night Richard's heart sank within him.

The river, the mountain, the quickening east swam before his eyes.

He shut them to recover his self-control.

In that brief interval, by some fantastic mental process, the little room at Simpson's Bar, and the figures of the sleeping father and son, rose upon him.

He opened his eyes widely, cast off his coat, pistol, boots, and saddle, bound his precious pack tightly to his shoulders, grasped the bare flanks of Jovita with his bared knees, and, with a shout, dashed into the yellow water.

A cry rose from the opposite bank as the head of a man and horse struggled for a few moments against the battling current, and then were swept away, amid uprooted trees and whirling driftwood.

*　　*　　*　　*　　*　　*

The Old Man started and awoke.

The fire on the hearth was dead, the candle in the outer

room flickering in its socket, and somebody was rapping at the door.

He opened it, but fell back with a cry before the dripping half-naked figure that reeled against the door-post

"Dick?"

"Hush! Is he awake yet?"

"No—but Dick?—"

"Dry up, you old fool! Get me some whisky *quick!*

The Old Man flew and returned with—an empty bottle!

Dick would have sworn, but his strength was not equal to the occasion.

He staggered, caught at the handle of the door, and motioned to the Old Man.

"Thar's suthin' in my pack yer for Johnny. Take it off. I can't."

The Old Man unstrapped the pack and laid it before the exhausted man.

"Open it, quick!"

He did so with trembling fingers.

It contained only a few poor toys—cheap and barbaric enough, goodness knows, but bright with paint and much tinsel.

One of them was broken; another, I fear, was irretrievably ruined by water; and on the other, ah me! there was a cruel spot.

"It don't look like much, that's a fact," said Dick ruefully . . . "But it's the best we could do . . . Take 'em, Old Man, and put 'em in his stocking, and tell him—tell him, you know—hold me, Old Man."

The Old Man caught at his sinking figure.

"Tell him," said Dick, with a weak little laugh—"tell him Sandy Claus has come."

And even so, bedraggled, ragged, unshaven and unshorn, with one arm hanging helplessly at his side, Santa Claus came to Simpson's Bar and fell fainting on the first threshold.

The Christmas dawn came slowly after, touching the remoter peaks with the rosy warmth of ineffable love.

And it looked so tenderly on Simpson's Bar that the whole mountain, as if caught in a generous action, blushed to the skies.

SURPRISING ADVENTURES OF MASTER CHARLES SUMMERTON

AT exactly half-past nine o'clock on the morning of Saturday, August 26th, 1865, Master Charles Summerton, aged five years, disappeared mysteriously from his paternal residence on Folsom Street, San Francisco.

At twenty-five minutes past nine he had been observed, by the butcher, amusing himself by going through that popular youthful exercise known as "turning the crab," a feat in which he was singularly proficient.

At a court of inquiry summarily held in the back parlour at 10.15, Bridget, cook, deposed to have detected him at twenty minutes past nine, in the felonious abstraction of sugar from the pantry, which, by the same token, had she known what was a-comin', she'd have never previnted.

Patsey, a shrill-voiced youth from a neighbouring alley, testified to having seen "Chowley" at half-past nine in front of the butcher's shop round the corner, but as this young gentleman chose to throw out the gratuitous belief that the missing child had been converted into sausages by the butcher, his testimony was received with some caution by the female portion of the court, and with downright scorn and contumely by its masculine members.

But whatever might have been the hour of his departure, it was certain that from half-past ten, A.M., until nine, P.M., when he was brought home by a policeman, Charles Summerton was missing.

Being naturally of a reticent disposition, he has since

resisted, with but one exception, any attempt to wrest from him a statement of his whereabouts during that period.

That exception has been myself.

He has related to me the following in the strictest confidence:

His intention on leaving the door steps of his dwelling, was to proceed without delay to Van Dieman's Land, by way of Second and Market Streets.

This project was subsequently modified so far as to permit a visit to Otaheite, where Captain Cook was killed.

The outfit for his voyage consisted of two car tickets, five cents in silver, a fishing line, the brass capping of a spool of cotton, which, in his eyes, bore some resemblance to metallic currency, and a Sunday-school library ticket.

His garments, admirably adapted to the exigencies of any climate, were severally, a straw hat with a pink ribbon, a striped shirt, over which a pair of trousers, uncommonly wide in comparison to their length, were buttoned, striped balmoral stockings, which gave his youthful legs something of the appearance of wintergreen candy, and copper-toed shoes with iron heels, capable of striking fire from any flag stone.

This latter quality Master Charley could not help feeling would be of infinite service to him in the wilds of Van Dieman's Land, which, as pictorially represented in his geography, seemed to be deficient in corner groceries and matches.

Exactly as the clock struck the half-hour, the short legs and straw hat of Master Charles Summerton disappeared around the corner.

He ran rapidly, partly by way of inuring himself to the fatigues of the journey before him, and partly by way of testing his speed with that of a North Beach car which was proceeding in his direction.

The conductor not being aware of this generous and lofty emulation, and being somewhat concerned at the spectacle of a pair of very short, twinkling legs so far in the rear, stopped his car, and generously assisted the youthful Summerton upon the platform.

From this point a hiatus of several hours' duration occurs in Master Charles's narrative.

He is under the impression that he "rode out" not only his two tickets, but that he became subsequently indebted to the company for several trips to and from the opposite termini, and that at last, resolutely refusing to give any explanation of his conduct, he was finally ejected, much to his relief, on a street corner.

Although, as he informs us, he felt perfectly satisfied with this arrangement, he was impelled, under the circumstances, to hurl after the conductor an opprobrious appellation, which he had ascertained from Patsey was the correct thing in such emergencies, and possessed peculiarly exasperating properties.

We now approach a thrilling part of the narrative, before which most of the adventures of the "Boys' Own Book" pale into insignificance.

There are times when the recollection of this adventure causes Master Charles to break out in a cold sweat, and he has several times since its occurrence been awakened by lamentations and outcries in the night season by merely dreaming of it.

On the corner of the street lay several large empty sugar hogsheads.

A few young gentlemen disported themselves therein, armed with sticks, with which they removed the sugar which still adhered to the joints of the staves, and conveyed it to their mouths.

Finding a cask not yet pre-empted, Master Charles set to work, and for a few moments revelled in a wild saccharine dream, whence he was finally roused by an angry voice and the rapidly retreating footsteps of his comrades.

An ominous sound smote his ear, and the next moment

he felt the cask wherein he lay uplifted and set upright against the wall.

He was a prisoner, but as yet undiscovered.

Being satisfied in his mind that hanging was the systematic and legalized penalty for the outrage he had committed, he kept down manfully the cry that rose to his lips.

In a few moments he felt the cask again lifted by a powerful hand, which appeared above him at the edge of his prison, and which he concluded belonged to the ferocious giant Blunderbore, whose features and limbs he had frequently met in coloured pictures.

Before he could recover from his astonishment, his cask was placed with several others on a cart, and rapidly driven away.

The ride which ensued, he describes as being fearful in the extreme.

Rolled around like a pill in a box, the agonies which he suffered may be hinted at, not spoken.

Evidences of that protracted struggle were visible in his garments, which were of the consistency of syrup, and his hair, which for several hours, under the treatment of hot water, yielded a thin treacle.

At length the cart stopped on one of the wharves, and the cartman began to unload.

As he tilted over the cask in which Charles lay, an exclamation broke from his lips, and the edge of the cask fell from his hands, sliding its late occupant upon the wharf.

To regain his short legs, and to put the greatest possible distance between himself and the cartman, were his first movements on regaining his liberty.

He did not stop until he had reached the corner of Front Street.

Another blank succeeds in this veracious history.

He cannot remember how or when he found himself in front of the circus tent.

He has an indistinct recollection of having passed through a long street of stores which were all closed, and which made him fear that it was Sunday, and that he had spent a miserable night in the sugar cask.

But he remembers hearing the sound of music within the tent, and of creeping on his hands and knees, when no one was looking, until he passed under the canvas.

His description of the wonders contained within that circle; of the terrific feats which were performed by a man on a pole, since practised by him in the back yard; of the horses, one of which was spotted and resembled an animal in his Noah's Ark, hitherto unrecognized and undefined, of the female equestrians, whose dresses could only be equalled in magnificence to the frocks of his sister's doll, of the painted clown, whose jokes excited a merriment, somewhat tinged by an undefined fear, was an effort of language which this pen could but weakly transcribe, and which no quantity of exclamation points could sufficiently illustrate.

He is not quite certain what followed.

He remembers that almost immediately on leaving the circus it became dark, and that he fell asleep, waking up at intervals on the corners of the streets, on front steps, in somebody's arms, and finally in his own bed.

He was not aware of experiencing any regret for his conduct, he does not recall feeling at any time a disposition to go home—he remembers distinctly that he felt hungry.

He has made this disclosure in confidence.

He wishes it to be respected.

He wants to know if you have five cents about you.

THE ILIAD OF SANDY BAR

BEFORE nine o'clock it was pretty well known all along the river that the two partners of the "Amity" claim had quarrelled and separated at day-break.

At that time the attention of their nearest neighbour had been attracted by the sounds of altercations and two consecutive pistol-shots.

Running out, he had seen, dimly, in the gray mist that rose from the river, the tall form of Scott, one of the partners, descending the hill toward the cañon; a moment later, York, the other partner, had appeared from the cabin, and walked in an opposite direction toward the river, passing within a few feet of the curious watcher.

Later, it was discovered that a serious Chinaman, cutting wood before the cabin, had witnessed part of the quarrel.

But John was stolid, indifferent, and reticent.

"Me choppe wood—me no fightee," was his serene response to all anxious queries.

"But what did they *say*, John?"

John did not "*sabe.*"

Col. Starbottle deftly ran over the various popular epithets which a generous public sentiment might accept as reasonable provocation for an assault. But John did not recognize them.

"And this yer's the cattle," said the Colonel, with some severity, "that some thinks ought'er be allowed to testify agin' a White Man! Git—you heathen!"

Still the quarrel remained inexplicable.

That two men, whose amiability and grave tact had earned for them the title of "The Peacemakers," in a community not greatly given to the passive virtues—that these men, singularly devoted to each other, should suddenly and violently quarrel, might well excite the curiosity of the camp.

A few of the more inquisitive visited the late scene of conflict, now deserted by its former occupants.

There was no trace of disorder or confusion in the near cabin.

The rude table was arranged as if for breakfast; the pan of yellow biscuit still sat upon that hearth whose dead embers might have typified the evil passions that had raged there but an hour before.

But Col. Starbottle's eye—albeit, somewhat blood-shot and rheumy—was more intent on practical details.

On examination, a bullet-hole was found in the doorpost, and another, nearly opposite, in the casing of the window.

The Colonel called attention to the fact that the one "agreed with" the bore of Scott's revolver, and the other with that of York's derringer.

"They must hev stood about yer," said the Colonel, taking position; "not mor'n three feet apart, and—missed!"

There was a fine touch of pathos in the falling inflection of the Colonel's voice, which was not without effect.

A delicate perception of wasted opportunity thrilled his auditors.

But the Bar was destined to experience a greater disappointment.

The two antagonists had not met since the quarrel, and it was vaguely rumoured that on the occasion of second meeting, each had determined to kill the other "on sight."

There was, consequently, some excitement—and, it is to be feared, no little gratification—when, at ten o'clock, York stepped from the Magnolia Saloon into the one, long, straggling street of the camp, at the same moment that Scott left the blacksmith's shop, at the forks of the road.

It was evident, at a glance, that a meeting could only be avoided by the actual retreat of one or the other.

In an instant, the doors and windows of the adjacent saloons were filled with faces.

Heads unaccountably appeared above the river-banks and from behind bowlders.

An empty waggon at the cross-road was suddenly crowded with people, who seemed to have sprung from the earth.

There was much running and confusion on the hill-side.

On the mountain-road, Mr. Jack Hamlin had reined up

his horse, and was standing upright on the seat of his buggy.

And the two objects of this absorbing attention approached each other.

"York's got the sun," "Scott'll line him on that tree," "he's waitin' to draw his fire," came from the cart—and then it was silent.

But above this human breathlessness the river rushed and sang, and the wind rustled the tree-tops with an indifference that seemed obtrusive.

Colonel Starbottle felt it, and, in a moment of sublime pre-occupation, without looking around, waved his cane behind him, warningly, to all nature, and said, "Shu!"

The men were now within a few feet of each other.

A hen ran across the road before one of them. A feathery seed-vessel, wafted from a way-side tree, fell at the feet of the other.

And, unheeding this irony of Nature, the two opponents came nearer, erect and rigid, looked in each other's eyes, and—passed?

Colonel Starbottle had to be lifted from the cart.

"This yer camp is played out," he said, gloomily, as he affected to be supported into the "Magnolia."

With what further expression he might have indicated his feelings it was impossible to say, for at that moment Scott joined the group.

"Did you speak to me?" he asked of the Colonel, dropping his hand, as if with accidental familiarity, on that gentleman's shoulder.

The Colonel, recognizing some occult quality in the touch, and some unknown quantity in the glance of his questioner, contented himself by replying—

"No, sir," with dignity.

A few rods away, York's conduct was as characteristic and peculiar.

"You had a mighty fine chance then—why didn't you

plump him?" said Jack Hamlin, as York drew near the buggy.

"Because I hate him," was the reply, heard only by Jack.

Contrary to popular belief, this reply was not hissed between the lips of the speaker, but was said in an ordinary tone.

But Jack Hamlin, who was an observer of mankind, noticed that the speaker's hands were cold, and his lips dry, as he helped him into the buggy, and accepted the seeming paradox with a smile.

When Sandy Bar became convinced that the quarrel between York and Scott could not be settled after the usual local methods, it gave no further concern thereto.

But presently it was rumoured that the "Amity Claim" was in litigation, and that its possession would be expensively disputed by each of the partners.

As it was well known that the claim in question was "worked out" and worthless, and that the partners, whom it had already enriched, had talked of abandoning it but a day or two before the quarrel, this proceeding could only be accounted for as gratuitous spite.

Later, two San Francisco lawyers made their appearance in this guiltless Arcadia, and were eventually taken into the saloons, and—what was pretty much the same thing—the confidences of the inhabitants.

The results of this unhallowed intimacy were many subpœnas; and, indeed, when the "Amity Claim" came to trial, all of Sandy Bar that was not in compulsory attendance at the county seat came there from curiosity.

The gulches and ditches for miles around were deserted.

I do not propose to describe that already famous trial.

Enough that, in the language of the plaintiff's counsel, "it was one of no ordinary significance, involving the inherent rights of that untiring industry which had developed the Pactolian resources of this golden land"—and, in the homelier phrase of Colonel Starbottle, "a fuss that gentlemen might hev settled in ten minutes over a social glass, ef they meant business; or in ten seconds with a revolver, ef they meant fun."

Scott got a verdict, from which York instantly appealed.

It was said that he had sworn to spend his last dollar in the struggle.

In this way Sandy Bar began to accept the enmity of the former partners as a life-long feud, and the fact that they had ever been friends was forgotten.

The few who expected to learn from the trial the origin of the quarrel were disappointed.

Among the various conjectures, that which ascribed some occult feminine influence as the cause was naturally popular, in a camp given to dubious compliment of the sex.

"My word for it, gentlemen," said Colonel Starbottle— who had been known in Sacramento as a Gentleman of the Old School—"there's some lovely creature at the bottom of this."

The gallant Colonel then proceeded to illustrate his theory, by divers sprightly stories, such as Gentlemen of the Old School are in the habit of repeating, but which, from deference to the prejudices of gentlemen of a more recent school, I refrain from transcribing here.

But it would appear that even the Colonel's theory was fallacious. The only woman who personally might have exercised any influence over the partners, was the pretty daughter of "old man Folinsbee," of Poverty Flat, at whose hospitable house—which exhibited some comforts and refinements rare in that crude civilization—both York and Scott were frequent visitors.

Yet into this charming retreat York strode one evening a month after the quarrel, and, beholding Scott sitting there, turned to the fair hostess with the abrupt query:

"Do you love this man?"

The young woman thus addressed returned that answer—

at once spirited and evasive—which would occur to most of my fair readers in such an exigency.

Without another word, York left the house.

"Miss Jo" heaved the least possible sigh as the door closed on York's curls and square shoulders, and then, like a good girl, turned to her insulted guest.

"But would you believe it, dear?" she afterward related to an intimate friend, "the other creature, after glowering at me for a moment, got upon its hind legs, took its hat, and left too; and that's the last I've seen of either."

The same hard disregard of all other interests or feelings in the gratification of their blind rancour characterized all their actions.

When York purchased the land below Scott's new claim, and obliged the latter, at a great expense, to make a long detour to carry a "tail-race" around it, Scott retaliated by building a dam that overflowed York's claim on the river.

It was Scott who, in conjunction with Colonel Starbottle, first organized that active opposition to the Chinamen, which resulted in the driving off of York's Mongolian labourers; it was York who built the waggon-road and established the express which rendered Scott's mules and pack-trains obsolete; it was Scott who called into life the Vigilance Committee which expatriated York's friend, Jack Hamlin; it was York who created the *Sandy Bar Herald*, which characterized the act as "a lawless outrage," and Scott as a "Border Ruffian;" it was Scott, at the head of twenty masked men, who, one moonlight night, threw the offending "forms" into the yellow river, and scattered the types in the dusty road.

These proceedings were received in the distant and more civilized outlying towns as vague indications of progress and vitality.

I have before me a copy of the *Poverty Flat Pioneer*, for the week ending August 12, 1856, in which the editor, under the head of "County Improvements," says:

"The new Presbyterian Church on C Street, at Sandy Bar, is completed. It stands upon the lot formerly occupied by the Magnolia Saloon, which was so mysteriously burnt last month. The temple, which now rises like a phœnix from the ashes of the Magnolia, is virtually the free gift of H. J. York, Esq., of Sandy Bar, who purchased the lot and donated the lumber. Other buildings are going up in the vicinity, but the most noticeable is the 'Sunny South Saloon,' erected by Captain Mat. Scott, nearly opposite the church. Captain Scott has spared no expense in the furnishing of this saloon, which promises to be one of the most agreeable places of resort in old Tuolumne. He has recently imported two new, first-class billiard-tables, with cork cushions. Our old friend, 'Mountain Jimmy,' will dispense liquors at the bar. We refer our readers to the advertisement in another column. Visitors to Sandy Bar cannot do better than give 'Jimmy' a call."

Among the local items occurred the following:

"H. J. York, Esq., of Sandy Bar, has offered a reward of 100 dols. for the detection of the parties who hauled away the steps of the new Presbyterian Church, C Street, Sandy Bar, during Divine service on Sabbath evening last. Captain Scott adds another hundred for the capture of the miscreants who broke the magnificent plate-glass windows of the new saloon on the following evening. There is some talk of reorganizing the old Vigilance Committee at Sandy Bar."

When, for many months of cloudless weather, the hard, unwinking sun of Sandy Bar had regularly gone down on the unpacified wrath of these men, there was some talk of mediation.

In particular, the pastor of the church to which I have just referred—a sincere, fearless, but perhaps not fully-enlightened man—seized gladly upon the occasion of York's liberality to attempt to re-unite the former partners.

He preached an earnest sermon on the abstract sinful‚ ness of discord and rancour.

But the excellent sermons of the Rev. Mr. Daws were directed to an ideal congregation that did not exist at Sandy Bar—a congregation of beings of unmixed vices and virtues, of single impulses, and perfectly logical motives, of preternatural simplicity, of child-like faith, and grown-up responsibilities.

As, unfortunately, the people who actually attended Mr. Daws' church were mainly very human, somewhat artful, more self-excusing than self-accusing, rather good-natured, and decidedly weak, they quietly shed that portion of the sermon which referred to themselves, and accepting York and Scott—who were both in defiant attendance—as curious examples of those ideal beings above referred to, felt a certain satisfaction—which I fear, was not altogether Christian-like—in their "raking down."

If Mr. Daws expected York and Scott to shake hands after the sermon, he was disappointed.

But he did not relax his purpose.

With that quiet fearlessness and determination which had won for him the respect of men who were too apt to regard piety as synonymous with effeminacy, he attacked Scott in his own house.

What he said has not been recorded, but it is to be feared that it was part of his sermon.

When he had concluded, Scott looked at him, not unkindly over the glasses of his bar, and said, less irreverently than the words might convey:

"Young man, I rather like your style; but when you know York and me as well as you do God Almighty, it'll be time to talk."

And so the feud progressed: and so, as in more illustrious examples, the private and personal enmity of two representative men led gradually to the evolution of some crude half-expressed principle or belief.

It was not long before it was made evident that those beliefs were identical with certain broad principles laid down by the founders of the American Constitution, as expounded by the statesmanlike A; or were the fatal quicksands, on which the ship of State might be wrecked, warningly pointed out by the eloquent B.

The practical result of all which was the nomination of York and Scott to represent the opposite factions of Sandy Bar in legislative councils.

For some weeks past, the voters of Sandy Bar and the adjacent camps had been called upon, in large type, to "RALLY!"

In vain the great pines at the cross-roads—whose trunks were compelled to bear this and other legends—moaned and protested from their windy watch-towers.

But one day, with fife and drum, and flaming transparency, a procession filed into the triangular grove at the head of the gulch.

The meeting was called to order by Colonel Starbottle, who, having once enjoyed legislative functions, and being vaguely known as a "war-horse," was considered to be a valuable partisan of York.

He concluded an appeal for his friend, with an enunciation of principle, interspersed with one or two anecdotes, so gratuitously coarse, that the very pines might have been moved to pelt him with their cast-off cones, as he stood there.

But he created a laugh, on which his candidate rode into popular notice; and when York rose to speak, he was greeted with cheers.

But, to the general astonishment, the new speaker, at once launched into bitter denunciation of his rival.

He not only dwelt upon Scott's deeds and example, as known to Sandy Bar, but spoke of facts connected with his previous career, hitherto unknown to his auditors.

To great precision of epithet and directness of statement,

the speaker added the fascination of revelation and exposure.

The crowd cheered, yelled, and were delighted; but when this astounding philippic was concluded, there was a unanimous call for "Scott!"

Colonel Starbottle would have resisted this manifest impropriety, but in vain.

Partly from a crude sense of justice, partly from a meaner craving for excitement, the assemblage was inflexible; and Scott was dragged, pushed, and pulled upon the platform.

As his frowsy head and unkempt beard appeared above the railing, it was evident that he was drunk.

But it was also evident, before he opened his lips, that the orator of Sandy Bar—the one man who could touch their vagabond sympathies (perhaps because he was not above appealing to them)—stood before him.

A consciousness of this power lent a certain dignity to his figure, and I am not sure but that his very physical condition impressed them as a kind of regal unbending and large condescension.

Howbeit, when this unexpected Hector arose from the ditch, York's myrmidons trembled.

"There's nought, gentlemen," said Scott, leaning forward on the railing—"there's nought as that man hez said as isn't true. I was run outer Cairo; I did belong to the Regulators; I did desert from the army; I did leave a wife in Kansas. But thar's one thing he didn't charge me with, and, may be, he's forgotten. For three years, gentlemen, I was that man's pardner——"

Whether he intended to say more, I cannot tell; a burst of applause artistically rounded and enforced the climax, and virtually elected the speaker.

That fall he went to Sacramento; York went abroad, and for the first time in many years, distance and a new atmosphere isolated the old antagonists.

With little change in the green wood, gray rock, and

yellow river, but with much shifting of human landmarks, and new faces in its habitations, three years passed over Sandy Bar.

The two men, once so identified with its character, seemed to have been quite forgotten.

"You will never return to Sandy Bar," said Miss Folinsbee, the "Lily of Poverty Flat," on meeting York in Paris —"for Sandy Bar is no more. They call it Riverside now; and the new town is built higher up on the river bank. By the bye, 'Jo' says that Scott has won his suit about the 'Amity Claim,' and that he lives in the old cabin, and is drunk half his time. O, I beg your pardon," added the lively lady, as a flush crossed York's sallow cheek; "but, bless me, I really thought that old grudge was made up. I'm sure it ought to be."

It was three months after this conversation, and a pleasant summer evening, that the Poverty Flat coach drew up before the verandah of the Union Hotel at Sandy Bar.

Among its passengers was one, apparently a stranger, in the local distinction of well-fitting clothes and closely-shaven face, who demanded a private room and retired early to rest.

But before sunrise next morning he arose, and drawing some clothes from his carpet-bag, proceeded to array himself in a pair of white-duck trousers, a white-duck overshirt, and a straw hat.

When his toilette was completed, he tied a red bandanna handkerchief in a loop, and threw it loosely over his shoulders.

The transformation was complete: as he crept softly down the stairs and stepped into the road, no one would have detected in him the elegant stranger of the previous night, and but few have recognized the face and figure of Henry York of Sandy Bar.

In the uncertain light of that early hour, and in the

change that had come over the settlement, he had to pause for a moment to recall where he stood.

The Sandy Bar of his recollection lay below him, nearer the river; the buildings around him were of later date and newer fashion.

As he strode toward the river, he noticed here a school-house and there a church.

A little farther on, "The Sunny South" came in view —transformed into a restaurant—its gilding faded and its paint rubbed off.

He now knew where he was; and running briskly down a declivity, crossed a ditch, and stood upon the lower boundary of the Amity Claim.

The gray mist was rising slowly from the river, clinging to the tree tops and drifting up the mountain side, until it was caught among those rocky altars, and held a sacrifice to the ascending sun.

At his feet the earth, cruelly gashed and scarred by his forgotten engines, had, since the old days, put on a show of greenness here and there, and now smiled forgivingly up at him, as if things were not so bad after all.

A few birds were bathing in the ditch with a pleasant suggestion of its being a new and special provision of Nature, and a hare ran into an inverted sluice-box, as he approached, as if it were put there for that purpose.

He had not yet dared to look in a certain direction.

But the sun was now high enough to paint the little eminence on which the cabin stood.

In spite of his self-control, his heart beat faster as he raised his eyes toward it.

Its window and door were closed, no smoke came from its *adobe* chimney, but it was else unchanged.

When within a few yards of it, he picked up a broken shovel, and shouldering it with a smile, strode toward the door and knocked.

There was no sound from within.

The smile died upon his lips as he nervously pushed the door open.

A figure started up angrily and came toward him: a figure whose bloodshot eyes suddenly fixed into a vacant stare; whose arms were at first outstretched and then thrown up in warning gesticulation; a figure that suddenly gasped, choked, and then fell forward in a fit.

But before he touched the ground, York had him out into the open air and sunshine.

In the struggle, both fell and rolled over on the ground.

But the next moment York was sitting up, holding the convulsed frame of his former partner on his knee, and wiping the foam from his inarticulate lips.

Gradually the tremor became less frequent, and then ceased; and the strong man lay unconscious in his arms.

For some moments York held him quietly thus, looking in his face. Afar, the stroke of a woodman's axe—a mere phantom of sound—was all that broke the stillness.

High up the mountain, a wheeling hawk hung breathlessly above them.

And then came voices, and two men joined them.

"A fight?"

No, a fit; and would they help him bring the sick man to the hotel?

And there, for a week, the stricken partner lay, unconscious of aught but the visions wrought by disease and fear.

On the eighth day, at sunrise, he rallied, and opening his eyes, looked upon York, and pressed his hand; then he spoke:

"And it's you. I thought it was only whisky."

York replied by taking both of his hands, boyishly working them backward and forward, as his elbow rested on the bed, with a pleasant smile.

"And you've been abroad. How did you like Paris?"

"So, so. How did *you* like Sacramento?"

"Bully."

And that was all they could think to say.

Presently Scott opened his eyes again

"I'm mighty weak."

"You'll get better soon."

"Not much."

A long silence followed, in which they could hear the sounds of wood-chopping, and that Sandy Bar was already astir for the coming day.

Then Scott slowly and with difficulty turned his face to York, and said,—

"I might hev killed you once."

"I wish you had."

They pressed each other's hands again, but Scott's grasp was evidently failing.

He seemed to summon his energies for a special effort.

"Old man!"

"Old chap."

"Closer."

York bent his head toward the slowly fading face.

"Do ye mind that morning?"

"Yes."

A gleam of fun slid into the corner of Scott's blue eye, as he whispered,—

"Old man, thar *was* too much saleratus in that bread."

It is said that these were his last words.

For when the sun, which had so often gone down upon the idle wrath of these foolish men, looked again upon them reunited, it saw the hand of Scott fall cold and irresponsive from the yearning clasp of his former partner, and it knew that the feud of Sandy Bar was at an end.

Poems

THAT HEATHEN CHINEE

TABLE MOUNTAIN, 1870

WHICH I wish to remark—
  And my language is plain—
That for ways that are dark
  And for tricks that are vain,
The heathen Chinee is peculiar,
  Which the same I would rise to explain.

Ah Sin was his name;
  And I shall not deny
In regard to the same
  What that name might imply,
But his smile it was pensive and child-like,
  As I frequently remarked to Bill Nye.

It was August the third;
  And quite soft was the skies;
Which it might be inferred
  That Ah Sin was likewise;
Yet he played it that day upon William
  And me in a way I despise.

Which we had a small game,
  And Ah Sin took a hand:

255

It was Euchre. The same
  He did not understand;
But he smiled as he sat by the table,
  With the smile that was child-like and bland.

Yet the cards they were stocked
  In a way that I grieve,
And my feelings were shocked
  At the state of Nye's sleeve:
Which was stuffed full of aces and bowers,
  And the same with intent to deceive.

But the hands that were played
  By that heathen Chinee,
And the points that he made
  Were quite frightful to see—
Till at last he put down a right bower,
  Which the same Nye had dealt unto me.

Then I looked up at Nye,
  And he gazed upon me;
And he rose with a sigh
  And said, "Can this be?
We are ruined by Chinese cheap labour"—
  And he went for that heathen Chinee.

In the scene that ensued
  I did not take a hand,
But the floor it was strewed
  Like the leaves on the strand
With the cards that Ah Sin had been hiding,
  In the game "he did not understand."

In his sleeves which were long,
  He had twenty-four jacks—
Which was coming it strong,
  Yet I state but the facts;
And we found on his nails, which were taper,
  What is frequent in tapers—that's wax.

Which is why I remark,
  And my language is plain,
That for ways that are dark,
  And for tricks that are vain,
The heathen Chinee is peculiar—
  Which the same I am free to maintain.

FURTHER LANGUAGE FROM TRUTHFUL JAMES

Nye's Ford, Stanislaus

1870

Do I sleep? do I dream?
  Do I wonder and doubt?
Are things what they seem,
  Or is visions about?
Is our civilization a failure?
  Or is the Caucasian played out?

Which expressions are strong:
  Yet would feebly imply
Some account of a wrong—
  Not to call it a lie—
As was worked off on William, my pardner,
  Which his name it was W. Nye.

He came down to the Ford
    On the very same day
Of that Lottery, drawed
    By those sharps at the Bay;
And he says to me, "Truthful, how goes it?"
    I replied, "It is far, far from gay—

"For the camp has gone wild
    On this Lottery game,
And has even beguiled
    'Injin Dick,' by the same."
Which said Nye to me, "Injins is pizen—
    Do you know what his number is, James?"

I replied, "7, 2,
    9, 8, 4, is his hand."
When he started—and drew
    Out a list, which he scanned;
Then he softly went for his revolver,
    With language I cannot command.

Then I said, "William Nye!"
    But he turned up to me,
And the look in his eye
    Was quite painful to see.
And he says: "You mistake; this poor Injin
    I protects from such sharps as you be!"

I was shocked and withdrew;
    But I grieve to relate.

When he next met my view
   Injin Dick was his mate;
And the two around town was a-lying
   In a frightfully dissolute state.

Which the war dance they had
   Round a tree at the Bend,
Was a sight that was sad;
   And it seemed that the end
Would not justify the proceedings,
   As I quiet remarked to a friend.

For that Injin he fled
   The next day to his band;
And we found William spread
   Very loose on the strand,
With a peaceful-like smile on his feature,
   And a dollar greenback in his hand.

Which the same when rolled out,
   We observed with surprise,
What that Injin, no doubt,
   Had believed was the prize—
Them figures in red in the corner,
   Which the number of note specifies.

Was it guile, or a dream?
   Is it Nye that I doubt?
Are things what they seem,
   Or is visions about?
Is our civilization a failure?
   Or is the Caucasian played out?

THE SOCIETY UPON THE STANISLAUS

I RESIDE at Table Mountain, and my name is Truthful
    James;
I am not up to small deceit, or any sinful games;
And I'll tell in simple language what I know about the row
That broke up our society upon the Stanislow.

But first I would remark, that it is not a proper plan
For any scientific gent to whale his fellow-man,
And, if a member don't agree with his peculiar whim,
To lay for that same member for to "put a head" on him.

Now nothing could be finer or more beautiful to see
Than the first six months' proceedings of that same
    society,
Till Brown of Calaveras brought a lot of fossil bones
That he found within a tunnel near the tenement of Jones.

Then Brown he read a paper, and he reconstructed there,
From those same bones, an animal that was extremely rare;
And Jones then asked the Chair for a suspension of the
    rules,
Till he could prove that those same bones was one of his
    lost mules.

Then Brown he smiled a bitter smile, and said he was at
    fault.
It seemed he had been trespassing on Jones's family vault:
He was a most sarcastic man, this quiet Mr. Brown,
And on several occasions he had cleaned out the town.

Now I hold it is not decent for a scientific gent
To say another is an ass,—at least, to all intent;
Nor should the individual who happens to be meant
Reply by heaving rocks at him to any great extent.

Then Abner Dean of Angel's raised a point of order—when
A chunk of old red sandstone took him in the abdomen,
And he smiled a kind of sickly smile, and curled up on the
    floor,
And the subsequent proceedings interested him no more.

For, in less time than I write it, every member did engage
In a warfare with the remnants of a palæozoic age;
And the way they heaved those fossils in their anger was a
    sin,
Till the skull of an old mammoth caved the head of Thomp-
    son in.

And this is all I have to say of these improper games,
For I live at Table Mountain, and my name is Truthful
    James;
And I've told in simple language what I know about the
    row
That broke up our society upon the Stanislow.

"JIM"

SAY there! P'r'aps
Some on you chaps
    Might know Jim Wild?
Well,—no offence:
Thar ain't no sense
    In gittin' riled!

Jim was my chum
　Up on the Bar:
That's why I come
　Down from up yar,
Lookin' for Jim.
Thank ye, sir! *You*
Ain't of that crew,—
　Blest if you are!

Money?—Not much:
　That ain't my kind:
I ain't no such.
　Rum?—I don't mind,
Seein' it's you.

Well, this yer Jim,
Did you know him?—
Jess 'bout your size;
Same kind of eyes?—
Well, that is strange:
　Why, it's two year
　Since he came here,
Sick, for a change.

Well, here's to us:
　　Eh?
The h—— you say
　　Dead?—
That little cuss?

What makes you star,—
You over thar?

Can't a man drop
's glass in yer shop
But you must rar'?
  It wouldn't take
    D—— much to break
You and your bar.

      Dead!
Poor—little—Jim!
—Why, thar was me,
Jones, and Bob Lee,
Harry and Ben,—
No-account men:
Then to take *him!*

Well, thar—Good-bye,—
No more, sir,—I—
    Eh?
What's that you say?—
Why, dern it!—sho!
No? Yes! By Jo!

      Sold!
Sold! Why, you limb,
You ornery,
    Derned old
Long-legged Jim!

CHIQUITA

BEAUTIFUL! Sir, you may say so. Thar isn't her match in
    the county.
Is thar, old gal,—Chiquita, my darling, my beauty?

Feel of that neck, sir,—thar's velvet! Whoa! Steady,—
    ah, will you, you vixen!
Whoa! I say. Jack, trot her out; let the gentleman look at
    her paces.

Morgan!—She ain't nothin' else, and I've got the papers to
    prove it.
Sired by Chippewa Chief, and twelve hundred dollars won't
    buy her.
Briggs of Tuolumne owned her. Did you know Briggs of
    Tuolumne?—
Busted hisself in White Pine, and blew out his brains down
    in 'Frisco?

Hedn't no savey—hed Briggs. Thar, Jack! that'll do,—quit
    that foolin'!
Nothin' to what she kin do, when she's got her work cut out
    before her.
Hosses is hosses, you know, and likewise, too, jockeys is
    jockeys;
And 'tain't ev'ry man as can ride as knows what a hoss has
    got in him.

Know the old ford on the Fork, that nearly got Flanigan's
    leaders?
Nasty in daylight, you bet, and a mighty rough ford in low
    water!
Well, it ain't six weeks ago that me and the Jedge and his
    nevey
Struck for that ford in the night, in the rain, and the water
    all around us;

Up to our flanks in the gulch, and Rattlesnake Creek just a
    bilin',
Not a plank left in the dam, and nary a bridge on the river.
I had the grey, and the Jedge had his roan, and his nevey,
    Chiquita;

And after us trundled the rocks just loosed from the top of
the cañon.

Lickity, lickity, switch, we came to the ford, and Chiquita
Buckled right down to her work, and afore I could yell to
her rider,
Took water jest at the ford, and there was the Jedge and
me standing,
And twelve hundred dollars of hoss-flesh afloat, and a drift-
in' to thunder!

Would ye b'lieve it? that night that hoss, that ar' filly,
Chiquita,
Walked herself into her stall, and stood there, all quiet and
dripping:
Clean as a beaver or rat, with nary a buckle of harness,
Just as she swam the Fork,—that hoss, that ar' filly, Chi-
quita.

That's what I call a hoss! and—What did you say?—O, the
nevey?
Drownded, I reckon,—leastways, he never kem back to
deny it.
Ye see the derned fool had no seat,—ye couldn't have made
him a rider;
And then, ye know, boys will be boys, and hosses—well,
hosses is hosses!

DOW'S FLAT

1856

Dow's FLAT. That's its name.
And I reckon that you
Are a stranger? The same?
Well, I thought it was true,—
For thar isn't a man on the river as can't spot the place at
first view.

It was called after Dow,—
　　Which the same was an ass,—
　And as to the how
　　Thet the thing kem to pass,—
Jest tie up your hoss to that buckeye, and sit ye down here
　　　in the grass:

You see this yer Dow
　　Hed the worst kind of luck;
He slipped up somehow
　　On each thing thet he struck.
Why, ef he'd a straddled that fence-rail the derned thing 'ed
　　　get up and buck.

He mined on the bar
　　Till he couldn't pay rates;
He was smashed by a car
　　When he tunnelled with Bates;
And right on the top of his trouble kem his wife and five
　　　kids from the States.

It was rough,—mighty rough;
　　But the boys they stood by,
And they brought him the stuff
　　For a house, on the sly;
And the old woman,—well, she did washing, and took on
　　　when no one was nigh.

But this yer luck of Dow's
　　Was so powerful mean
That the spring near his house
　　Dried right up on the green;
And he sunk forty feet down for water, but nary a drop to
　　　be seen.

Then the bar petered out,
 And the boys wouldn't stay;
And the chills* got about,
 And his wife fell away:
But Dow, in his well, kept a peggin' in his usual ridikilous
  way.

One day,—it was June,—
 And a year ago, jest,—
This Dow kem at noon
 To his work like the rest,
With a shovel and pick on his shoulder, and a derringer†
  hid in his breast.

He goes to the well,
 And he stands on the brink,
And stops for a spell
 Jest to listen and think:
For the sun in his eyes, (jest like this sir!) you see, kinder
  made the cuss blink.

His two ragged gals
 In the gulch were at play,
And a gownd that was Sal's
 Kinder flapped on a bay:
Not much for a man to be leavin', but his all,—as I've
  heer'd the folks say.

And—That's a peart hoss
 Thet you've got,—ain't it now?
What might be her cost?
 Eh? Oh!—Well, then, Dow—
Let's see,—well, that forty-foot grave wasn't his sir, that
  day anyhow.

---

* Fever and ague.
† A derringer, revolver.

For a blow of his pick
　　Sorter caved in the side,
And he looked and turned sick,
　　Then he trembled and cried.
For you see the dern cuss had struck—"Water?"—
　　　Beg your parding, young man, there you lied!

It was *gold*,—in the quartz,
　　And it ran all alike;
And I reckon five oughts
　　Was the worth of that strike;
And that house with the coopilow's his'n,—which the same
　　　isn't bad for a Pike.

Thet's why it's Dow's Flat;
　　And the thing of it is
That he kinder got that
　　Through sheer contrairiness:
For 'twas *water* the derned cuss was seekin', and his luck
　　　made him certain to miss.

Thet's so. Thar's your way
　　To the left of yon tree;
But—a—look h'yur, say?
　　Won't you come up to tea?
No? Well, then the next time you're passin'; and ask after
　　　Dow,—and thet's *me*.

————

IN THE TUNNEL

Didn't know Flynn,
　　Flynn, of Virginia,—
Long as he's been 'yar?
Look'ee here, stranger,
Whar *hev* you been?

Here in this tunnel
  He was my pardner,
That same Tom Flynn,—
  Working together,
  In wind and weather,
Day out and in.

Didn't know Flynn!
  Well, that *is* queer;
Why, it's a sin
To think of Tom Flynn,
  Tom with his cheer,
  Tom without fear,—
Stranger, look 'yar!

Thar in the drift,
  Back to the wall,
He held the timbers
  Ready to fall;
  Then in the darkness
I heard him call:
  "Run for your life, Jake!
Run for your wife's sake!
Don't wait for me."

And that was all
  Heard in the din,
  Heard of Tom Flynn,—
    Flynn of Virginia.

That's all about
  Flynn of Virginia.
That lets me out.
  Here in the damp,—
Out of the sun,—
  That 'ar derned lamp
Makes my eyes run.
Well, there,—I'm done!

But, sir, when you'll
Hear the next fool
   Asking of Flynn,—
Flynn of Virginia,—
   Just you chip in,
Say you knew Flynn;
Say that you've been 'yar.

"CICELY"

Alkali Station

Cicely says you're a poet; maybe; I ain't much on rhyme:
I reckon you'd give me a hundred, and beat me every time.
Poetry!—that's the way some chaps puts up an idee,
But I takes mine "straight without sugar," and that's what's
    the matter with me.

Poetry!—just look round you,—alkali, rock, and sage;
Sage-brush, rock, and alkali; ain't it a pretty page!
Sun in the east at mornin', sun in the west at night,
And the shadow of this 'yer station the on'y thing moves in
    sight.

Poetry!—Well now—Polly! Polly run to your mam;
Run right away, my pooty! By by! Ain't she a lamb?
Poetry!—that reminds me o' suthin' right in that suit:
Jest shet that door thar, will yer?—for Cicely's ears is cute.

Ye noticed Polly,—the baby? A month afore she was born,
Cicely—my old woman—was moody-like and forlorn;
Out of her head and crazy, and talked of flowers and trees;
Family man yourself, sir? Well, you know what a woman
    be's.

Narvous she was, and restless,—said that she "couldn't
   stay."
Stay,—and the nearest woman seventeen miles away.
But I fixed it up with the doctor, and he said he would be
   on hand,
And I kinder stuck by the shanty, and fenced in that bit o'
   land.

One night,—the tenth of October,—I woke with a chill and
   fright,
For the door it was standing open, and Cicely warn't in
   sight,
But a note was pinned on the blanket, which it said that
   she "couldn't stay,"
But had gone to visit her neighbour,—seventeen miles away.

When and how she stampeded, I didn't wait for to see,
For out in the road, next minit, I started as wild as she:
Running first this way and that way, like a hound that is
   off the scent,
For there warn't no track in the darkness to tell me the way
   she went.

I've had some mighty mean moments afore I kem to this
   spot,—
Lost on the plains in '50, drowned almost, and shot;
But out on this alkali desert, a hunting a crazy wife,
Was ra'ly as on-satis-factory as anything in my life.

"Cicely! Cicely! Cicely!" I called, and I held my breath,
And "Cicely!" came from the canyon,—and all was as still
   as death.
And "Cicely! Cicely! Cicely!" came from the rocks below,
And jest but a whisper of "Cicely!" down from them peaks
   of snow.

I ain't what you call religious,—but I jest looked up to the
  sky,
And—this 'yer's to what I'm coming, and maybe ye think I
  lie:
But up away to the east'ard, yaller and big and far,
I saw of a suddent rising the singlerist kind of star.

Big and yaller and dancing, it seemed to beckon to me:
Yaller and big and dancing, such as you never see:
Big and yaller and dancing,—I never saw such a star,
And I thought of them sharps in the Bible, and I went for
  it then and thar.

Over the brush and bowlders I stumbled and pushed ahead:
Keeping the star afore me, I went wharever it led.
It might hev been for an hour, when suddent and peart and
  nigh,
Out of the yearth afore me thar riz up a baby's cry.

Listen! thar's the same music; but her lungs they are
  stronger now
Than the day I packed her and her mother,—I'm derned if
  I jest know how.
But the doctor kem the next minit, and the joke o' the
  whole thing is
That Cis never knew what happened from that very night
  to this!

But Cicely says you're a poet, and maybe you might, some
  day,
Jest sling her a rhyme 'bout a baby that was born in a
  curious way.

And see what he says; and, old fellow, when you speak of
    the star, don't tell
As how 'twas the doctor's lantern,—for maybe 'twon't sound
    so well.

PENELOPE

SIMPSON'S BAR, 1858

So you've kem 'yer agen,
    And one answer won't do;
Well, of all the derned men
    That I've struck, it is you.
O Sal! 'yer's that derned fool from Simpson's cavortin'
    round yer in the dew.

Kem in, ef you *will*.
    Thar,—quit! Take a cheer
Not that; you can't fill
    Them theer cushings this year,—
For that cheer was my old man's, Joe Simpson, and they
    don't make such men about 'yer.

He was tall, was my Jack,
    And as strong as a tree.
Thar's his gun on the rack,—
    Just you heft it, and see.
And *you* come a courtin' his widder. Lord! where can that
    crittur, Sal, be!

You'd fill my Jack's place?
    And a man of your size,—
With no baird to his face,
    Nor a snap to his eyes,—
And nary—Sho! thar! I was foolin',—I was Joe, for sar-
    tain,—don't rise.

Sit down. Law! why, sho!
I'm as weak as a gal,
Sal! Don't you go, Joe,
Or I'll faint,—sure, I shall.
Sit down,—*anywheer*, where you like, Joe,—in that cheer, if
you choose,—Lord, where's Sal!

————

THE MIRACLE OF PADRE JUNIPERO

THIS is the tale that the Chronicle
Tells of the wonderful miracle
Wrought by the pious Padre Serro,
The very reverend Junipero.

The Heathen stood on his ancient mound,
Looking over the desert bound
Into the distant, hazy south,
Over the dusty and broad champaign
Where, with many a gaping mouth,
And fissure cracked by the fervid drouth,
For seven months had the wasted plain
Known no moisture of dew or rain.
The wells were empty and choked with sand;
The rivers had perished from the land;
Only the sea fogs, to and fro,
Slipped like ghosts of the streams below.
Deep in its bed lay the river's bones,
Bleaching in pebbles and milk-white stones,
And tracked o'er the desert faint and far,
Its ribs shone bright on each sandy bar.

Thus they stood as the sun went down
Over the foot-hills bare and brown;

Thus they looked to the South, wherefrom
The pale-faced medicine-man should come.
Not in anger, or in strife
But to bring—so ran the tale—
The welcome springs of eternal life,
The living waters that should not fail.

Said one, "He will come like Manitou,
Unseen, unheard, in the falling dew."
Said another, "He will come full soon
Out of the round-faced watery moon."
And another said, "He is here!" and lo,—
Faltering, staggering, feeble and slow,—
Out from the desert's blinding heat
The Padre dropped at the heathen's feet.
They stood and gazed for a little space
Down on his pallid and careworn face,
And a smile of scorn went round the band
As they touched alternate with foot and hand
This mortal waif, that the outer space
Of dim mysterious sky and sand
Flung with so little of Christian grace
Down on their barren, sterile strand.

Said one to him: "It seems thy god
Is a very pitiful kind of god;
He could not shield thine aching eyes
From the blowing desert sands that rise,
Nor turn aside from thy old grey head
The glittering blade that is brandished
By the sun he set in the heavens high;
He could not moisten thy lips when dry;
The desert fire is in thy brain;
Thy limbs are racked with the fever-pain:
If this be the grace he showeth thee
Who art his servant, what may we,

Strange to his ways and his commands,
Seek at his unforgiving hands?"
"Drink but this cup," said the Padre straight,
"And thou shalt know whose mercy bore
These aching limbs to your heathen door,
And purged my soul of its gross estate.
Drink in His name, and thou shalt see
The hidden depths of this mystery.
Drink!" and he held the cup. One blow
From the heathen dashed to the ground below
The sacred cup that the Padre bore;
And the thirsty soil drank the precious store
Of sacramental and holy wine,
That emblem and consecrated sign
And blessed symbol of blood divine.

Then, says the legend (and they who doubt
The same as heretics be accurst),
From the dry and feverish soil leaped out
A living fountain; a well-spring burst
Over the dusty and broad champaign,
Over the sandy and sterile plain,
Till the granite ribs and the milk-white stones
That lay in the valley—the scattered bones—
Moved in the river and lived again!

Such was the wonderful miracle
Wrought by the cup of wine that fell
From the hands of the pious Padre Serro,
The very reverend Junipero.

AN ARCTIC VISION

WHERE the short-legged Esquimaux
Waddle in the ice and snow,
And the playful polar bear
Nips the hunter unaware;

Where by day they track the ermine
And by night another vermin,—
Segment of the frigid zone,
Where the temperature alone
Warms on St. Elias' cone;
Polar dock, where Nature slips
From the ways her icy ships;
Land of fox and deer and sable,
Shore end of our western cable,—
Let the news that flying goes
Thrill through all your Arctic floes,
And reverberate the boast
From the cliffs of Beechey's coast,
Till the tidings, circling round
Every bay of Norton Sound,
Throw the vocal tide-wave back
To the isles of Kodiac.
Let the stately polar bears
Waltz around the pole in pairs,
And the walrus, in his glee,
Bare his tusk of ivory;
While the bold sea unicorn
Calmly takes an extra horn;
All ye polar skies, reveal your
Very rarest of parhelia;
Trip it, all ye merry dancers,
In the airiest of lancers;
Slide, ye solemn glaciers, slide,
One inch farther to the tide,
Nor in rash precipitation
Upset Tyndall's calculation.
Know you not what fate awaits you,
Or to whom the future mates you?
All ye icebergs make salaam,—
You belong to Uncle Sam!

On the spot where Eugene Sue
Led his wretched Wandering Jew,
Stands a form whose features strike
Russ and Esquimaux alike.
He it is whom Skalds of old
In their Runic rhymes foretold;
Lean of flank and lank of jaw,
See the real Northern Thor!
See the awful Yankee leering
Just across the Straits of Behring
On the drifted snow, too plain,
Sinks his fresh tobacco stain
Just beside the deep inden-
Tation of his Number 10.

Leaning on his icy hammer
Stands the hero of this drama.
And above the wild duck's clamour,
In his own peculiar grammar,
With its linguistic disguises.
Lo, the Arctic prologue rises:
"Wa'll, I reckon 'tain't so bad,
Seein' ez 'twas all they had;
True the Springs are rather late
And early falls predominate;
But the ice crop's pretty sure,
And the air is kind o' pure;
'Tain't so very mean a trade,
When the land is all surveyed
There's a right smart chance for fur-chase
All along this recent purchase,
And, unless the stories fail,
Every fish from cod to whale;
Rocks, too; mebbe quartz; let's see,—
'Twould be strange if there should be,—

Seems I've heerd such stories told;
Ah!—why, bless us,—yes, it's gold!"

While the blows are falling thick
From his Californian pick,
You may recognise the Thor
Of the vision that I saw,—
Freed from legendary glamour,
See the real magician's hammer.

TO THE PLIOCENE SKULL

A Geological Address

"Speak, O man, less recent!   Fragmentary fossil!
Primal pioneer of pliocene formation,
Hid in lowest drifts below the earliest stratum
            Of volcanic tufa!

"Older than the beasts, the oldest Palæotherium;
Older than the trees, the oldest Cryptogami;
Older than the hills, those infantile eruptions
            Of earth's epidermis!

"Eo—Mio—Plio—whatsoe'er the 'cene' was
That those vacant sockets filled with awe and wonder,—
Whether shores Devonian or Silurian beaches,—
            Tell us thy strange story!

"Or has the professor slightly antedated
By some thousand years thy advent on this planet,
Giving thee an air that's somewhat better fitted
            For cold-blooded creatures?

"Wert thou true spectator of that mighty forest
When above thy head the stately Sigillaria
Reared its columned trunks in that remote and distant
             Carboniferous epoch?

"Tell us of that scene,—the dim and watery woodland
Songless, silent, hushed, with never bird or insect
Veiled with spreading fronds and screened with tall club-
    mosses,
             Lycopodiacea,—

"When beside thee walked the solemn Plesiosaurus,
And around thee crept the festive Ichthyosaurus,
While from time to time above thee flew and circled
             Cheerful Pterodactyls,

"Tell us of thy food,—those half-marine refections,
Crinoids on the shell and Brachipods *au naturel*,—
Cuttle-fish to which the *pieuvre* of Victor Hugo
             Seems a periwinkle.

"Speak, thou awful vestige of the Earth's creation,—
Solitary fragment of remains organic!
Tell the wondrous secret of thy past existence,—
             Speak! thou oldest primate!"

Even as I gazed, a thrill of the maxilla,
And a lateral movement of the condyloid process,
With post-pliocene sounds of healthy mastication,
             Ground the teeth together.

And, from that imperfect dental exhibition,
Stained with expressed juices of the weed Nicotian,
Came these hollow accents, blent with softer murmurs
   Of expectoration;

"Which my name is Bowers, and my crust was busted
Falling down a shaft in Calaveras County,
But I'd take it kindly if you'd send the pieces
   Home to old Missouri!"

THE BALLAD OF THE EMEU

O SAY, have you seen at the Willows so green,—
 So charming and rurally true,—
A singular bird, with a manner absurd,
 Which they call the Australian Emeu?
    Have you
Ever seen this Australian Emeu?

It trots all around with its head on the ground,
 Or erects it quite out of your view;
And the ladies all cry, when its figure they spy,
 O, what a sweet pretty Emeu!
    Oh! do
Just look at that lovely Emeu!

One day to this spot, when the weather was hot,
 Came Matilda Hortense Fortescue;
And beside her there came a youth of high name,—
 Augustus Florell Montague:
    The two
Both loved that wild, foreign Emeu.

With two loaves of bread then they fed it, instead
  Of the flesh of the white cockatoo,
Which once was its food in that wild neighbourhood
  Where ranges the sweet Kangaroo;
          That too
  Is game for the famous Emeu!

Old saws and gimlets but its appetite whets
  Like the world famous bark of Peru;
There's nothing so hard that the bird will discard,
  And nothing its taste will eschew,
          That you
  Can give that long-legged Emeu!

The time slipped away in this innocent play,
  When up jumped the bold Montague:
"Where's that specimen pin that I gaily did win
  In raffle, and gave unto you,
          Fortescue?"
  No word spoke the guilty Emeu!

"Quick! tell me his name whom thou gavest that same,
  Ere these hands in thy blood I imbrue!"
"Nay, dearest," she cried, as she clung to his side,
  "I'm innocent as that Emeu!"
          "Adieu!"
  He replied, "Miss M. H. Fortescue!"

Down she dropped at his feet, all as white as a sheet,
  As wildly he fled from her view;
He thought 'twas her sin,—for he knew not the pin
  Had been gobbled up by the Emeu;
          All through
  The voracity of that Emeu!

THE AGED STRANGER

An Incident of the War

"I was with Grant—" the stranger said;
  Said the farmer, "Say no more,
But rest thee here at my cottage porch,
  For thy feet are weary and sore."

"I was with Grant—" the stranger said;
  Said the farmer, "Nay, no more,—
I prithee sit at my frugal board,
  And eat of my humble store.

"How fares my boy,—my soldier boy
  Of the old Ninth Army Corps?
I warrant he bore him gallantly
  In the smoke and the battle's roar!"

"I know him not," said the aged man,
  "And, as I remarked before,
I was with Grant—" "Nay, nay, I know,"
  Said the farmer, "say no more;

"He fell in battle,—I see, alas!
  Thou'dst smooth these tidings o'er,—
Nay: speak the truth, whatever it be,
  Though it rend my bosom's core.

"How fell he,—with his face to the foe,
  Upholding the flag he bore?

O, say not that my boy disgraced
    The uniform that he wore!"

"I cannot tell," said the aged man,
    "And should have remarked before,
That I was with Grant,—in Illinois,—·
    Some three years before the war."

Then the farmer spake him never a word,
    But beat with his fist full sore
That aged man, who had worked for Grant
    Some three years before the war.

GRIZZLY

COWARD,—of heroic size,
In whose lazy muscles lies
Strength we fear and yet despise;
Savage,—whose relentless tusks
Are content with acorn husks;
Robber,—whose exploits ne'er soared

O'er the bee's or squirrel's hoard;
Whiskered chin, and feeble nose,
Claws of steel on baby toes,—
Here, in solitude and shade,
Shambling, shuffling, plantigrade,
Be thy courses undismayed!
Here, where Nature makes thy bed,
Let thy rude, half human tread
    Point to hidden Indian springs,

Lost in ferns and fragrant grasses,
   Hovered o'er by timid wings,
Where the wood-duck lightly passes,
Where the wild bee holds her sweets,—
Epicurean retreats,
Fits for thee, and better than
Fearful spoils of dangerous man.

In thy fat-jowled deviltry
Friar Tuck shall live in thee;
Thou mayst levy tithe and dole;
   Thou shall spread the woodland cheer,

From the pilgrim taking toll;
   Match thy cunning with his fear;
Eat, and drink, and have thy fill;
Yet remain an outlaw still!

MADRONO

CAPTAIN of the Western wood,
Thou that apest Robin Hood!
Green above thy scarlet hose,
How thy velvet mantle shows;
Never tree like thee arrayed,
O thou gallant of the glade!

When the fervid August sun
Scorches all it looks upon,
And the balsam of the pine

Drips from stem to needle fine,
Round thy compact shade arranged,
Not a leaf of thee is changed!

When the yellow autumn sun
Saddens all it looks upon,
Spreads its sackcloth on the hills,
Strews its ashes in the rills,
Thou thy scarlet hose dost doff,
And in limbs of purest buff
Challengest the sombre glade
For a sylvan masquerade.

Where, O where, shall he begin
Who would paint thee, Harlequin?
With thy waxen burnished leaf,
With thy branches' red relief,

With thy poly-tinted fruit,
In thy spring or autumn suit,—
Where begin, and O, where end,—
Thou whose charms all art transcend?

COYOTE *

Blown out of the prairie in twilight and dew,
Half bold and half timid, yet lazy all through;
Loath ever to leave, and yet fearful to stay,
He limps in the clearing,—an outcast in grey.

----

* The prairie-wolf (Mexican, *coyote*). This animal lives in cracks and crevices made in the prairies and plains by the intense summer heat.

A shade on the stubble, a ghost by the wall,
Now leaping, now limping, now risking a fall,
Lop-eared and large-jointed, but ever alway
A thoroughly vagabond outcast in grey.

Here, Carlo, old fellow,—he's one of your kind,—
Go, seek him, and bring him in out of the wind.
What! snarling, my Carlo! So—even dogs may
Deny their own kin in the outcast in grey.

Well, take what you will,—though it be on the sly,
Marauding, or begging,—I shall not ask why;
But will call it a dole, just to help on his way
A four-footed friar in orders of grey!

TO A SEABIRD

SANTA CRUZ, 1869

SAUNTERING hither on listless wings,
  Careless vagabond of the sea,
Little thou heedest the surf that sings,
The bar that thunders, the shale that rings,—
  Give me to keep thy company.

Little thou hast, old friend, that's new,
  Storms and wrecks are old things to thee;
Sick am I of these changes, too;

Little to care for, little to rue,—
  I on the shore, and thou on the sea.

All of thy wanderings, far and near,
  Bring thee at last to shore and me;
All of my journeying end them here,
This our tether must be our cheer,—
  I on the shore, and thou on the sea.

Lazily rocking on ocean's breast,
  Something in common, old friend, have we;
Thou on the shingle seek'st thy nest,
I to the waters look for rest,—
  I on the shore, and thou on the sea.

———

HER LETTER

I'M sitting alone by the fire,
  Dressed just as I came from the dance.
In a robe even *you* would admire,—
  It cost a cool thousand in France;
I'm be-diamonded out of all reason,
  My hair is done up in a cue;
In short, sir, "the belle of the season"
  Is wasting an hour on you.

A dozen engagements I've broken;
  I left in the midst of a set;
Likewise a proposal, half spoken,
  That waits—on the stairs—for me yet.

They say he'll be rich,—when he grows up,—
  And then he adores me indeed.
And you, sir, are turning your nose up,
  Three thousand miles off, as you read.

"And how do I like my position?"
  "And what do I think of New York?"
"And now, in my higher ambition,
  With whom do I waltz, flirt, or talk?"
"And isn't it nice to have riches,
  And diamonds and silks, and all that?"
"And aren't it a change to the ditches
  And tunnels of Poverty Flat?"

Well, yes,—if you saw us out driving
  Each day in the park, four-in-hand,—
If you saw poor dear mamma contriving
  To look supernaturally grand,—
If you saw papa's picture, as taken
  By Brady, and tinted at that,—
You'd never suspect he sold bacon
  And flour at Poverty Flat.

And yet, just this moment, when sitting
  In the glare of the grand chandelier,—
In the bustle and glitter befitting
  The "finest *soirée* of the year,"—
In the mists of a *gaze de Chambéry*,
  And the hum of the smallest of talk,—
Somehow, Joe, I thought of the "Ferry,"
  And the dance that we had on "The Fork."

Of Harrison's barn, with its muster
  Of flags festooned over the wall;
Of the candles that shed their soft lustre
  And tallow on head-dress and shawl;
Of the steps that we took to one fiddle;
  Of the dress of my queer *vis-à-vis;*
And how I once went down the middle
  With the man that shot Sandy McGee;

Of the moon that was quietly sleeping
  On the hill, when the time came to go;
Or the few baby peaks that were peeping
  From under their bedclothes of snow;
Of that ride,—that to me was the rarest;
  Of—the something you said at the gate:
Ah, Joe, then I wasn't an heiress
  To "the best-paying lead* in the State."

Well, well, it's all past; yet it's funny
  To think, as I stood in the glare
Of fashion and beauty and money,
  That I should be thinking, right there,
Of some one who breasted high water,
  And swam the North Fork, and all that,
Just to dance with old Folinsbee's daughter,
  The Lily of Poverty Flat.

But goodness! what nonsense I'm writing!
  (Mamma says my taste still is low,)
Instead of my triumphs reciting,
  I'm spooning on Joseph,—heigh-ho!

---

* Pronounced *leed.* Western expression for mine or digging.
"Flat" is the common term for any low alluvial land.

And I'm to be "finished" by travel,—
  Whatever's the meaning of that,—
O, why did papa strike pay gravel
  In drifting on Poverty Flat?

Good night,—here's the end of my paper;
  Good night,—if the longitude please,—
For maybe, while wasting my taper,
  Your sun's climbing over the trees.
But know, if you haven't got riches,
  And are poor, dearest Joe, and all that,
That my heart's somewhere there in the ditches,
  And you've struck it,—on Poverty Flat.

DICKENS IN CAMP

ABOVE the pines the moon was slowly drifting,
  The river sang below;
The dim Sierras, far beyond, uplifting
  Their minarets of snow:

The roaring camp-fire, with rude humour, painted
  The ruddy tints of health
On haggard face and form that drooped and fainted
  In the fierce race for wealth;

Till one arose, and from his pack's scant treasure
  A hoarded volume drew,
And cards were dropped from hands of listless leisure
  To hear the tale anew;

And then, while round them shadows gathered faster,
    And as the fire-light fell,
He read aloud the book wherein the Master
    Had writ of "Little Nell."

Perhaps 'twas boyish fancy—for the reader
    Was youngest of them all—
But, as he read, from clustering pine and cedar
    A silence seemed to fall;

The fir-trees, gathering closer in the shadows,
    Listened in every spray,
While the whole camp, with "Nell" on English meadows
    Wandered and lost their way.

And so in mountain solitudes—o'ertaken
    As by some spell divine—
Their cares dropped from them like the needles shaken
    From out the gusty pine.

Lost is that camp, and wasted all its fire;
    And he who wrought that spell?—
Ah, towering pine and stately Kentish spire,
    Ye have one tale to tell!

Lost is that camp! but let its fragrant story
    Blend with the breath that thrills
With hop-vines' incense all the pensive glory
    That fills the Kentish hills.

And on that grave where English oak, and holly,
     And laurel wreaths entwine,
Deem it not all a too presumptuous folly—
     This spray of Western pine!

July, 1870.

THE LOST GALLEON

In sixteen hundred and forty-one,
The regular yearly galleon,
Laden with odorous gums and spice,
India cottons and India rice,
And the richest silks of far Cathay,
Was due at Acapulco Bay.

Due she was, and over-due,—
Galleon, merchandise, and crew,
Creeping along through rain and shine,
Through the tropics, under the line.
The trains were waiting outside the walls,
     The wives of sailors thronged the town,
The traders sat by their empty stalls,
     And the viceroy himself came down;
The bells in the tower were all a-trip,
Te Deums were on each father's lip,
The limes were ripening in the sun
For the sick of the coming galleon.

All in vain. Weeks passed away,
And yet no galleon saw the bay:
India goods advanced in price;
The governor missed his favourite spice;
The señoritas mourned for sandal,

And the famous cottons of Coromandel;
And some for an absent lover lost,
  And one for a husband,—Donna Julia,
Wife of the captain, tempest tossed,
  In circumstances so peculiar:
Even the fathers, unawares,
Grumbled a little at their prayers;
And all along the coast that year
Votive candles were scarce and dear.

Never a tear bedims the eye
That time and patience will not dry;
Never a lip is curved with pain
That can't be kissed into smiles again:
And these same truths, as far as I know,
Obtained on the coast of Mexico
More than two hundred years ago,
In sixteen hundred and fifty-one,—
Ten years after the deed was done,—
And folks had forgotten the galleon:
The divers plunged in the Gulf for pearls,
White as the teeth of the Indian girls;
The traders sat by their full bazaars;
  The mules with many a weary load,
And oxen, dragging their creaking cars,
  Came and went on the mountain road.

Where was the galleon all this while:
Wrecked on some lonely coral isle?
Burnt by the roving sea-marauders,
Or sailing north under secret orders?
Had she found the Anian passage famed,
By lying Moldonado claimed,
And sailed through the sixty-fifth degree
Direct to the North Atlantic sea?

Or had she found the "River of Kings,"
Of which De Fonté told such strange things
In sixteen forty?   Never a sign,
East or West or under the line,
   They saw of the missing galleon;
Never a sail or plank or chip,
They found of the long-lost treasure-ship,
   Or enough to build a tale upon.
But when she was lost, and where and how,
Are the facts we're coming to just now.

Take, if you please, the chart of that day
Published at Madrid,—*por el Rey;*
Look for a spot in the old South Sea,
The hundred and eightieth degree
Longitude, west of Madrid: there,
Under the equatorial glare,
Just where the East and West are one,
You'll find the missing galleon,—
You'll find the "San Gregorio," yet
Riding the seas with sails all set,
Fresh as upon the very day
She sailed from Acapulco Bay.

How did she get there?   What strange spell
Kept her two hundred years so well,
Free from decay and mortal taint?
What? but the prayers of a patron saint!
A hundred leagues from Manilla town,
The "San Gregorio's" helm came down;
Round she went on her heel, and not
A cable's length from a galliot
That rocked on the waters, just abreast
Of the galleon's course, which was west-sou-west.

Then said the galleon's commandante,
General Pedro Sobriente
(That was his rank on land and main,
A regular custom of old Spain),
"My pilot is dead of scurvy: may
I ask the longitude, time, and day?"
The first two given and compared;
The third,—the commandante stared!

"The *first* of June? I make it second."
Said the stranger, "Then you've wrongly reckoned;
I make it *first*: as you came this way,
You should have lost—d'ye see—a day;
Lost a day, as plainly see,
On the hundred and eightieth degree."

"Lost a day?" "Yes: if not rude,
When did you make east longitude?"
"On the ninth of May,—our patron's day."
"On the ninth?—*you had no ninth of May!*
Eighth and tenth was there; but stay"—
Too late; for the galleon bore away.

Lost was the day they should have kept,
Lost unheeded and lost unwept;
Lost in a way that made search vain,
Lost in a trackless and boundless main;
Lost like the day of Job's awful curse,
In his third chapter, third and fourth verse;
Wrecked was their patron's only day,—
What would the holy fathers say?

Said the Fray Antonio Estavan,
The galleon's chaplain,—a learned man,—

"Nothing is lost that you can regain:
And the way to look for a thing is plain
To go where you lost it, back again.
Back with your galleon till you see
The hundred and eightieth degree.
Wait till the rolling year goes round,
And there will the missing day be found;
For you'll find—if computation's true—
That sailing *east* will give to you
Not only one ninth of May, but two,—
One for the good saint's present cheer,
And one for the day we lost last year."

Back to the spot sailed the galleon;
Where, for a twelve-month, off and on
The hundred and eightieth degree,
She rose and fell on a tropic sea:
But lo! when it came to the ninth of May,
All of a sudden becalmed she lay
One degree from that fatal spot,
Without the power to move a knot;
And of course the moment she lost her way,
Gone was her chance to save that day.

To cut a lengthening story short,
She never saved it. Made the sport
Of evil spirits and baffling wind,
She was always before or just behind,
One day too soon, or one day too late,
And the sun, meanwhile, would never wait:
She had two eighths, as she idly lay,
Two tenths, but never a *ninth* of May;
And there she rides through two hundred years
Of dreary penance and anxious fears:
Yet through the grace of the saint she served,
Captain and crew are still preserved.

By a computation that still holds good,
Made by the Holy Brotherhood,
The "San Gregorio" will cross that line
In nineteen hundred and thirty-nine:
Just three hundred years to a day
From the time she lost the ninth of May.
And the folk in Acapulco town,
Over the waters, looking down,
Will see in the glow of the setting sun
The sails of the missing galleon,
And the royal standard of Philip *Rey;*
The gleaming mast and glistening spar,
As she nears the surf of the outer bar.
A *Te Deum* sung on her crowded deck,
  An odour of spice along the shore,
A crash, a cry from a shattered wreck,—
  And the yearly galleon sails no more,
In or out of the olden bay;
For the blessed patron has found his day.

———

Such is the legend. Hear this truth:
  Over the trackless past, somewhere,
Lie the lost days of our tropic youth,
  Only regained by faith and prayer,
Only recalled by prayer and plaint:
Each lost day has its patron saint!

———

THE STAGE-DRIVER'S STORY

It was the stage-driver's story, as he stood with his back
    to the wheelers,
Quietly flecking his whip, and turning his quid of tobacco;

While on the dusty road, and blent with the rays of the
    moonlight,
We saw the long curl of his lash and the juice of tobacco
    descending.

Danger! Sir, I believe you,—indeed, I may say on that
    subject,
You your existence might put to the hazard and turn of
    a wager.
I have seen danger? Oh, no! not me, sir, indeed, I assure
    you:
'Twas only the man with the dog that is sitting alone in
    yon wagon.

It was the Geiger Grade, a mile and a half from the sum-
    mit:
Black as your hat was the night, and never a star in
    the heavens.
Thundering down the grade, the gravel and stones we
    sent flying
Over the precipice side,—a thousand feet plumb to the
    bottom.

Half-way down the grade I felt, sir, a thrilling and creaking,
Then a lurch to one side, as we hung on the bank of the
    cañon;
Then, looking up the road, I saw, in the distance behind
    me,
The off hind wheel of the coach just loosed from its axle,
    and following.

One glance alone I gave, then gathered together my ribbons,
Shouted, and flung them, outspread, on the straining necks
    of my cattle;

Screamed at the top of my voice, and lashed the air in
    my frenzy,
While down the Geiger Grade, on *three* wheels, the vehicle
    thundered.

Speed was our only chance, when again came the ominous
    rattle:
Crack, and another wheel slipped away, and was lost in the
    darkness.
Two only now were left; yet such was our fearful mo-
    mentum,
Upright, erect, and sustained on *two* wheels, the vehicle
    thundered.

As some huge bowlder, unloosed from its rocky shelf on
    the mountain,
Drives before it the hare and the timorous squirrel, far-
    leaping,
So down the Geiger Grade rushed the Pioneer coach, and
    before it
Leaped the wild horses, and shrieked in advance of the
    danger impending.

But to be brief in my tale. Again, ere we came to the
    level,
Slipped from its axle a wheel; so that, to be plain in my
    statement,
A matter of twelve hundred yards or more, as the distance
    may be,
We travelled upon *one* wheel, until we drove up to the
    station.

Then, sir, we sank in a heap; but, picking myself from
    the ruins,

I heard a noise up the grade; and looking, I saw in the
    distance
The three wheels following still, like moons on the horizon
    whirling
Till, circling, they gracefully sank on the road at the side
    of the station.

This is my story, sir; a trifle, indeed, I assure you.
Much more, perchance, might be said; but I hold him, of
    all men, most lightly
Who swerves from the truth in his tale—No, thank you—
    Well, since you *are* pressing,
Perhaps I don't care if I do: you may give me the same,
    Jim,—no sugar.